HEADGAMES

Nick Earls is the author of bestselling novels *Zigzag Street* and *Bachelor Kisses* and two novels for young adults – the award-winning *After January* and *48 Shades of Brown*.

His work has been published internationally in English and in translation. His previous jobs include suburban GP and storytelling armchair. He lives in Brisbane.

HEADGAMES

NICK EARLS

PENGUIN BOOKS

If you would like to write to Nick Earls,
his email address is nickearls@peg.apc.org

Penguin Books Australia Ltd
487 Maroondah Highway, PO Box 257
Ringwood, Victoria 3134, Australia
Penguin Books Ltd
Harmondsworth, Middlesex, England
Penguin Putnam Inc.
375 Hudson Street, New York, New York 10014, USA
Penguin Books Canada Limited
10 Alcorn Avenue, Toronto, Ontario, Canada M4V 3B2
Penguin Books (NZ) Ltd
Cnr Rosedale and Airborne Roads, Albany, Auckland, New Zealand
Penguin Books (South Africa) (Pty) Ltd
5 Watkins Street, Denver Ext. 4, 2094, South Africa
Penguin Books India (P) Ltd
11, Community Centre, Panchsheel Park, New Delhi 110 017, India

First published by Penguin Books Australia Ltd, 1999
This edition published by Penguin Books Australia Ltd, 1999

1 3 5 7 9 10 8 6 4 2

Cover photography by Jacqui Henshaw
Author photography by Mick Toal
Design by Ellie Exarchos, Penguin Design Studio
Typeset in Joanna by Post Pre-press Group, Brisbane
Printed and bound in Australia by Australian Print Group, Maryborough, Victoria

National Library of Australia
Cataloguing-in-Publication data:

Earls, Nick, 1963– .
Headgames.

ISBN 0 14 028350 1.

I. Title.

A823.3

www.penguin.com.au

CONTENTS

green

In our year at uni, Frank Green is it. The style council, the big man on campus, the born leader. From day one, Frank Green has been the definition of cool. Frank Green, frank in all colours, shameless and sure as a peacock. Peach jeans, pink jeans, Frank Green.

Queensland Uni, Medicine, 1981. Nothing counts here if Frank's not a part of it.

Frank Green juggles so many girls he's nearly juggling all of them. He juggles so many girls they all know. They all know and don't care. It's the price to pay, if it's a price at all. Frank Green has magic in his hands, the poise of a matador, the patter of a witless, irresistible charm.

I juggle girls the same way possums juggle Ford Cortinas. I'm road-kill out there, bitumen paté, seriously unsought-after. Quiet, dull-dressed, lurking without impact on the faculty peripheries. Lurking like some lame trap, like a trap baited with turd and I'm not catching much.

I have – my mother says I have – a confidence problem.

Frank Green has bad bum-parted hair, mild facial asymmetry and teeth like two rows of dazzling white runes, but he ducked the confidence problem like a limbo dancer.

Frank Green makes entrances. I turn up. When Frank Green is the last to leave I'm still there, but no-one's noticed. Frank Green dances like a thick liquid being poured out of something. I dance like I'm made of Lego, like I'm a glued-up Airfix model of something that dances. Better still, I don't dance. I retreat quite imperceptibly like a shadow in bad clothes.

My mother says I have lovely eyes, and just wait, they'll all get sick of Frank Green. My mother thinks he has no staying power, but I beg to differ. Frank, those pants and Countdown, I've told her, are three things that are here to stay. And she says, If you say so Philby, if you say so.

And I've told her there's no more Philby now, but does she listen? I've told her I'm Phil, this is uni, I'm Phil. And I'm sure I was only even Phillip for about five minutes before Philby surfaced in Moscow loaded up with Orders of Lenin. Philby the Russian spy. Philby the Third Man. Philby the bug-eyed, black-haired baby just born in London. Me. Seventeen years of Philby now. And what chance does a philby have? Philbies sound so pathetic you shouldn't let them out. Philby: a soft, hopeless marsupial that without a great deal of mollycoddling will drift into irrelevant extinction. A philby. A long-nosed, droop-eared wimp of a marsupial with lovely eyes, destined to die. Inevitably nocturnal, and very afraid.

Outside the house you don't call me that, I tell her. Okay? Outside the house, no Philby.

On weekends I lie on my back with my physics book open over my head and I dream of girls. Girls who come up and talk to me at faculty functions. Who approach quite deliberately and talk to me with a calculating seductiveness. Glamorous, desirable girls who tell me quite openly that they crave me with a painful urgency, that Frank is all style and no substance, that they hope they're not making fools of themselves, but they know what they want. And in the dream under the physics book I don't shake with fear and lose the grip on my burger, I maintain calm, I sip at my plastic cup of Coke, I let them have their say and I acquiesce to their outrageous desires. In my dreams, I am a peach-jeaned man of cool. I am lithe and quite elegant. I am all they could want, I am highly supportive of their expectation of orgasm and I treat them kindly.

And unlike Frank, I'd be happy with one, though admittedly any one of several. I have a list, a list of four girls I would be quite unlikely to turn down, should I figure in their desires. I have spoken to one on three occasions and another once. Other than that, nothing happens. But that's okay, I've got six years in this degree.

Chemistry pracs begin on Fridays, and this is where things get weird. I'm in Frank's group (alphabetically) and his friends aren't. Week Two and the group divides to do titrations and I'm standing next to Frank and a little behind him when the division occurs so I'm his partner.

I learn things about Frank. Close-up things. Unglamorous things, but quite okay things just the same. Frank twiddles his pencil when he doesn't know much. Frank says Hey several times whenever he has an idea, or has something he thinks is an idea. Frank is very distractable and has no great interest in organic chemistry. In the first prac we talk a lot about bands we like. Frank sings like someone with terrible sinuses and fills beakers up with varying amounts of water and plays them with his pencil with no concession to the dual concepts of rhythm and melody. Our titration goes very poorly. Our tutor takes us aside and says, Listen guys, I'm worried about your attitude, that prac was piss easy. Frank sings several lines of 'The Long and Winding Road' but all on one note, and the tutor doesn't know what to do.

Frank says Hi to me three times over the next four uni days. Frank actually says Hi to me, and people notice every time. People look at me and I can see them thinking, Hey, he's Frank's friend.

Friday in the chem lab, Frank says, I think I can get it right this time, and he sings 'The Long and Winding Road' again, but still all on one note. We spend the first forty minutes of the prac (Caffeine Extraction from a Measured Sample of Instant Coffee) discussing how profoundly the death of John Lennon has affected both us as individuals, and society as a whole. The tutor asks if we could please do the chem prac and I tell him he should treat Frank's deeply held feelings about the death of John Lennon with respect.

The tutor says he feels really bad about the death of John Lennon too, and agrees that the implications are undeniably global, but could we please do the chem prac. And he says 'The Long and Winding Road' is actually one of his favourite songs and could Frank please possibly never, ever sing it again, because Frank's version of it makes him very angry. Frank starts to sing 'Hey Jude', all on one note (the same note as that used for 'The Long and Winding Road'), and then thinks better of it.

We take a look at the chem prac. Frank admits he's done none of the prep we're supposed to and apologises to me, saying he's not really doing his bit for the partnership. I tell him I spent a few minutes on it last night, and as I see it we have two options. The first is to do the prac the way the book says, bearing in mind that this involves several titrations and the result will be very bad. The second option has two parts, which I explain to Frank quietly. The first part is the maths. I have done the maths, and I know exactly what our yield should be. The second part is the extra instant coffee in my pocket.

Frank chooses option two. We end up with 120 per cent of the caffeine we are supposed to, and we tip just enough down the sink to give us an impressive but subtle 96 per cent yield.

After the prac Frank asks me if I'm doing anything tonight, not realising how unnecessary the question is. He says, We're going down the pub if you want to join us. I say, Sure, but I try so hard to be cool when I say it that I gag slightly. I try to disguise it as a cough, but that only makes

things worse. Frank looks at me. It seems I have to say
something, so I say Mucus, and he says, Sure, I've got these
sinuses, you know? So I get away with it. When Frank's not
looking I take my pulse. It's 154. I hate the confidence
problem.

So I go home after the chem prac. I have to think about
this and I can't do that in lectures. This is it. This is a big
moment. This is tribal. This is right out of our anthropology subject, not out of my life. This is the bit where the
anthropology lecturer said, All tribes have rituals, and if
you don't know them you're not in the tribe.

There are problems with this. It took me seconds to
realise I'd never had a drink in a pub before (and this is
where the gritty issues of ritual will come into play), but it
wasn't till I was in the backyard thrashing the guts out of
the Totem Tennis ball at 4.20 that I realised I didn't know
which pub to go to. With the *Yellow Pages* and a map I work
out the half-dozen pubs nearest uni. At some point this
evening I will enter one nonchalantly, and probably fash-
ionably late (if late's still fashionable), and say Hi to Frank
and whoever he drinks with, and I won't say a word about
the other pubs I've been to first. I understand ritual. Step
one – appear to know which pub.

I shower and put on a lime green shirt with a yachting
motif and regular jeans. Will there be girls? I wish my
teeth were straighter, my lips more full. I lace up my white
canvas shoes and my mother stands me in front of the
body length mirror and I just can't believe this is as good
as it gets. I don't know what she expected, standing me

here. I don't know if she thought I could still go out after seeing this.

I think I'll tell Frank I came down with something, some bug. If I was a real contender I could tell him I got a better offer. Sorry I didn't make it Friday, Frank: girl trouble, you know? I'll go with the bug. I'll see him Monday morning and affect some queasy face that suggests a whole weekend of gastric discontent, and this'll all be fine. And no prep for chem pracs in future, that's where this trouble started.

My mother will have none of this. She's seen the map and tells me I'll need a driver. I'll drive you round till we find the right place, and I'll give you the money for a cab home, she says. And even though I'm protesting and telling her I'm really not feeling well, we seem to be having this conversation in her car and I seem to be taking ten bucks from her when we're stopped at a traffic light.

This is really bad, this whole thing. I'm aware of that. Imagine if Frank sees me, being dropped off by my mother, my mother fussing over me before I'm allowed out of the car. I say none of this, but she knows it, anyway. This the plan, she says, slipping on sunglasses even though it's early evening, driving faster than she needs to, braking late, talking with maybe just a hint of an accent. And I think it's a hint of the accent she used sporadically but to good comic effect in a minor role in the Arts Theatre's recent production of *Uncle Vanya*.

I'm hating this.

At the Royal Exchange I'll park in the back car park, she

says, going on in that damn accent. There appears to be a lane leading south-west from there, between two shops. You will walk down that lane. You will then turn right and walk along Toowong High Street until you arrive at the hotel, as though from the bus stop. I shall wait ten minutes, during which time I shall be reading this book. She holds up a Robert Ludlum novel she has borrowed from the library. If you are not back in ten minutes, I shall assume you have been successful. I shall drive down the lane, turn left and be gone.

My mother, when she takes the piss, really takes the piss. I am hating this evening even more. Hating this evening, hating Uncle Vanya and his whole family, hating Chekov, hating my parents whose abiding strangeness means I don't have a chance out there. You've damaged me, I want to tell her. You've given me no idea of normal, damn you. If I die like a philby in there it's all because of you.

She parks in the most secluded spot in the car park. I do the lane thing as she has directed. The Royal Exchange, it seems, has several different parts to it. I hadn't expected that. (What had I expected? A barn? How could I not expect rooms?) It's amazing how relaxed the people are in here, all of them, how conversant with ritual in a way that seems innate. How none of them has white canvas shoes, but maybe Frank won't notice. I'm running round working up a sweat, running down my ten minutes, finding new bits of the Royal Exchange Hotel, not finding Frank Green.

I run back to the car park, to the secluded spot where

my mother has opened her Robert Ludlum novel but is only pretending to read.

He's not there, he's not there, I tell her, and I don't like the slightly desperate tone I use.

Calm now, Philby, she says. The mission has just begun. All will be well.

She guns the car out onto the High Street, loops back and parks in front of a panel beater's shop round the corner from the Regatta.

Usual drill, she says, and reaches for Robert Ludlum.

I run to the Regatta, telling myself not to run. Telling myself Frank Green wouldn't run. I'm sweating quite a lot now. I'm smelling like a wet dog, I'm sure of it. And I don't see Frank Green, despite copious amounts of stupid looking. Everyone here is so relaxed. No-one's wearing a shirt like mine. No-one's wearing white canvas shoes. I feel sick, some bug, maybe.

Hey Phil, Frank says from behind, tapping me on the shoulder and catching me quite unprepared. We're outside, on the verandah.

Pink Floyd *Dark Side of the Moon* T-shirt, peach jeans tonight. White canvas shoes. Frank Green is wearing white canvas shoes.

I just came in to buy a round, he says, and we walk to the bar. So what do you want?

I'm not prepared for this moment. Damn it, I didn't think this through. I'm an anthropological idiot. What do I want? My palms sweat, my tongue rattles round in my mouth like a cricket bail. What do I want? I'm thinking all those beer words, but I have to pick the right one. I've never done this before. Do I want a pot? A schooner? A middy? Do I have to say which beer? What are the names of beers? I'm dying here. How many Xs was it? Or something involving spirits, spirits mixed with something. Frank's waiting. Frank's becoming confused. But Frank isn't dizzy. Frank's heart rate is well short of 200. Frank isn't about to throw up and get frog-marched out of the tribe on his first day. I'm visualising my parents' drinks cabinet. Damn them. Damn them and their stupid English people's drink cabinet. You amateur theatre-loving bloody G and T drinking British colonial bloody bastards, I'm thinking when Frank says, What do you want? again.

I tell him beer, Fourex, a pot. In my head this is what I tell him, but my mouthparts are against me and say, Creme de Menthe.

Frank looks as though I've slapped him. Cream de menth, he says. You want cream de menth?

Yeah. I say yeah, because what else can I say now?

Righto, he says and shrugs his shoulders. You want ice?

Yeah.

So he orders three pots and a Creme de Menthe with ice.

He carries two pots out to the verandah. I carry one pot and the Creme de Menthe. And I visualise my parents' drink cabinet and I curse the bright green bottle at the front. I see my father pouring it, offering me a glass with a con man's smile and a white linen napkin over his arm, saying, And do we want it *frappé*, sir?

The others, Vince and Greg, friends of Frank's from our

year, stare at my drink from some distance away. I am about to begin a long journey into the wilderness. The urge to apologise for my drink choice is almost irresistible. I want to start again. I want a pot. I want to go outside and pay a cabbie ten bucks to drive over my head.

What's that? Vince says, pointing to my drink (as if there's any need to point).

I tell him and he nods, nods like he knew but he hoped he'd been wrong. He wants to ask why. He wants to ask why, but he doesn't.

And I want to tell him. I want to say Look, it's not my fault. My parents are so northern hemisphere, so insufferably strange. They drink this. They've made me drink it three times in company, but you shouldn't think I'm one of them. I meant to get a pot.

We drink quickly.

My shout, Greg says, and goes inside. He's back in a few minutes with three beers and a Creme de Menthe with ice.

And I can't change now. I know I can't change now. To say No, I'll have a pot would be to admit a gross error of judgement, so I sit in my lonely, soft cloud of mint, sipping away. I take the next shout. Three beers and a Creme de Menthe with ice.

Frank is looking comfortable, leaning back in the white plastic seat and crapping on about uni, specifically about the chem prac and the coffee in my pocket, pinging a fingernail repeatedly against the rim of his beer glass and grinning at me while singing 'The Long and Winding Road' with the aid of no actual notes at all.

Shit, 96 per cent yield, Vince says, shaking his head. We got 88 and we thought that was okay.

I'm smiling, laughing with Frank about Vince who doesn't quite get it and thinks we're champion titrators, laughing with him about the coffee in my pocket, about how we wouldn't have got 50 per cent without the coffee in my pocket. I'm sweating peppermint. I'm stinking of sweet mint and many parts of me are starting to relax, starting to become loose and less interested in direction. I'm laughing at almost anything now, just thinking about turning up at the chem prac with coffee in my pocket and laughing heaps.

This is very refreshing, I'm saying. Very refreshing with a little ice, you know. But I think I'm only saying this in my head, doing a secret ad for Creme de Menthe, turning to the camera with a James Bond smile and saying, Damn' refreshing, and giving a little tilt of the head.

Vince says, Hey, what's that like, that cream de menth? And he takes a sip from my glass. He scrunches up his eyes and thinks hard. He passes it to Greg and says, What do you reckon?

It's not great with the beer, Greg says. It's not great after ten beers, but maybe it's not the best time, you know? Jeez, it's strong though. I reckon if you wanted to get pissed, you'd get pissed pretty quick on this. What do you reckon, Phil? Get pissed pretty quick on this, do you?

I want to say, Shit yeah. I really want to say, Shit, yeah, but I can't work out with any confidence which order the words go in, and while I'm thinking about it, while I'm trying really hard not to say, Yeah, shit, he says, I reckon Phil's pissed on this, you know?

Well he would be, wouldn't he? Frank says.

I can't get up when it's my shout any more, so I just hand Vince the money and he automatically comes back with three beers and a Creme de Menthe with ice.

My sinuses feel very clear, I say to Frank. Very, very clear.

And Frank says, Good on you.

I tell him it must be the mint. The mint clears the sinuses, I say quite loudly. I can recommend it. And Frank thinks I am recommending it, in an immediate and personal way and, aware that he has a problem with his sinuses, orders himself two Creme de Menthes with his next beer, taking them both quickly and earnestly, like medicine.

I am now feeling hot all over, and there is a ringing in my head coming from a long way off. I want to warn Frank about this, to say there might be side effects, but I can't possibly be heard over his singing, particularly while Vince is shouting, Yeah I think they're a bit clearer, your sinuses. Yeah. That's sounding bloody good, mate.

So he joins in.

Hey, how about some Five Hundred, Greg says, pulling a deck of cards from his pocket. Just for small stuff, for ones, twos and fives, hey?

First I think he means dollars and I wonder what I've let myself in for, and then he scoops a handful of small change onto the table and organises it into three wobbly piles. So I say, Sure, and then realise I've never played Five Hundred before.

And just when I think I'm about to be thwarted by the

tribal problem, I remember the Solo my father taught me to play. The Solo he had played when in the British Armed Forces in India. No-one in the Punjab could touch me lad, when I had a bit of form going, he told me once. And he's always said that Five Hundred was an inferior version of the great game, and that anyone who mastered Solo could make the best Five Hundred player in the world look like a fool.

So, after a brief clarification of house rules, we play. We play, and I hear myself shouting, but, I hope, not ungenerously as I take hand after hand. Boldly, flamboyantly, elegantly, like an impresario, like a hussar, feeling nothing below the waist, watching the table sway in front of me and rise on one occasion only to strike me softly in the face. And I feel nothing, nothing at all but mint and victory. And there are times when I'm sure my brain is resting and my arms play on without me, flourishing strategies that haven't been seen outside the British Armed Forces in India since the late nineteenth century, passing Creme de Menthe to my shouting mouth, raking money across the table.

From this point, my recollections are non-linear.

I lie on my bed with my room full of well-established daylight and stinking of old mint. Crusty green debris around my nostrils, hidden Creme de Menthe oozing from my sinuses whenever I roll over. There is a bucket on the floor near the bed. A blue bucket with a slick of bubbly green swill on the bottom.

We sang 'Across the Universe', I recall. Sang it, or at least shouted it at the cars on Coro Drive, and they honked their horns, and I think I saluted. I recall myself shouting at all stages of the card game, loudly and in a ridiculous English accent, and saying very pukka things that today mean little. I remember giving the anthropology lecturer the bagging of a lifetime in his absence. At least, I assume it was in his absence. I can see him rearing up through my rickety dreams saying, You just got lucky kid, but I don't think he did.

And some of my large pile of small-change winnings went on a bottle of Creme de Menthe and we toasted many things, including the way the game is, or was, played in the Punjab, back when it was played by experts and the sun had yet to set on the long twilight of the empire.

And I took the pack and started ripping out card tricks at high speed, just the way my father showed me, shouting at the others in a private parody of his voice, Come on then Charlie, pick a card, any card. And I fooled them every time, baffled them, and I can hear Vince's voice saying, The man's a genius, a genius.

And I'm still in the middle of this slow, green, glorious death, heaving up some more unnecessary gastric juices into the blue bucket when my mother comes in.

Your friend Frank's called a couple of times, she says. He said to tell you that there's a barbecue at his place tonight, and that three of the four girls you mentioned last night will be turning up. He said to tell you that it's BYO – but don't worry, he'll have plenty of ice.

She watches me nod and lose a little more gastric juice.

You're doin' well, Philby, she says, perhaps in the accent she used to try out (unsuccessfully) for the part of Blanche in *A Streetcar Named Desire*. Doin' fine.

the haircut of a
more successful man

Ellen doesn't know me, mainly because I tell her so many lies. She knows someone else, a different person I've created and told her about. And I like it better that way. It has so many more possibilities.

She cuts my hair, round about every fourth Saturday. I'm her 11.45, her last appointment. That's a regular thing. She does me like she's in no hurry, as though it's not bad to linger, spend some time in the vicinity of my unspectacular hair, my modest trimming requirements.

It was only a few haircuts into our relationship that I decided I wanted to be a little more glamorous, at least to someone. So when Ellen asked me those hairdresser questions, those broad open-ended How have things been? questions, I really started telling her. And week by week a strange glamour crept into my life, a very measured, down-played, sophisticated, natural kind of glamour. Stories of considerable, though never boastful, prowess. My work as an international banker, my private adventures.

My trip to Melbourne a few years ago at the time of the Australian Open, meeting Gabriella Sabatini through a mutual friend, playing a set of singles with her. She won six–two and didn't work up a sweat, but four of the games went to deuce.

My lecture tour of the universities of northern Spain, though I never told her what I'd lectured about. My behind-the-scenes work on the Sydney Olympic bid.

Kylie Minogue's twenty-first in '89, the hassles we had with the papparazzi, and the secret name Kylie uses in hotels to screen her calls. And I made this secret part of our relationship, and Ellen swore to tell no-one.

And once she said she'd counted up and she figured I must know at least eleven of the *Who Weekly* list of the world's twenty-five most beautiful people, and she didn't know anyone else who knew even one of them.

So I chose to become a very complex international kind of man, someone very different to the person I could have told her about, the transport economist who drives a ten-year-old Ford Laser and lives alone in a two-bedroom flat a few streets away. And it's a choice I'm usually glad I've made. I'm glad the second or third or fourth time she asked me how things had been I told her about things that were never likely to be.

I ask her about her life, too, and she always prefaces any remarks by telling me it's nowhere near as exciting as mine. She lives over the river where she and her husband Garry are renovating a turn-of-the-century cottage. They have two young daughters, and Garry's always keen for more, and keen for a son or two as well. He just loves kids, she tells me. And it doesn't sound like a bad life at all.

And she washes my hair, washes it slowly before each trim and massages the conditioner deep into my scalp. Works her elegant fingers forcefully into me with a rhythm that sends me into a temporary ecstatic trance. I close my eyes to make the most of every touch. I shut down all other sensations. And she doesn't talk while she's doing this. I think she respects the serene state into which I've drifted and she doesn't do anything that might break it. All the time those fingers, working, working away, working up a lather, rinsing, then hands on again for the conditioner.

And all I can feel is this, all I can see is the dull red inside my eyelids. And I imagine a world where hair-dressing is a nude art, where you walk into the salon and the gear comes off, for everybody. So I'm sitting naked with my head tipped back and Ellen working peacefully away. And in this better world my body hair is distributed in a more concise manner, my muscle mass is just a little more impressive and some days I have a dick that would measure up well against the leg of a fat four-year-old child.

In this place only beautiful people cut hair. Ellen still cuts hair there. Ellen with her grey eyes and her straight blonde hair that she dismisses as boring, her breasts loaded into a snug white T-shirt like something danger-ous, her black jeans. Nude of course in this other place that only exists while she's washing my hair, her magical liberated breasts dipping down close to my wet head. Breasts growing larger and becoming troublesome, bumping against my head repeatedly like generously inflated balloons, and she's apologising and I'm telling her it's okay, I don't mind. Wet shining large breasts with my head between them.

And she towels me down like a boxing coach and leads me over to the chair. Cuts my hair. Takes the Samson power of my blind, dizzy dream away, just a little. We're both still dressed when I leave.

Sometimes I even want to tell her that I miss her between visits. If I'm having a really shitty time of it I want to go back the next day, just for the wash. But then she'd be onto me for sure.

Sometimes I walk out of there still on a high, hot enough to burn a hole right through my pants, sometimes I'm already crashing down. Walking into the glare of the outside and hating it instantly, all of it. The ugly people who in any better world would never make the grade as hairdressers, the bright raging daylight, the crappy car that I have to leave round the corner where she won't see it, the crappy, brown-brick flat where I'll be parking it, sleeping nights. The place where I watch TV and eat takeaway. Where I drink beer and eat barbecue chips in front of the one-day cricket night games, lounging around on the old sofa night after hot summer night wearing only the haircut of a more successful man. Falling asleep eventually, dreaming the crappy dreams I expect to, waking without enthusiasm.

I think I'm in a rut.

Sometimes I also think I could kill Garry. Garry the daughter-maker. Garry the dream husband. Perfect Garry who found her first. I imagine myself in their leafy suburban street with a sniper's rifle, zeroing the cross hairs in on his chest, blowing him away. I can only think this because I'm far too dull to do it. There are days, though, when it's the first part of a quite unstoppable fantasy. Me lying there on the old sofa with a few beers in me, gazing up at the ceiling and inadvertently making the oral gun noises of childhood.

It's been a while since there has been anyone else in my life, and I suppose that's not surprising if I spend much of my spare time lying around naked drinking beer and fantasising about murdering someone I don't even know. I suppose if I actually did it people would talk about what a quiet neighbour I was, and how they would never have guessed I could have done something like that. But then the *Courier Mail* would build up a picture of me as some psychotic loner, and this end would come to seem inevitable.

Worse than that, though, it's such a self-defeating fantasy. I shoot the man she loves, Ellen hates me forever, for ten or fifteen years I get a series of very unattractive prison haircuts and it's a long, long time till I come across hands like hers again. And I don't imagine the prison barber works the conditioner into your scalp with any tenderness at all. And I expect it would take a hell of an imagination to fantasise about his breasts enlarging around your wet head. But in times of deprivation, I suppose all such things are possible.

So the fantasy persists, but only on the old sofa, only in my crappy flat. Sometimes I doze while I'm still working on it and a late wicket falls in the night cricket and I'm suddenly awake again. Awake in the flickering lights of replays, still tumescent in the last lingering drift of the dream, still expecting to look down and see a dick like a hot, basking reptile reclining across my belly. But finding instead something more like a moist pink kangaroo baby beginning its slow crawl to the pouch.

The big, bold dreams of lonely men with unimportant dimensions.

When I was young I used to go to a barber with my father. His name was Ron and all he could do was a short back and sides. None of those fancy hairstyles. He was bald and myopic and very ugly in an old-fashioned sort of way. When I worked out, much more recently, that the best hairdressing was done nude, I thought back to Ron the barber. But only once.

In the country of nude hairdressing, Ron would be forever turned back at the border, sent to roam the wilderness with his scissors and his shaving brush, cursing for the rest of his days the cruelties of the world and its unreasonable preoccupation with beauty. And he'd hold up his hands, his stumpy clean little fingers, his tidy nails and he'd moan to the harshly beautiful, grey-eyed goddess of hairdressers, and he'd wail about the land of unseen plenty where they wouldn't even let him get his gear off to shear a few sheep.

I call the salon one Thursday, even though I've seen Ellen

just twelve days before. Something big? she says. Yeah, I tell her, and she pencils me in for Saturday, 11.45. I think I might tell her I'm going to Bangkok on Monday because I've found a loop-hole in Thai foreign investment law that will sink a big deal a multi-national is sewing up. I have two days to fine-tune the details.

Two days thinking only of Ellen. Two days hard as a bat handle sitting in my one-window office in my senior project officer chair looking out at Spring Hill. Two days thinking only of soap, shampoo, hands in my hair, fuck the traffic lights, fuck the ring-road plans, fuck the minister who wants to take something to cabinet next week. The minister and his ministerial hair, black luxuriant hair always looking well cared for and important. With hair like that, he could be the next premier.

Friday night is of course a night of precocious masturbation, lying in my long bath in body-temperature water, reasonably well shampooed where it counts. Taking the bat handle and playing several innings of indoor cricket. Afterwards, I sleep quite well, and I wake late.

When I arrive, the salon's still busy dealing with the families lining up in numbers for Saturday morning cuts. Ellen says, Hi babe, in a slightly weary way and goes back to the wriggling blond six-year-old in front of her.

When it's my turn she takes me to the basin. I tell her my hair feels really dirty today, and she says she'll be thorough. She works my head so hard I think I'll moan if I'm not careful. I can't imagine what she'd do if I moaned, because the nature of the moan would be quite apparent.

My mouth goes dry at the best of it and I feel quite dizzy. She lifts my head and wraps it in a towel and I can move only slowly to the chair.

Big night? she says.

Yeah. Yeah, fairly big.

How do you want it?

Just a trim. Not much off at all. I just want it to be a little neater.

She doesn't talk as much today. She doesn't initiate conversation in quite the usual way. I see her looking at me sometimes, and I wonder if I moaned, after all.

I ask her how things are and she says, Fine. She doesn't go into any details. Doesn't tell me how the re-wiring's going. Doesn't tell me about Stephanie and Alexandra. Doesn't even tell me about Garry. Maybe somebody's shot him. I should ask.

I don't. I say very little. She doesn't ask me anything, either. This is strange. I almost need to ask her what's going on, but I don't know if I can. And I keep my Thailand story to myself. I know I can't believe it at the moment. Right now I know I stole it from somewhere and it seems like the most transparent of lies, like a lie that could unravel a whole desirable identity. And that'd be it. I'd have to get up and leave with wet partly cut hair and never come back. And Ellen is far too important for me to contemplate that. I realise that now as she's taking millimetres from the ends of my hair, and unless I'm very careful I could become deeply depressed in an instant.

I watch her hands, combing and measuring and trim-ming. Her face that seems quite far from me today. The reflection of her back view a million times, caught between the mirrors that line both walls.

How's that? she says, when it's done. But she says it as though she's presenting me with nothing, as though it's really just a way of telling me the haircut's over and it's time to go.

Good, really good, I tell her, and in the mirror I'm sure my smile looks unconvincing, perfunctory.

I walk to the cash register. I give her fifteen dollars. She gives me fifty cents. She says, See you next time, then. And I go.

And I feel like shit today, really bad after the cut, like it's got me nowhere. Like the whole weekend is shot, and maybe more. Like the rest of my life is just beer and TV and seasonal sporting fluctuations. So it makes sense that today is the day I lose my car keys. My bulky plastic Captain Haddock keyring that no-one could lose. I am a man facing a ten-year-old white Laser with nothing but his empty pockets, his keys forsaken in some transitional moment. Waiting chair to basin. Basin to cutting chair. Back there, back with Ellen, back where I just can't go right now.

So I stand by the roadside next to my ten-year-old white Laser hoping I will see the blue plastic jumper of Captain Haddock, his slightly startled, bearded, plastic face, lying somewhere on the ground with my keys. Despite my hair-cut, I feel at this moment very unsuccessful.

Hey.

Ellen's voice says, Hey, just behind me. Says it in a tough kind of way, and I turn. She's different now. A totally different person to the haircutting Ellen at the salon. And she's swinging my Captain Haddock keyring like it's a nunchaku, like, Don't mess with me or the plastic captain will be just a blur when he hits you.

She's crazy and powerful now. She tells me Garry's a shit, stands in this quite busy street and tells me Garry's a shit. That it never worked. That she wanted kids and he just laughed at her and it never looked like happening. She looks at my car, the ten-year-old white Laser I am standing near in a way that says it must be my car. And she says to me, I don't care if it's all lies, okay? I don't give a shit if this isn't the black Saab it's supposed to be. Just get in.

I start to walk to the driver's door and she says, Go round the other side.

She gets in behind the wheel and unlocks the passenger door. I do what I'm told.

Tell me where you live, she says.

I tell her Bishop Street and she says, Right, puts it in gear and drives.

Three and a half minutes it takes. Three and a half minutes of Ellen staring straight ahead. Three and a half minutes of wondering what the hell is going on. It occurs to me, and I don't know why, but it occurs to me that she might be going to kill me. She looks like she could kill me. Maybe she will. Maybe that's fair. I don't know. I know I have an erection of quite fearsome proportions, but it never was a part of my body to show much judgement.

The fact that part of me, a small part of me, thinks it's reasonable to have an erection doesn't mean she isn't going to kill me. As though she's read my mind while she's washed my hair, watched every minute of two years of appalling fantasies and today was the day it all became too much and I'm about to get what I deserve.

We park in front of my block of units. It is a visibly crappy block of units, but she says nothing other than Let's go in.

She unlocks the door, shuts it behind us.

I'm putting a lot on the line here, all right? she says. I know you might never come back to me after this.

She's not going to kill me. Maybe the erection wins.

I've been thinking about you, she says, staring out the window with the alarming intensity she's maintained throughout the last six minutes. Even when I'm not cutting your hair. I've been thinking about you and soap. You and me and a shitload of soap. You and me and a lot of shampoo. I've been thinking you might be hairy, she says. Like, really hairy. I've been wanting you to be really hairy, and really in need of a good wash.

I am really hairy, I tell her. Like, really fucking hairy. Hair suit, my friends call me, since they say hirsute doesn't do me justice.

I think this is a joke, but she doesn't laugh.

Garry isn't hairy, she says. Garry has a chest like a boy. Did you get the shampoo I told you to? The Decoré in the flesh-coloured bottle?

Yeah.

We go into the bathroom and start running the water.

Got anything with bubbles? she says.

Yeah, maybe.

She goes to the cupboard and throws a handful of crystals into the bath and it suds up right away, filling the room with the complicated fragrance of flowers of the forest.

She takes my shirt off, then my pants, and tells me to get in.

My God you're hairy she says, with a strange, hungry smile.

Yeah.

She undresses and my dick climbs through the bubbles like a periscope.

She moves on top of me, splashes herself with the warm water and she glistens. She runs the water through her hair and gives me a smile that shows her teeth.

I hope to Christ I'm not going to wake up now to see Steve Waugh being run out. Some crappy highlights package waking me at this moment of exhilaration. Flickering lights, a lonely room, a pointless, raging hard-on.

We'll start with your head, she says. Familiar territory. Then we'll take it one inch at a time.

And she foams the shampoo in my hair with both hands, moves her face close, her grey eyes, and I see another flash of the white teeth just before her warm wet mouth is onto mine.

She soaps my shoulders, and my chest, rubs handfuls of the suds up and down her own body, breathes heavily. She works her way lower, lower.

Right now I wouldn't care if she did kill me. They'd never get the lid down.

She shampoos between my thighs, rubbing rhythmically from my knees to my groin on both sides. Still crouching over me, straddling me.

And the shampoo runs into my eyes, starts inflicting that stiff pain on them when it runs there and you don't wash it away. And I can't wash it away. I can't move. My eyes start to close and I'm still watching her, hypnotised by her like never before, squatting over me, the foot-long, flesh-coloured bottle of Decoré held right in front of her with both hands, low down and squeezing, squeezing out large amounts of the thick off-white shampoo, squeezing it all over me down there.

And just for a moment, with my near-blinded eyes, this is all very disempowering.

I have no control. None at all.

But I don't care.

Garry is as dead as he needs to be and I didn't have to do a thing. And my crappy flat is right now a far, far better world.

Later we drink beer and eat barbecue chips and lie on the old sofa. Ellen flicks between channels. Old movies, repeats, cricket highlights. Steve Waugh is run out for next to nothing. I don't care.

TV's crap, she says. Tell me a story. I like stories.

problems with a girl
and a unicorn

I've always been a big advocate of share-housing. At least, I was until the girl came along.

I now realise it's something that can work well or quite badly, and it all gets down to personalities.

And the girl and the unicorn are very different. It hadn't occurred to me that a person might differ quite so greatly from a unicorn, and then might choose to be so thoroughly dogmatic about it. But that's her, I guess.

Of course, it does mean I've come to know the unicorn's more sensitive side, and sometimes we're up all night talking. About all kinds of things. Apples, the case for and against the opposable thumb, some of the more attractive racehorses about town, the early short fiction of Peter Carey, magic realism (a genre for which the unicorn has little regard). The girl, our housemate, girls in general.

'I could do without them,' the unicorn says. 'Imagine a world without girls. Without girls for so long no-one could even be sure if they'd ever existed. If they were just, you know, mythical beasts in fairy tales, or something.'

'Like . . .'

'Yeah,' the unicorn says. 'Like trolls. Just like them.'

'She's not so bad.'

'Not so bad? Not so bad?'

'Yeah. I mean, I don't like her, or anything, but she's not a problem. She's okay, for a housemate, you know? You can't expect to be best friends with people just because you share a house with them.'

'You see that room there?' the unicorn says, pointing to the toilet and obviously unhappy with what I've said.

'Yeah . . .'

'You know what she does in there?'

'What do you mean?'

'I think she shits in there.' The unicorn pauses, for effect. 'If you want to know. What I'm saying is, I think the girl shits in a room inside the house. Shits in the reading room. I really thinks she does. Right where you've got every back issue of HQ. I've heard her. Somewhere near the font, I reckon. Now, what do you think of that?'

'Well . . .'

'And it gets worse. I've taken a look in there. And next to the font there's this paper. A roll of paper hanging on this thing on the wall, and not a word on it. You might not have noticed it, but . . .' The unicorn pauses, sucks on the cigarette, gives a flicker of nictitating membrane. 'This is pretty disgusting . . .'

'What?'

'I think she sticks it up her end. Like, her hind quarters. I think we've got to have a word with her. Probably you, you've got to have a word with her. She'll listen to you. I don't think she likes me.'

'Yeah . . .'

'Look, if you don't believe me, just hang around nearby some time. I'm not lying to you. It's fucking disgusting. She gets that paper from somewhere. I don't know where, I don't know how. I can't believe it's legal. But she gets it. Stanley, it's fucking pornographic. Think about it. This soft, patterned, scented paper, and she sticks it up her end. Deliberately. Practically every day. I can't believe you haven't noticed. But why would you, I suppose? I only worked it out myself when I thought, one day, hang on, she was only in there a couple of minutes. She can't have read a single article, not so that she would've got anything out of it, anyway. You know the way, when *you're* in there, you'd be there for, oh, half an hour, at least . . .'

'Yeah.'

'Not her. Have you noticed? Well I have. So I stood outside and listened one day. Nearly threw up in the garden afterwards when I worked it out.'

'Well, you always have had that funny stomach.'

'For godsakes. Do you realise what you're condoning?'

'Um . . .'

And it's a difficult issue, this one. Just because unicorns are exotic creatures doesn't mean that you expect them to have no grasp of plumbing, but what do you say? They can tend to take offence easily.

'There's probably no harm in it,' is the best I can do. 'What about live and let live?'

But I know I don't sound convincing. And I'm right.

'Well done, chinless,' the unicorn says. 'Well fucking done. I can't believe you sometimes. I mean, I was sick when I worked it out. This is really upsetting me, and she's pretending she doesn't even know.'

And I suppose I can see the unicorn's point. The girl isn't very sensitive, and I suppose I have been condoning that, when maybe I should have done more. If she's doing things that upset the unicorn, she really shouldn't. I don't. It's not hard.

Things were okay here, till she came along. And now the two of them aren't getting on at all, and I keep getting caught in the middle. The girl's the problem, most of the time. She gets shitty with the unicorn for counting the rent money by tapping its hooves on the polished wooden floor.

But, as the unicorn says, 'How the fuck can I count if I can't hear it? If I did it on the carpet we wouldn't know what was going on.'

And so what if the unicorn spills a bit of chaff about the place? So what if the unicorn smokes that much? It's never inside. The girl should cut the unicorn some slack. That's what I think.

Not that the unicorn's perfect. After all, I can't use the toilet at home any more. That's pretty clear. Unless I'm only going there to read one of my back issues of HQ. But it's all about being sensitive (something the girl isn't) and taking your housemate's needs into account, even if the housemate is being a bit, well, over-sensitive.

And these things, things like shitting in the toilet at home, they're just habits, and easy to change if it's for the best. As if there aren't thousands of toilets in the western suburbs, and all of them built for just that purpose. Why doesn't she realise how upset the unicorn is, and change her ways? It's not too much to ask, surely. I'd be so embarrassed if it was me doing it.

The last thing I'd want to do is upset the unicorn (or anyone, really), but why can't the girl be that reasonable? Then we wouldn't have these problems.

In the evenings, the unicorn and I spend more and more time sitting on the back steps talking. Sometimes I go inside to watch TV with the girl, but the unicorn's starting to get jealous when I do that, so I have to do it pretty selectively. I've tried to explain. I'm just watching TV. I'm not being with her watching TV. We both just happen to be watching TV. Besides, the girl says less and less, anyway. I've tried not to take sides, but neither of them has made it easy.

So I have to put a lot of time in on the back steps. Me just sitting, staring off into space, the unicorn smoking and telling me anti-girl jokes downloaded from the Internet and laughing that deep, gurgling laugh.

And it was all okay, well, not okay, but sort of manageable, until the unicorn got stressed about the reading room. That, I suppose, was when I knew we were in trouble, that some of our problems as a household were more than superficial.

So I organise a house meeting to try to fix the situation before it's too late. But it doesn't work. Of course it doesn't work, and the girl starts it, getting at the unicorn with the usual stupid accusations. Bringing flies into the house. Chewing the brim of her straw hat. That kind of thing. One baseless allegation after another.

'Well, you,' the unicorn says, unable to take it any more, 'you go into that room there,' pointing at the toilet, 'and you don't even read. I know what you do.'

'What?' The girl is confused.

'Garden not good enough for you, then?'

'What?' More confused.

'You go in there,' the unicorn says, only just keeping control, 'and you shit, girl. I know you do. You can't deny it. You shit in there. And you,' pause for effect, 'stick paper up your end.'

For a few seconds nothing happens.

'Perfumed paper,' the unicorn says, as though it's necessary.

And the girl looks perplexed, looks at me, and I realise she might be going to cry. She blinks, she goes red. She's angry. More than angry, it's not that straightforward. And I'm pretty sure she is going to cry.

'It may not be quite like that,' I say, in my usual gutless, peacemaker voice.

'Don't tell me,' the unicorn says. 'I don't want to know.'

The girl takes a quick breath in, and then another. She turns, and runs to her room. These walls are thin, and I can hear crying, muffled not quite enough by her pillow.

'And what is that now?' the unicorn says. 'Fuck, she makes some silly noises. Can you understand a word of it?'

'I think she's upset.'

'Upset? She,' pause for emphasis, 'shits in your reading room. If I had half your attachment to those magazines I'd be slinging her out. Get some chin about you, Stanley. Stand up for yourself for Christ's sake.'

And that, pretty much, is that.

We adjourn to the back steps. The unicorn smokes. Sings the blues in a frivolous falsetto, clops his front hooves together and says, 'Sounds just like coconuts, doesn't it?' As though nothing's happened.

I go inside and make myself a cup of tea. I don't know what I'm going to do to fix this. I go out onto the verandah and round to the girl's French doors and I tap on the glass.

'You want some tea?'

'No. Thanks. No.'

'Look, that all got a bit out of hand.'

She says nothing.

'There were things said that . . .'

'Don't. Don't even try. We just don't get on, and that's how it is. Stop trying to fix it. I mean, thanks, but it won't do any good. And in the end . . . in the end, you'll always take the unicorn's side.'

'But I don't want there to be sides.'

'You'd better get back out there.'

'Yeah. So . . . are you up for the X-Files at eight-thirty?'

'Maybe.'

I go back inside, drop my teabag in the bin, join the unicorn on the steps again.

'Took you a while,' the unicorn says.

'Yeah. I just thought I'd offer her some tea. No big deal. I'd make tea for you if you liked it. You know that.'

'Oh yeah.'

And the unicorn coughs, and its eyes bulge and it leans forward until it sicks the ragged ribbon from the girl's straw hat up out of its mouth.

'Fucking ribbons,' it says. 'What are they about? They're bloody dangerous.'

'Have you eaten her hat? The rest of her hat.'

The unicorn says nothing, toys with moist shreds of ribbon.

'I can't believe you'd do that,' I tell the unicorn. 'I defended you in there. I defended you when she said you'd been eating her hat.'

'Yeah, well. Didn't ask you to.'

'I just wish we could all get on.'

'Yeah. But, it's not going to happen, is it? She's just not like you and me. Not really. We'll never understand her, will we? And one day, hopefully, she'll just fuck off. Back to wherever she's come from. And we can be a bit more choosy about Number Three next time. Or maybe keep the place for just the two of us.'

Said by the unicorn as a good thing, but it worries me. The girl pisses the unicorn off so easily, and I can't help but think I could be next. That one of any twenty things about me might enrage the unicorn if it so much as noticed them.

And the chaff the unicorn spills probably is what brings the rats in. That's what the girl says, and I've been dismissing it as some vendetta. And the unicorn blames the rats on the fact that the girl wears only edible fibres. So I buy polyester now. But I don't think that's the issue any more. I think the girl might be right.

And twice we've had to fix the bit of the floor where the unicorn counts, and the girl has said the landlord won't stand for much more of it. She said she's talked to the landlord and the unicorn said that was bullshit. Said, 'What did the landlord expect us to do? Stop counting? Guess the rent money?'

And later the unicorn said to me, 'I never see her count a thing, you know. She just hands it over. I think she's got something going with the landlord. I think they want us out of here. That's what I think.'

So I got used to counting by tapping the floor with my shoe, or at least telling the unicorn I'd done it in my room. And that seems a bit silly, now. But it's like the reading room. There's nothing I can do to fix this situation between them. Maybe it's just that the girl holds such a hard line on all these things. When really, it's no problem to go to the toilet in other places, and make sure you never need to at home. She knows how much that upsets the unicorn, and she just won't budge. It'd upset anyone if she shitted in any other room, after all, and how's the unicorn to know the difference?

If only she'd just give a little, if they'd both give a little. But they're both so stubborn.

When the X-Files comes on, I go back inside and leave the unicorn to it, muttering away, saying things like 'I reckon you like her,' under its breath. And calling me slack and spineless and 'just plain fucked in the head sometimes'.

All of which I ignore. The girl's still in her room. I go round and tap on the glass again.

'X-Files,' I tell her.

'Could you tape it?'

'Come and watch.'

'I don't want to go out there.'

'But this is where you live. You should be able to go into the lounge room.'

'Tell that to your friend.'

'Nothing's stopping you going into the lounge room.'

'Stan, I don't know how to say this nicely, but wake up.'

'Yeah, look, I know. I know there are problems. I spend my life trying to fix them. Now please, let's just be normal. Just a bit normal. Come out of your room, please. Come and watch the X-Files.'

She says, 'Okay,' and opens the French doors. 'Okay.'

But it's not okay. That's where she stops. And says, 'Oh, shit,' and starts to cry again.

And I move forward as though I can help somehow. And she puts her hand up as though she can push the whole thing away, and her hand ends up on my chest, steadying her.

With her other hand she rubs at her eyes. And then she looks up at me.

'Stupid, really,' she says. 'I shouldn't let it get to me.'

'Yeah, but it's not easy. I know it's not easy.'

And I kiss her on the mouth. She looks at me, looks funny about it.

'Sorry,' I say to her. 'I'm really sorry. I don't know . . .'

'It's all right.' She smiles, hugs me in a brisk, business-like forgiving way. 'Let's go and watch the X-Files.'

I can't concentrate, of course. I'm sitting there wondering why the hell I kissed the girl. Wondering if it's some bad thing to do with her vulnerability, the vulnerability that she had about her, just for that moment. And that really sucks. It's a bad reason to kiss someone. And then I think, maybe I wanted to kiss her, maybe I have for ages. And I shouldn't think that. Maybe I know the unicorn's weird and nasty, and maybe I haven't been brave enough to say anything. But I shouldn't have kissed the girl, whatever.

So I apologise again in the ad break, and she says it's still fine. And she gives me a look, quite a nice look. Not a look that says (if looks can ever say) 'kiss me again'. But a look that might say at least something like, 'I bet you don't kiss the unicorn.' And it's good watching the X-Files with her, and I'm glad the unicorn's outside. Smoking, singing at the night sky.

But I realise this could be trouble if I'm not careful. If the girl and I talk too much, something like that. So next ad break, I decide I should go out to the back steps and even things up, time-wise.

And the girl gives me a different look, a look that says that I should know better, but that also says she kind of knew I wouldn't know better. Disappointment.

Maybe it's not that kind of look, but if it isn't it should be. Maybe she's not even looking at me, but she should be and she should be making it clear I'm letting her down. I shouldn't have kissed her. It was like taking a side. I've got to be more careful here.

'You,' the unicorn says, as though I've been away ages and my return's a surprise.

'Yeah.'

'You must have drowned her in tea by now.'

'Do you want some?'

'I don't drink tea. You know I don't drink tea.'

'Yeah. I think it's okay to do things for people. Cups of tea and things.'

The unicorn harrumphs and looks away. Stubs the cigarette butt into the fibro wall of the house. Breathes out smoke.

'A beer'd be good,' the unicorn says. 'We should both have a beer.'

So I go into the kitchen for a couple of stubbies and flip the tops off while the girl watches. It's disdain now. The look has gone from disappointment to disdain. I make a face at her that's supposed to say 'well what the hell can I do?', but I don't think she gets it. She goes blank, looks back at the TV. As though I'm not worth the trouble. As though I should get out. And I shouldn't have kissed her.

Back on the steps, the unicorn is shaking another cigarette out of the packet. It takes the beer and it's about to drink when its nostrils flare.

'What's that?' it says.

'What?'

'That smell.'

'What smell?'

'Don't play dumb, Stanley.' And there's a hint of menace now and I just don't get it. 'I smell girl. There's girl on your breath.'

'What?'

'You heard me.'

'Look . . .'

'Look nothing. I don't believe it. She did that mouth thing to you didn't she?'

'What?'

'She did that mouth thing. And you didn't even stop her. You and the girl have done the mouth thing. I could just spew.'

'No . . .'

'Oh come on. Don't lie as well. You chinless, gutless, dribbly piece of shit.'

And there's nothing I can say. Nothing that wouldn't make things worse.

'I'm going to fix her,' the unicorn says. 'I'm going to fucking fix her. She should have gone long ago.'

'No.'

But the unicorn is on its feet and striding into the house before I can say more. Before I can think of anything helpful.

And then there's shouting going on, from both of them. Shouting at the same time, and I can't bear it. All kinds of anger and accusations. And I'm stuck on the steps. Stuck out here with the beer I didn't want, looking out into the back-yard, and darkness.

The unicorn kicks a chair over. I know it's the unicorn, because the girl wouldn't. And she's crying again, and that's how we got into some of these problems in the first place. I wish she wouldn't cry.

And she's shouting about leaving and the unicorn's shouting about it being about bloody time. And I hear something medium-sized, maybe the coffee table, maybe a speaker, hit the wall and splinter.

And the unicorn bellows and bellows and the girl doesn't say much now. She shouldn't have turned this into a fight. She should know how mad the unicorn gets. Sometimes you just go to your room till it blows over. She should know that.

But I've never heard the unicorn like this before. Louder and louder. Bellowing. Hooves taking chunks out of the floor. And then a thump. And quiet.

I don't want to go in, but I know I have to. The talking's stopped in there. Everything's stopped. And it can't be good.

I go in, and the girl is up against the far wall, with her feet off the ground. Stuck there on the end of the unicorn's horn. Hanging there with her head cocked to one side and her eyes wide open. And the unicorn's horn has driven right through her, up through her chest and out through her back and lodged in the wall behind her.

And the unicorn looks at me, sideways, still stuck there through the girl and into the wall, blood splattered all over its face and all the muscles in its shoulders twisting to get it free.

'Jesus, Stan,' it says. 'I think I've gored her. Gored her something wicked. Why the fuck didn't you tell me I had that thing up there?'

sausage sizzle

Second year starts as it was always likely to. Frank Green is pissed on Creme de Menthe again.

Which would be fine, if we hadn't volunteered for barbecue duty at the faculty orientation sausage sizzle. Fine, if his naughty-French-maid apron didn't keep flapping so close to the heat beads.

'It's how to meet 'em,' he said, when he volunteered us for it weeks ago. 'Be the man with the tongs. Save the biggest snags for the spunks and offer them up with some witticism.'

And he was about to move right into the witticism, I could tell, so I held up my hand and said, 'Save a little magic for the day, Frank. It's got to sound fresh.'

'Sure,' he said, the magic already on his mind. 'Mate. First years.' Said like a carnivore talking about gazelle flank. 'First years.' Said as though he was telling me right then he'd be rooting himself stupid by sundown.

First years. I was far too scared when I started first year to think that sex might actually happen. But deciding to be a lot less scared lately hasn't made it any more likely, and that doesn't seem fair. Hanging around with Frank was, I thought, a bit of a plus. Now I'm not so sure.

'So how long's it been since you've been close to a root?' Frank says, eyeing off the herd of grazing first years, as though he's doing it on my behalf. While reading my mind, but maybe it's easily read.

'Dunno,' I tell him, which is a lie, since it's no problem to add nine months to my age and come up with something just over nineteen years.

Already, I'm thinking today will not be the day that changes my luck. Already I'm thinking that maybe my best possible outcome would be that we both miss out. Then at least I won't have to get the phone call from Frank in the morning. The lurid, sweaty detail. I just hate imagining Frank naked. I wish he didn't feel the need to call.

He takes a sip of his tall green drink and the ice cubes clink against the sides. He's famous for it now, his Creme de Menthe. And its strategic implications. 'Much quicker than beer,' he's said regularly. 'You'd be a fool to try to get pissed on beer once you know the green drink.'

So we've swapped, in a way. I'm okay with beer now, a few beers. And with the barbecue fired up and a few dozen sausages to turn, I'm on my second light for the afternoon, alternating with water. Which reminds me. Today I was gone before I started, really.

My mother drove me here, never a good beginning to an event.

'But I'm heading that way, Philby,' she said.

And I said, 'No you aren't.'

And she half-pursed her lips and said, 'Get in the car.'

And I sat there in the traffic in the foul sun, every second talking myself closer to ruin. Sweating and wanting to stay home and wallow in the pool. Hating barbecues and preferring watermelon and feeling the mad fluttering of trouble let loose once again in my stomach as I thought about the next few hours.

She talked on and on, in vague and offensively encouraging tones, but didn't quite say anything encouraging enough that I could go off at her about it. She's getting better at me being a loser, and the only thing worse than that is, so am I.

'It's stinking hot today,' she said as I peeled myself from the passenger seat upholstery and climbed out of the car, trying not to hear her say things like 'tenner for a cab home' (though I took it, of course) and 'I'll make a bed up for Frank, shall I?'

I just wanted her to go away, go away, let me sneak away from her privately, and I'd made it as far as the refec steps when I heard her shout, 'Be careful, Philby. Watch your fluids.'

And I ignored her utterly, but the world knew just whose mother she was, and I got several pieces of good advice about fluids over the next half-hour or so.

It's my confidence problem, and it just isn't going. And putting a name to it's only made it seem like some disease

I've got, and helped me to anticipate everything it puts me through.

Any time I'm in the vicinity of a heterosexual female of approachable age, I get a bit edgy. I think I've been saving myself for a little too long without ever meaning to. I am comprehensively inexperienced. I am stuck at the stage just before the conversation stage, and I know enough to know that that's very stuck, and far removed from the main game.

It's all down to attitude, I know that, and I've worked on it. I rehearse in my room, saying plenty of clever things quietly into my pillow, factoring in a range of possible girl responses and working out where I might take the conversation from there. And my mother thinks my sensitive side's a plus and my pillow thinks I'm a right charmer, but in the real world I'm like a pencil-drawn outline of my better self.

I go to the faculty functions. Frank makes me. I'm the man with the plan (he makes me say that, over and over), and soon enough, I'm as dynamic as paint in there. Silent and desperately two-D up against the wall and wanting to try again some other night. Or never. Looking around at the casual talk and the coupling and realising I'm so seriously behind in this faculty that I have to have some form about me first time up, and practice (verbal or otherwise) just isn't going to get me there.

I thought this'd get better. It's got so bad my mother even told me that she'd thought it'd get better. It's so bad she offered to buy me a book on it, and in that instant it got much worse.

I think the eighteenth century was good, plenty of

other centuries were probably good. I think you could write poems for girls then (or sometimes even just quote someone else's), and make them love you before you even met. At least, in some cases. I'd be up for that. I write the odd poem.

Frank doesn't. Well, occasional limericks, but only when he can find two rhymes for 'hornbag', and that's not the same thing. But it works for him. He keeps the limericks for the guys and gets the girl action he wants, better than 30 per cent of the time, and he never gets stuck in a relationship.

We work the barbecue and heat wells up from the beads and the sun flogs us from behind, through the spindly trees that grow out of the rockery. And there's not much enthusiasm today for meat.

Frank toys with a fat ten-inch sausage and says, 'This beast'd be mine,' any time a first year (female) comes up to the barbecue area, but it usually only costs him eye contact and doesn't get him far.

He's surprisingly resilient though, when it comes to things like this. He calls it 'the numbers', reckoning he's got nothing to lose, a 2 per cent chance of success each time and an awful lot of sausages to serve. Frank's more strategic than he looks. Frank knows intercourse never happens by chance, even though you have to make it look as though it does.

'Never had a root I didn't have to work two hours for,' he once told me, as though it was advice.

I ask him if he wants just a plain water next, and he

says, 'Nuh.' Quaffs a mouthful of green. He points out possibles in the crowd, telling me, 'I'd go her. I'd go her in a flash. Sizzle, baby, sizzle,' he says, staring shamelessly, poking his now-favourite sausage with the tongs and giving a bit of a jiggle of his hips.

'Those three over there,' he says. 'Those three. Second-year physios, aren't they? I've seen them at a few of these things before. I'm giving them heaps of eye, mate. You can even have first pick and I'll take the other two. Can't say fairer than that.'

And he slurps Creme de Menthe, gives me a dirty man's wink. Frank Green is the only person I know who expects to both get drunk and have sex every time he leaves the house, and that ends up giving him a great outlook on life. Even though most of the time he only manages to get drunk.

But he's going to get lucky today. I can tell. He's got the confidence going, more than usual even, mainly because of the sausage. He doesn't often get to operate with the aid of such an overt symbol of his penis. People like confidence. Frank told me once, or several times, that someone had described him as 'fully self-actualised', and he's quite proud of that. Sometimes he even tells girls. Sometimes he explains it to them as meaning that he's 'pretty much 100 per cent horn, baby'. On two occasions known to me, he has alleged that this claim has led to intercourse, reasonably quickly.

There are days when Frank Green's whole world scares me, even though I'm a part of it. Days when I know the maths is stacked against me, and I know that I'm only about 20 per cent self-actualised, and feeling no more than fifteen.

'So pick,' he says. 'Which one?'

'The one with the nose,' I tell him, but I know that I'm fucked.

I slip into a tail spin and sludge a few onions around on the hotplate. I like the smell of onions cooking. I like it when people don't talk to me or when they just go, 'Hey, great onions.' I like the idea of someone wanting you, in a nice way, wanting to be with you and things, and other things arising as a consequence. I like days that are not dominated by performance anxiety and fear of the unknown, and I have them sometimes. Most recently, there was a day two weeks ago just like that.

I serve more onions, to low-key acclaim.

Meanwhile Frank has spiked his massive sausage with a fork and is passing one end of it in and out of his mouth in order to attract attention.

So far, no attention.

Frank, again, has managed to be the first person at a faculty function to have far too much to drink. So his Creme de Menthe theory's holding up.

And I'm here, the loser onion boy in the rain shadow of Frank's dumb porn display, and it's more than possible that we could both be looking like idiots.

'Put it down,' I tell him. 'I'll never have sex in my whole life if you don't put that down.'

'Oh,' he says, a little surprised. 'Okay, sorry.'

And my outburst costs us a customer, but it had to be said.

Then for quite a while nothing happens. Frank stares at
the same three physio students, continues to deliver them
heaps of eye. They laugh and show him the finger and stay
right where they are, squirting more cask red into their
plastic cups and looking impressively unenticed.

'Jeez, we're not doing so well,' Frank says, swigging a
mouthful of Creme de Menthe right from the bottle and
swaying subtly to the left and then back again.

'I think people have enough meat for now. There'll be
some back for seconds.'

'You know that's not what I mean.'

And the day's about to get easier. He's about to join me
in the tail spin. His confidence has risen to foolish heights
and he's about to do the Icarus thing. It's a semi-regular
pattern, and I can pick when it's going to happen. From
Greek mythology, Frank has learned nothing.

'I can't believe we could both leave here today without
pulling some action,' he says, totally believing it. 'I don't
know what's going on. What's going on?'

'The usual. The 70 per cent of the time for you 100 per
cent of the time for me usual, dickhead.'

'Might have to pick up a mag on the way home. Would
you be up for that?'

'What, buying you another porn mag?'

'No. Go you halves. The usual.'

'Frank, this is very depressing. No-one even wants our
food any more.'

'What is this?' he says. 'It's still only the fucking afternoon. I can't believe we're gone already.'

'Yeah, but it's too hot. Too hot to eat this stuff.'

'I don't care if they eat it or not. We're not cooking it so people can eat it. Will you stop talking about the fucking food?'

I'm finding it easier to deal with in terms of the food, but all of a sudden Frank's finding nothing easy. A shitty kind of silence seems to descend upon us. The three women, now no longer being worked on by Frank's eye, seem to have noted the substantial semi-circle of space in front of us, and seem to be smirking. He tips a couple of steaks and another tray of sausages onto the barbecue, but half-heartedly and only so that he's got something to do.

And I actually like Frank better when he's depressed, but it's not as though I don't feel guilty about it.

Fat spits and the sausages sizzle and one of them sticks on the hot metal and rips and Frank mutters something that begins with, 'Can't even fuckin' . . .'

'It's okay,' I tell him. 'I quite like the crunchy bits. That one can be mine.'

At the edge of the crowd, one of the three women (the one with the nose) crushes their empty wine cask under her foot and starts to make her way over to the bar. And then the other two start heading our way. They must have seen Frank put the new stuff on. I give him a nudge, and his instincts have kicked in by the time they get to us.

'Can I tempt either of you ladies with my meat?' he says, mustering his most seductive patter from somewhere and emphasising the word meat as much as possible.

'Not really,' one of them says and smirks again. 'Not our scene.'

'Can't believe you've come all this way for Philby's onions,' he says, and I could kill him for it, but it's already too late.

'No. Listen,' she says. 'We were just thinking. You guys, you're working hard, and you're not looking too cheery. Specially you.' Looking at me. Which is bad, since Frank's still looking pretty glum. 'We were thinking, you'd be due for a break round about now, wouldn't you?'

'For sure,' Frank says, as though all the eye work's paying off and the day's finally starting to make sense.

'Yeah. That's what we were thinking. And, well . . .' she pauses, looks at the one who hasn't spoken, and gets a nod. 'We were feeling like a bit of a break from this ourselves, hey Lisa?'

'Yeah.'

And even Frank is gawking at them, at the possibilities of this, and how easy it's looking for both of us. Even Frank doesn't think he's this good with the eye, and knows it's the kind of scenario he normally only lies about when we're driving to uni, not something that actually happens. And even though, in the usual way, I don't expect I'll be able to speak for the next couple of hours, it might not be a problem, since I guess I'm with Lisa, and she doesn't seem like much of a talker.

'So what have you got in mind?' Frank says, pretty sure of what they've got in mind.

Am I ready for this? No. No way. Can I stop it? Can I go

home now? Could I please meet someone nice, and have some say in what happens to me? My hand pokes around with the tongs, and shakes. I imagine Lisa without clothes, and me in the vicinity. The shake gets worse.

'Well, this is the interesting bit,' the non-Lisa one says. 'You know that totally bullshit guy fantasy? The one about getting to watch two lesbians?'

And Frank says, 'Yeah,' just as I'm saying 'What?'

And she looks at me and says, 'That fantasy. The one about watching two women doing it. Well, we just thought, we were feeling kind of sorry for you. And sometimes we quite like to be watched.'

And she's saying this right at me, so I have to say something back, but all I can say is, 'God. Are you serious? Isn't it kind of a private thing?'

She gives a shrug. 'All right. Just asking. Just thought it could be, you know, fun.'

'Um,' Frank says, to stop them going, as he makes a big deal of turning a steak that doesn't need it.

'Yeah?'

'You'd be thinking, like, now? Inside somewhere?'

'Yeah.'

He turns the steak again, two or three times.

'Oh, I could be up for it,' he says. 'It's getting hot out here. And I reckon we've fed everyone. Hey Phil?'

And now I remember a few times when we've bought the mags. And how we often, well, usually, end up with one featuring an alleged lesbian scenario. And that whenever Frank's made me chip in, the lesbian scenario always ends up in his half. There may be a pattern at work, and one not quite covered by Frank's usual explanation of, 'Hey Philby, twice the norks.'

'Um,' he says, in a way that makes it clear there's more to it than um. 'Any chance of one of you, you know, giving me a bit of a working over?'

'What do you mean?'

'Oh, you know, physically. Whatever. Nothing funny. Just, like, with something. Like a belt, or . . .'

'Aw, yuk. What do you think this is?'

'Hey, just asking.'

And Lisa says, quietly but firmly, 'I think I could.'

'And could you, you know, talk and stuff?'

'Not much of a talker.'

'I'm not looking for anything fancy.'

'Maybe, then. But, you know, it's not totally sexual. To be honest, you really shitted me off all last year at any of the faculty things we had. So, you know, I'm up for it.'

'Look, if we're being honest, I don't mind if you hate me,' And he passes me his tongs and says, 'You'll be right?' And I nod and he says, 'Well. Girls. What are we waiting for?'

He picks up his bottle of Creme de Menthe, and the three of them walk off into the crowd, like people on their way to a lecture, no hint of what they're planning.

And now that I think about it, all the leather and pain stuff tends to end up in Frank's half of the mag as well. Actually, it's possible that we've never bought a mag that hasn't had at least one alleged lesbian scenario and something to do with riding crops, but the whole pain thing makes me very uneasy, so I've never complained when Frank guts the raunchy bits and I end up with only the articles. Which, come to think of it, always seems to be the way.

And the third of the women, the one who went inside first, the one with the nose, is now out again with a jug of red wine, and she comes over to me.

'So they've gone, have they?' she says.

'Yeah. Frank and your two . . . friends? Yeah.'

'Not your thing, hey?'

'Well, no, to be honest. I don't actually get it.'

'So what do you get?'

'God, not much really.'

Somehow it's easy to say this to her, so I tell her I've never had brilliant results with girls, much as I'd like to. It's almost like talking to a guy, talking about girls with a lesbian, and knowing there's nothing at stake. So I tell her, sort of as a joke, that I think it must have been easier in other centuries, and I run my poetry theory by her. And she laughs, but nicely. I've never told anyone my poetry theory before.

And I say to her, 'Maybe you can help me. I've got this thing. This thing where I can't get started. It's like, I can't even start a conversation with a girl, a straight girl, in case it doesn't work out. Frank says I should play the numbers, and not care if it doesn't work out, but I just don't think that's me, because I do care. And I'd like to, you know, get to know them a bit. I can't start the conversation maybe partly because I like it. I like the talking. I like the idea that one thing leads to another when you're ready for it to, but I don't think that's how things work. It's a dumb idea.'

'Is this some line?' she says, and laughs.

And I laugh too, since we both know how useless a line would be. 'No. I'm not that dumb.'

I ask her her name, realising I can't keep thinking about her as Lesbian Number Three, and it turns out it's Melissa.

It also turns out that I like her and, without the possibility of sexual tension, that's much easier to do than usual. In other circumstances, though clearly not these, I could find her attractive. But even as things are we could be friends, which wouldn't be so bad.

I can make her laugh, and she seems to like it. I certainly do.

She takes Frank's tongs and we cook the food together for the people who want seconds. She tells me a few things about girls, straight girls, and I don't mind listening, even if she is making them up.

Demand dies down again, and it's just the two of us, turning things.

'You're looking a bit sweaty there,' she says.

'Well, yeah. It's thirty-seven degrees and I'm stuck behind a barbecue.'

'You know what? I think it's somebody else's turn.'

'Probably.'

'A swim'd be good.'

'I've been thinking that all day.'

'Yeah, but I live in a flat a couple of streets away, and we've got a pool.'

'Oh, that'd be great. So are you going to round up a few people?'

'No, I hadn't really thought of it that way. I was thinking you and me. It's not a big pool, but it'd be nice. And no-one ever uses it. And maybe we could have something to eat other than this shit,' she says, turning a steak I'm in the process of thoughtlessly charring.

'Oh yeah?'

'Yeah.'

She pours herself more red wine from the jug, takes a sip.

And I'm thinking, can you actually ask someone if they aren't a lesbian? Can you actually get someone to confirm right now that they're the lesbian you'd thought they were, so that you can relax again and get back to the conversation.

'Yeah. Just us,' she says. 'A jug of wine, a loaf of bread and thou,' in a voice that turns self-consciously Elizabethan at the end.

She shuffles a few crispy onion bits.

'Oh right. Once more into the breech, dear friends,' I say in something like panic, then crash internally as I contemplate simultaneously the sudden strange obstetric overtones, and the fact that I think the next line has something to do with our English dead. 'Sorry. I . . .'

'It's fine. I like *Henry V*. It was a bit of a surprise, but . . .'

'Can I've another go?'

'Sure. Got anything less war-like?'

'That's the plan. Um . . . give me a sec.' Someone wanders

up and I dish out another couple of overdone sausages, thinking frantically, thinking till I'm in such a knot it almost hurts. But there's nothing. Nothing that'll work. And, damn it, I've come so far. Tail spin. Nose dive. Warning. This woman may not be a lesbian. 'No,' I tell her, and then I hear myself continue, ignoring the loud internal voice that's shouting, idiot, idiot, shut up you stupid dumb virgin, 'I'm stuck. I've got one from Marlowe, but it's a bit much. For just having a swim.'

'That's okay.'

'Even with the wine and bread. And the thou. A bit much.'

'It's okay.'

Frank lurches out from behind the building, waving his empty bottle and stumbling down the stairs. He staggers over our way, lifts up his apron front and shows me welts.

Where his shirt's gone, I don't know. And his shorts too, unfortunately. And did Lisa get his underpants as part of the deal?

'Snug fit you've got down there, Frank,' I tell him, but he just says 'Woo-woo, woo-woo,' jerking his right hand up and down as though he's pulling on something round about shoulder level. 'Woo-woo.' Like The Little Engine That Just Did. 'And they reckon rubber doesn't show,' he shouts. 'They should try the tubes on the Bunsen burners in Two Twelve.'

'They've practically perished. They're pretty grungy. They'd sting.'

'Oh, yeah. And she really fucking hated me. You too.'

'What?'

'I kept saying to her, it's Frank, it's Frank, but all she wanted to scream was "All men are bastards".' He burps, in a dangerous kind of way, as though there's much more than gas at stake. 'Fuck,' he says, in a deep, spooky voice. 'I smell mint.'

And he scrambles for the rockery.

'The man's an idiot,' Melissa says, as we listen to him turning most of his internal organs inside out among the cacti. 'Why would anyone . . . he's an idiot. Sorry, he's your friend, isn't he?'

'Yeah, but . . . Let's go for that swim. Let's go now.'

dog one, dog two

You are unsure of all of this, but maybe that's just you.

Ever since the dean lined you up for 'The Influence, If Any, of Maternal Low-dose Piroxicam on the Development of the Sublingual Fat Pad in Foetal Marmosets' as your doctoral thesis, you have realised that the world progresses in particularly small steps – some of them (some of the biggest) backwards, and a great many sideways in scream-ing lunatic tangents, arms flapping, lips slathering, eyes bulging with the glee of infinitesimal discovery. Such, you feel, is your work with, for, and on behalf of the mar-mosets. They didn't thank you. Their eyes bulged only with a feral, shuffling ignorance. Ignorance of your intent, igno-rance of their antenatal exposure to piroxicam and its implications (if any), ignorance even of their own sublin-gual fat pads. Science barely thanked you, either. It gave you your doctorate, one paper, one lecture, and a one-way ticket to more of this.

So now you are here, at Kranfield Pharmaceuticals, with perhaps your only progress the fact that you no longer work under the insipid gaze of marmosets. This is not an insipid lab. It is under the control of a man called Robert who is far from insipid. He is, in fact, a complete shit.

He seems to ooze when he moves, and he has great difficulty controlling flatulence. At times, when you are updating him about your work, his cheeks redden, his eyes bulge (though not with the innocence of marmosets) and he stares a good distance away, manoeuvring uncomfortably on his lab stool. It is as though he is carefully digesting what you are telling him and, realising its worthlessness, he is about to shit it in front of you. You go out of your way to make your reports hard, nuggety, pointed, just to put pain on his face as he purges himself of your cleverness.

All of this is part of the unspoken collective consciousness of the lab. That which has been spoken allows a disgruntled worker to refer to a bad day as one that would really give you the Roberts.

The man is a shit, and though it's not just your problem you feel it more keenly than most, as the only other person in the lab with a doctorate.

The main thrust of your present work involves dogs. Someone at Kranfield has taken the familiar piroxicam molecule (a fine drug and a great earner, but, regrettably, someone else's), fiddled with a side-chain, and slapped a patent on the end result. You have to prove that it's safe for humans, or, at least, unlikely to be downright dangerous.

You do this with dogs, and in increasingly large doses.

Now, dogs aren't cheap, so you can't do it with thousands. Unfortunately, you have a small enough number to name them, chat to them, invent personalities for them with the help of the technicians. Dog One becomes Rowan, after your large and lazy brother-in-law, Dog Two becomes AB following his excellence in specific physical tests, the fact that he's an all-round good bloke with the respect of the whole team and a general feeling that he would be more than willing to stand up to the most venomous eight-foot West Indian fast bowler, and with a straight bat, too. And so it goes.

You are clearly bored with the work, but perhaps you should have thought this naming business through. You should have learned all the necessary lessons about scientific detachment around the time you were snipping the tongues from new-born marmosets. But revulsion soon gave way to statistics, writing, proofreading, revising, waiting, waiting, waiting. And then word from the dean that the examiners were giving the thumbs up.

And the dean had a contact at Kranfield Pharmaceuticals, and here you are.

And out comes the new piroxicam derivative, so where are the marmosets? But this time, it's labradors. And they wag their tails when you feed them something munchy after giving them forty times the recommended human dose of the drug. You know you have to do this, you know that people can't be the first. But what about Rowan, AB, Wozza, Nataly and the rest? All so happy to see you in the morning.

You exercise them vigorously twice a day to maximise opportunities for wear and tear. Periodically you X-ray their knees. Eventually, you will look at the tissues of their knee joints under a microscope, administering various stains to assess progression of disease, or degree of cartilage preservation.

One night, in a dream, you set them free. All of them. You see them bounding through the night with knees glowing from numerous X-rays. Wafting silently into the distance like a blissful cloud of fireflies. And you are alone. There is an unpleasant smell, and a fart cracks the night like a walnut, and Robert is beside you. Questioning you. Oozing again. You depress his tongue with a spatula and pump in several litres of the drug, which then sets like concrete. His face goes red and he looks over your shoulder, grunting with some discomfort. In the enormous effort to shit he splits in two, the last thing to collapse into the rubble his bewildered, puffed-up face.

But you are unlikely to do the world this much good in your entire life. You are a known killer of marmosets, about to move on to animals that actually like you.

On the bus into the city you would tell people, explain yourself. Explain that you are doing it for them. But striking up a conversation about marmosets, your marmosets, or even your labradors, would be as welcome as telling them how much better your life has been since you met Jesus. And offering them some helpful literature. A woman once did this to you on a bus and then she hit you for a donation. So now if anyone says hi you just look straight ahead. No-one says hi.

You change buses in town. In the second bus, too, no-one says hi. People talk only to people they already know, so you have no chance to unburden yourself, or to make any religious purchases. The bus works its way through the commuter traffic, and the passengers, who all appear to be students, are talking about their distaste for eight o'clock lectures and their plans to seek extensions for assignments. And you want to tell them about the real world. You want to tell them that when they were born someone might have cut their tongues out to check the fat pads. But no-one did, and they don't know how lucky they are.

But one or two of them do look a little like marmosets. And you imagine that the bus is rocking along a lonely, dirt road late at night and you are a prisoner of the marmosets. And they look at you with those eyes again. They turn and they look at you over the seats and they say nothing. They show you their empty mouths, they show you they have no tongues, and they never take their eyes off you. Dozens of them. You find an old pamphlet pushed down next to the seat. You pull it out as though it might distract them and you say, Jesus anyone?

At this moment you realise you are holding an empty barbecue-chip packet between the heads of the two students sitting in front of you. They decline politely, as if it is clear to them you are disturbed, but not dangerous. They move up to the front of the bus to tell their friends about the madman who just offered them Cheezels from an empty barbeque-chip packet. There is considerable laughter at your expense. Students are like that. Despite the embarrassment you are not glad when your stop arrives.

At morning tea you crunch through a plateful of the hard, wheaty biscuits of which you have grown fond, and real life doesn't hold too many answers.

And Robert doesn't make things any easier. He's becoming even more territorial, even more protective of what he's doing. Less willing to let you into his office, even though access to the computer is essential to your work. He sits in the corner scratching himself, grumbling under his breath, making smells. And you are glad to enter your data and leave.

You tell him you should wait a good time before killing the dogs, or the work will have little value. You're not going soft, are you, he says. You wouldn't catch me going soft. And he laughs a hoarse laugh and he bares his teeth. He is a compendium of unpleasant habits, and they're only getting worse.

You return to the exercise yard to run the dogs. They're pleased to see you. They jump up to you, paw you like drunk friends, sniff your pockets for biscuits, start raising their own doubts with you, like, why are we here? Does all this, this life thing, have any meaning? And you tell them they have been chosen. For what, they ask? Not unreasonably. Well, this is basically a holiday camp, a sort of Club Med thing, lots of team activities, you tell them. And they've won a prize, each of them, and the prize is that they get to spend a very long holiday here. Three meals a day and plenty of exercise and fun. And you tell them you have to return to work now, and you go inside.

You notice a calendar and realise it's a long time since you took your worm tablets. You pop two from a blister pack and you mix them in with a bowl of appetising soft food, and devour it enthusiastically. But of course, you then spit the tablets back into the bowl, and get fairly pissed off with yourself. You've never been good with tablets.

You mix up the next few days' worth of the drug, at a higher dose now for some of the dogs. And you aren't happy about this, but it tastes okay.

The next day is someone's birthday, so you all bring along lunch. One of the others has brought soy chicken wings, a known favourite of Robert's. He watches you all as he pulls the flesh from the bones, watches you all 'cause he knows you want it too. And then he crunches the bones, but in his haste starts spluttering, coughing, turning purplish. Some dickhead hits him in the back and he coughs up the bone fragment, turns pinkish again, drools quietly with relief.

The man is a shit, and you'd like nothing more than to see him whitening by the roadside, crumbling into powder, slowly dissipated by the wind.

You have a bit of a doze after lunch and when you wake you give yourself a good going over with a stiff brush. And you feel all shiny and clean, even though the others don't notice.

And Rowan's not looking well. He makes it clear he's feeling distinctly queasy, and he wonders if it's what you're pumping into him. It could be just the birthday lunch, you tell him. Labradors can eat too much too quickly and not feel the best. But he was feeling sick before lunch. He didn't eat any lunch. Let's see how it goes, you say, there's a bit of it around and in fact I'm not feeling so well myself. And you feel your nose, just to show you're monitoring things. Rowan really isn't looking well, and he goes for a lie down.

It's hard to concentrate on your work after this. After you haven't even bothered to come up with a good lie for him. Surely he's worth more than this, you tell yourself. And you really don't feel well and you want to go home for the afternoon. You'd tell Robert about it, but he's pacing up and down in his office, grumbling and scratching himself and obviously anxious about something. He's tugging at his uncomfortable shirt and you notice how old and worn the collar looks. And he scratches under his arms and he scratches his flanks and he scratches behind his ears.

So you just go home.

The next morning is one of those mornings when you wake up feeling as though you've copped a bait, and you're off your breakfast and you head for work with no enthusiasm whatsoever.

And Rowan's cage is empty. Big, happy Rowan. One of the others tells you he started throwing up blood during the night, and no-one came when they called for help, and it didn't last long.

Robert's somewhere with his knee joints, and he's not very happy. This could bugger up the whole thing. It's not the result the company wants at all. Great knees, maybe, but not a great drug if the patient's dead.

And Robert will have to hold someone responsible for this. And even though you stuck strictly to protocol, you know it will be you.

You are told he wants to see you at five, when all the others have gone. And at five, all the others go, and it's no use curling up in the corner on your blanket whimpering.

You hear his feet on the lino, his heavy panting breathing, smell that Robert smell. He snarls at you with contempt when he sees you cowering there, growls cruelly. And you know he's offering you only one way out.

You back across the room and he follows you, checking your ineffectual moves to escape, growling ever more menacingly. And you back into the empty Dog One cage and he shuts the wire door. He prowls around the cage, obviously tense and you sit in the basket looking pathetic and making inadvertent whining noises. He comes right up to the wire, shows you all his teeth, backs off again. His smell is suffocating. Before he leaves, to make his position clear, he squats at the cage door, his face goes bulge-eyed and distant, and he drops a large shit to the lino floor.

He laughs at you with heavy, wet breathing, and he clatters off down the hallway.

And as you wait for the morning, a morning meaning a heavy, pasty dose of the piroxicam derivative, a bowl of something crunchy and more exercise than you're used to, Robert bounds through the night, baying at the moon in anger and triumph.

He stops, to concentrate hard on another shit, and as he lets it go, feels that calm feeling of letting it go, he is clubbed from behind by the proprietor of a nearby Chinese restaurant who is finding the going tough in these times of recession, and needs to come by his Mongolian lamb through other than conventional means.

He drags the body onto the back of his ute, making sure not to step in the shit, which over the following several months whitens by the roadside, crumbles into powder and is slowly dissipated by the wind.

And in his absence – and with a number of the dogs developing side effects – the new molecule is abandoned, the experiment erased, and you end up with a nice family in the suburbs. In summer they take you to their holiday house at the coast, where you run on the beach for hours. And at sunset you jump and snap, but only playfully, at the fireflies.

all those ways
of leaving

You left Brisbane in a bus. The first time, anyway. Several times by plane, since. You left Darren to backpack in Thailand, but mainly to leave Darren. Not that you realised Thailand was so incidental at the time. You left school with writing on your back. You left uni and threw up in the foyer of the Crest. You left most of your toiletries in a cheap hotel room in Paris in an addled moment. You left parties later than most. You left no stone unturned. You left when you wanted to every time.

That's seven, three of them new.

It's a game, all this itemising. All this lying with your eyes closed, listing all those ways of leaving. Besides, all that leaving and something's brought you back here. Leaving only matters, only seems like leaving, when you're doing it.

You left home under some kind of cloud that you don't remember. Some argument about the usual nothing with your mother.

Who is next to you now. Beside your bed. Restless as ever in your chair, pretending flowers slumped past their best could do with some arranging, pretending that the tilt of your window is fifteen ways wrong, and she's tried to fix it only fourteen times so she's back there again.

And it's nice of people to send you flowers but, from your lying-down position, the bit you can see most is the cut ends of the stems, and that's kind of sad. Sometimes, you'd like people to grow flowers with you in mind, rather than cutting them down to bring to you. Is that political? It sounds like it might be.

You left-wing, greenie person, you. There's another 'You left'. That must be about a million now. Four of them new today. But it's not that you're bored. You're just recapitulating. Turning over every moment a few more times, getting the full value of it. And 'recapitulating' was your maths teacher's favourite thing in grade nine. You remember that, too.

'Take it easy with that window,' you tell your mother, still without opening your eyes. 'For godsakes. I like the breeze. It's okay.'

'That's the fan, Shelly,' she tells you. 'I brought you a fan.'

'Well, it's good. So thank you. Don't be perturbed about any of the movement of air, mother. The fan is perfect, and the window's all it might be.'

'You're still reading Jane Austen, aren't you?'

'You say that as though it's porn, as though it could do me harm.'

'No, it was just . . . a question.'

But she's right. Jane Austen's a bit specific, but you have to admit she picked up on the dialect. You've been reading too many nineteenth-century novels with wan, consumptive heroines to stop yourself playing around with those indulgent speech patterns. You want to dab your lips with a lace hankie and laugh. And stop to sigh, 'Oh mother,' as though your next breath out might carry something impossibly meaningful, impossibly mournful. But you'd only laugh again. And then she'd start some telling off, and pull up abruptly when she realised again that she's not allowed to tell you that you should be taking this seriously.

You open your eyes, so that you can see her hand pat-patting away on the blue vinyl armrest of the chair in just that way that has come to really annoy you. It annoys you more if you look, so you look.

'We should get you one of those executive stress toys,' you tell her.

'No, I'm quite happy doing this,' she says.

'Chinese bloody armrest torture?'

'I thought I made it up myself.'

Your eyes focus in on something just in front of you, something on the pillow. A long golden hair.

'Bugger,' you say to your mother, but really to no-one in particular. 'Lost another one.'

It's been a long time since your hair was at its best. The last day, perhaps, was the day when you were just starting to believe you weren't going to lose it with the chemo, and then it came out by the brushful. That was the day after your oncologist said, 'I think you might be going to get away with it,' since things had gone so well. And by the time you saw him a couple of weeks later you were like an over-loved rag doll up there and you had the dreaded chemo beanie on.

And you looked him in the eye and said, 'Don't worry about it. I've just got this thing for gangsta rap, bro.'

And you weren't sure if 'bro' was right for gangsta rap, but the whole sentence baffled him, so that was fine. And anyway, he was busy checking out your beanie and in the grip of remorse about the comment he'd made the week before.

It grew back. Your hair grew back, but nothing like your old hair. It turned to straw, some kind of crappy, skanky flax that all the provitamin B5 in the world couldn't save (whatever promises the shampoo bottles made). It grew straight out from your head, thick and strange.

'Weave the word *welcome* into it, and you'd have a good doormat,' you told your mother. And you had to say to her, 'It's only hair. It's only hair.' And you had to say it to yourself, too.

And you'd had such good hair. And a good liver without all that tumour (and all those asterisks on your biochem reports), good legs when they had some muscle about them. But some lists are just plain stupid to get into. Some things are gone.

And sometimes a wavy golden one makes it, just to show it can. To hide in the straw and be found on your pillow. Or played with, the way you always played with your hair. Your famously bad habit of sucking your hair. The one you were supposed to grow out of, but kept until chemo blasted the hair from your head and gave you this other unsuckable thing. But still the occasional golden one to play with, knot, suck. All's not lost.

Your mother reaches for today's single pillow hair, to tidy it away, but you stop her. It's precious, you won't get many more.

The resident visits. 'How's it going?' she asks you.

'Fine. About the same,' you tell her. 'How are you?'

'Pretty good. Can't complain. Everything under control?'

'Pretty much. I had to go for a top-up of the morphine in the night, but it's okay now.'

'Was it your back again?'

'Yeah.'

'And you've got the sheepskin on the bed, and we have tried zapping that particular deposit . . .' she says, beginning her own list.

'Yeah. It's fine. The morphine did it.'

'Do you think we need to up your regular dose?'

'Not yet.'

'Okay. And the eating? How's that going?'

'Don't feel like much.'

'Shall we get the dietitian to see you?'

'I think you've lined her up for tomorrow. Hang on, let me check my diary.' And you find the piece of paper stuck in a magazine on your bedside table. 'Yeah, ten o'clock.'

'Good,' she says. 'Anything else?'

And just when you try hard to come up with a smart remark, there isn't one there. She's waiting, you know she's waiting.

'Why would I ask you for anything else? I waited all yesterday for the jet ski, but did you deliver?'

After she goes, you lie there flicking rubber bands up at the light, partly to irritate your mother. It doesn't irritate her enough, so you make her pick them up.

She goes along with that too, and it's only when you flick one into her hair that she stops, and says, 'One day, you're going to get yourself into a lot of trouble.'

'That's more like it,' you tell her.

She's been gone for two hours and you've just turned down dinner when the registrar arrives.

'You should probably be eating some of that,' he says.

'Would you? It's that institutional smell. It spoils everything. It even wrecks mashed potato.'

He talks you into trying the jelly, but you only agree if he tries the silverside first.

'I spent six years in a boarding school, Michelle,' he says, as though you've blown it. 'This is practically cuisine.'

So you end up eating four spoonfuls of the jelly, and then a fifth when he says, 'One more, or we do the choo-choo train.'

Then you play draughts. Two games, and you take one each.

You like Alex. He's been the unit's registrar for months now, and you get a new resident every eight weeks, so you never have the chance to get as used to them. Or them to you. Each time it takes a few days to break them in, make them aware in a subtle way that you're the ward's favourite patient. Barbara's not a bad resident. She's getting there, but she's no Alex. She dresses better than Alex. Until his wardrobe started becoming repetitive, Alex amazed you day after day with the worst dress sense conceivable. You told him once that you found it reassuring, since maybe it meant that he'd studied really hard and never ventured into the outside world long enough to get a sense of how fashion operated.

The best thing was, he wasn't really paying attention when you said it, and he'd started to thank you before he realised you were completely crapping on him.

And sometimes you call him Alex, sometimes you call him *Youngster*, since you were born four days before him, both of you in this hospital.

In other circumstances, it would have been obvious that you would have been friends. He is a big dag, and you can call him that. From you, he takes it as a term of endearment, and that's only partly to do with the way you say it.

And he worked out early on that you're the kind of person who laughs at the world's worst jokes, who can't stop themselves. So he comes in with jokes, deliberately bad jokes, and now you know you're going to laugh even before he tells them.

'I can't believe you laugh at that kind of thing,' he's said, plenty of times. 'You are such a loser.'

But this evening he says, 'Barbara tells me you're not eating,' after the second game of draughts.

'I wouldn't go that far. Particularly not after all that jelly. But I'm seeing the dietitian tomorrow, anyway. I think I'm going to ask for lobster bisque, round about fourth-hourly.'

'It is such as specialty of the hospital kitchen, after all. Always my favourite at boarding school, too.'

'Exactly.'

'Bisque,' he says, and laughs. 'I think they only know it as the first syllable of biscuit, but you can try.'

The next day, your mother cracks, the way you've been trying to make her crack for a while. In the end she does it independently, so you're not quite ready for it.

Something small starts it. You play canasta badly, make a fundamental error since your concentration's going, and suddenly she's getting upset about you throwing out a jack when obviously she's got jacks.

'Well, take it then,' you tell her, momentarily appalled that you might have had your last canasta victory over your mother, ever.

And it was last Tuesday, and no-one had the decency to notice, and make something of it. So many things you're ready for, and it's some of these little ones that take you by surprise, both of you. To think of all those summer holidays when canasta irritated you endlessly, and now you're going to miss it. Sometime in the night your canasta brain fell out, and it's never coming back. And you wonder what went with it, what other faculties crept off in the gentle morphine fog and won't return.

It'd be better if you got a choice. There are several things

you'd give up without a fuss. Clever ways of pegging particular laundry items. Everything you ever learned at netball
coaching before your knee went. Anything you ever knew
about the taxonomy of anything, not that that's really
much. The knots your father taught you when he thought
you might like sailing. And sailing bored you stupid, but
the knots are in your brain forever, probably the last thing
that'll go.

You make an active effort to forget knots, in case you
can relearn canasta into that part of your brain, but while
you're doing that you flick yesterday's golden hair around
a nearby pencil and secure it with a round turn and two
half-hitches.

And maybe it's just a bad day for the canasta, a concentration lapse, but it's better not to hope that.

You change the subject, talk about your cousin. She's
just moved in with a guy, so you ask how she's going.

'She's bought a fridge,' your mother says. 'Auto-defrost.'

'Serious stuff, fridge co-ownership. It's a big deal to
push the commitment level all the way to whitegoods.'

And that's when your mother cracks properly. You never
got round to co-owning a whitegood with anyone. A sandwich toaster with Darren, but it was something he way
over-emphasised, and Justin thought you should get a dog
(but he never was practical). The sandwich toaster is the
biggest-deal thing you've ever co-owned, goddamn it. Were
you ducking the whole issue of relationships, or what?

'But there's so much you're not getting to do,' your
mother says, as though it's a conversation she can start in

the middle the moment she's realised your cousin's reached a level you never will. And then she says, 'Sorry.'

But it's not news to you. Damn it, you're a list maker. As if you hadn't worked through the list of things you're not getting to do before now.

'I'm okay with that,' you tell her, because it's at least partly true and it's totally what you think she needs to hear. 'There's plenty that I've done, as well. Not everyone gets to do everything. And I'm pretty happy with what I have done. I think I covered a certain range, a pretty good range, overall. Including some things most people don't get to do. Almost no-one has had the chance to eat as much excellent, shitty food as I have without worrying about their weight, or their health, or their coronary arteries. It's like my whole life is made up of movie snack food, but better than movie snack food. And tell me that's not a dream come true.'

And the one about not getting to do everything is just the intro to your 'Not everyone gets to' list.

Not everyone gets to watch the next generation grow up, and make all the stupid mistakes they once made and still survive. Not everyone gets to be sufficiently mid-life that they qualify for the crisis. Not everyone gets to look back years later on all of their missed opportunities. Not everyone gets to take thirty in their stride, or fall all over it as though it's some disaster.

See? It's not so bad. Here for a good time, not a long time. Here for a good time, not a long time. You've adjusted to it – most of the way, anyway. That's what your mother needs to know. And, besides, it's not so much of a good time any more.

You've done a lot, enough now maybe, and the 'Not everyone gets to' list is too long for keeping, really. Too long to matter. Some things you get to do, some things you don't. And that's all of us.

Not everyone gets to know if they've ever really been in love. But plenty of people get a worse deal than that, and don't even get round to telling other people how they feel at all. Most of the world's most important conversations never end up happening, just because people won't put themselves on the line.

You've had relationships. Maybe you have been in love. You aren't now.

You didn't marry. You didn't want to. You had two offers, one of them serious (Darren), and both times it was the beginning of the end. The moment of emergence of plenty of different expectations. And you'd never led them to believe you'd be different. You've lost count of the number of times you looked Darren fair in the face and said, 'Wedlock,' good and slowly. 'Have you noticed that the second part of that is the word lock, Darren?'

You need to roll over. Your back is sore. Darren lives in America. He has a child already, last you heard. You've told him nothing.

You up your baseline morphine dose a little, and it stays up. You're needing more now.

Alex's evening visit begins with him saying, 'Shell, the weight, it's not good.'

'I'm planning to escape, a molecule at a time. I'm leaving, you know.'

'I'd heard that. But have you seen how you're dropping weight,' he says, as though you're an ailing thoroughbred (an approach you find quite appealing).

'I'm just not hungry. But don't worry, I've talked to the dietitian. We've got a plan.'

'Yeah?'

'Just wait. It's pretty gourmet.'

And he says, 'I bet it is,' and then he tells you he's got another joke for you. It involves an oversized cowboy hat and several vegetable items. 'Do you really want to hear it?' he says. 'It's pretty crass.'

And it's the crass jokes that you like most of all. Particularly the way you sense that he's really keen to tell them, at the same time as being slightly embarrassed about the crassness. He's an old-fashioned kind of joke teller, without realising it's old-fashioned. These days people tell funny stories about themselves (and beef them up so they've got punchlines), but not many tell actual classically structured jokes. That's how it seems, anyway. To you, not to Alex. Alex doesn't know that. Some of his even involve actresses and bishops, and probably pre-date World War One.

You are leaving a molecule at a time. You've warned him of that now. You are leaving by allowing your abilities to lapse and slip away uncontested, one by one.

It's night and sometimes you're asleep and sometimes

you're awake, and you're dreaming up ways of leaving. You are swelling muscles and striding out, as though this has never happened. You are leaving from the roof by a hang-glider that's been waiting for you there all this time. You are leaving in a cab, the cab that took you home leg-less last Melbourne Cup, six days before you stopped being perfectly healthy. Same cab, same driver. You are leaving in a big marrying car, but shouting to people that you never planned to do that, anyway. You are leaving on a jet plane in three-part harmony dressed for the early seventies.

You are leaving, and only Alex, the registrar, misses you. You tell him you'll call, and maybe you will. He's a nice guy but, Jesus, those ties. You are leaving and he's wearing the worst one, the skinny woven one with the alternating chocolate and caramel bands and the square-cut bottom.

You are leaving, with the horrible feeling that Alex is not quite ready for the real world. Which is stupid, prob-ably. A dream-logic thing. Alex is just as twenty-nine as you are. But a home-owner, married, career-bound. Alex is the real world, he just doesn't dress for it yet.

Lunch arrives the next day, and your mother and the dietitian both live up to their part of the deal, and the 'will provide own food in consultation with the dietitian' box on the form.

Your mother's ancient coaxing skills surface and you say to her, 'Next you'll be telling me there are bunnies at the bottom if I eat it all.'

'Well, you won't know if you don't, will you?' she says.

'That's what the bunnies are about.'

So today you manage four teaspoonfuls of Irish Cream ice-cream, with breaks for appreciation in between. Your second course is a mouthful of single-malt whiskey, which you hold on to slightly too long, and you cough and some of it comes out your nose. And in the mixture of spluttering and laughing at yourself, several people run to your bed in case you're breathing your last, and it's all you can do to tell them, 'Scotch. Down the wrong way,' as they start to pull at the curtains.

You're starting to block up abdominally, but you don't talk about that with Alex when he comes round at the end of the day. You know it won't be too long now. You just have that feeling.

You ask him about his renovations. Alex is the nicest cliché you know.

'Still somewhere between the before photo and the after photo,' he tells you, 'but the pet-piss smell has gone. So I'm starting to like the place a bit more.'

'You mean your aim's improving?'

'No, Kelly makes me do it off the verandah. Thanks, Shell. This may surprise you, but I'm fully house-trained. We threw out the last of the carpets a couple of weekends ago, and we've been polishing.'

'Where do you get that from? Is there some renovator gene?'

'I didn't say we were good at it. They tell you to start off in a corner you don't care about first, and now I know why.

Anyway, it's a money thing, doing your own renovating. You buy the place, you scare yourself stupid with the mortgage and then you realise there's just no living with the pet piss smell, and you have to take serious action now. And, of course, you have to do it yourself.'

'But it does give you a sense of satisfaction.'

'Yeah.'

'See. You are a renovator, really, even if you're pretending you aren't. And the corner you don't care about?'

'It looks like someone sprayed toffee on the wall.'

'You?'

'Might've been. But anyway, today's joke.'

'Sure.'

He pulls the curtain round and explains that today's joke is nothing unless he feels free to use the term butt fuck repeatedly. And, yes, he's aware the curtains do nothing for the noise but (and he whispers this), 'There's the illusion of privacy. People try not to listen if you've got the curtains round.'

'Really? I try to listen more.'

'Yes, well that's you. Now, do you want this joke?'

You do a deal with Barbara. Then you page Alex and you tell him, 'I should buy you a tie.'

'Sorry?'

'I'd like to buy you a tie.'

'Um. Thank you.'

'So I've got it organised. We're going to go out and get it at lunchtime.'

'What? I'm not sure I can go out at lunchtime. There's this job I've got . . .'

'Barbara's arranged the cover.'

'Barbara can't really cover me. She's just an intern.'

'No, she's arranged for one of the other registrars to cover you.'

'Oh.'

'And I've booked one of those big cabs that takes a wheel-chair. We won't be long. And, trust me, you need the tie.'

And it's probably not that that does it but he relents, for whatever reason, and he's there at twelve-thirty, ready to wheel you to the lift. Still not exactly at ease with the concept of going out for a tie, but playing along.

He and the cabbie load you into the car.

'Hey, you were right about that joke,' you tell Alex, as he does up his seat belt. 'I tried it a couple of times last night, and if you go with *sodomise* it just doesn't work. It has to be *butt fuck*.'

'Well, I told you, didn't I?'

The cabbie gets in and the car pulls slowly away from the entrance. A couple of young doctors cross the road in front of you, see Alex in the cab, and wave.

'They'll think you've got a date,' you say to him.

'No-one's going to think it's a date,' he says, and gives a small laugh.

'Why? Cause I'm long past rootable?'

'Sorry,' he says to the cab driver. 'It's the medication.'

'You lying bugger,' you say to him.

'She's actually totally mad.' And he turns back to you

and says, 'No. No-one's going to think it's a date, and that's nothing to do with you. There'd be a certain ethical bind involved in a date. And I think you know that. Plus, I am a permanently committed, married person. They're not going to think it's a date, because they know me. There's this bizarre idea out there about the sex lives of hospital medical staff. We're not all shagging machines, you know.'

'You and me both,' you say, and then you tap the cabbie on the shoulder. 'How about you? Are you a shagging machine?'

'Um, not really,' he says, taking a sideways look at Alex, who nods, as though that constitutes advice to continue. 'To be honest. Not since May at least. May, wasn't bad.'

'Ages ago now, buddy.'

'Hey, tell me about it.'

The jacarandas are flowering, vibrant lilac in today's wild late-spring sun. And the hospital windows are tinted so the glare out here seems amazing, quite hyper-real. It's been weeks since you were out here, or at least since you were out on a bright day like this, and anywhere outside the grounds. Weeks since this has been anything other than the view from a first-floor window, and now you're part of it. And your bones and other parts of you ache and send you shots of a more pointed kind of pain and it hurts to breathe and your mouth is dry and you didn't bring water.

'So what kind of tie are we getting you, Alex?' you say.

And he says, 'I'm guessing one that's not much like my other ties.'

'Good start.'

'One that's wider, a little more attention-seeking. Something memorable. But I'm hoping there's some room for negotiation.'

'Some. Maybe.'

'It's still got to be me, you know. I mean, it's got to be you, but it's got to be me, too. I plan to get a lot of wear out of this tie. I don't take on a new tie lightly. You know that.'

'Well, I'd figured.'

And the freeway is busy but moving, and you look into the cars, at the nonchalance of all the drivers and passengers having days that aren't in any way irregular. Uncounted, unremembered mid-life days, for most of them. Days in traffic, at work, home to another Thursday night in the nineties and the TV they're anticipating.

So how many ties have you bought before? Three, all of them for your father, as fall-back Father's Day gifts. It seemed like such a slack choice then. The 'oh my god, what am I going to get him' kind of embarrassing gift that you went for the day before when you realised imagination wasn't going to kick in. But your father takes on new ties very lightly indeed, so that's the difference.

Alex wakes you gently when the car pulls up in town.

'Shell,' he says, in a voice designed to be small. 'Shell.' Brushing your shoulder with his knuckles.

'Hi,' you say. 'Back with you.' Even though it's quite a lurch to get there.

You arrange the return trip with the cabbie, and you tell Alex, 'Don't fuss. Ties take time.'

You get him to wheel you to a specialty tie shop, and even the concept amazes him.

'God, what next?' he says. 'Sock shops?'

'Now, that's a joke, isn't it?'

'No. Who knows what people might try?'

'You hardly get out at all, do you?'

'What do you mean? I get out. Sometimes. I just hate paying for parking in town.'

'Alex, you've got to watch this. I'm worried that you're only a year or two away from being unable to participate at all, from being socially unsalvageable. Today's tie is going to help, but I don't know that I can do it all for you. I might have to talk to Kelly. I'm sure she'd like to get out more.'

'Well, yeah, but there's the mortgage . . .'

'There's life Alex. Oh, maybe it's too easy for me. I've never had a mortgage. Let's get purchasing. And watch. It's surprisingly painless.'

You search through racks of ties and agree on more of them than you expected to. You both hate most of them, and there's not a tie in the shop that looks anything like an Alex regular, so that helps, too. You get it down to a short list of half a dozen.

Alex goes 'Hmmm' a lot and you say, 'You want my advice?' And then you give it. 'Go for that one, the one with the yellow, or at least one of those two. There's a certain boldness to them. And you can cover boldness better than you think.'

'I'm not really sure what that means, but it sounded kind of complimentary.'

'Yes.'

'So one of these two?'

'Yes.'

'But, preferably, this one?'

'I think so.'

'All right, then. Let's do it.'

So he lets you get him the tie you want to get him, and he does it in a way that suggests it will be worn. That's good. And he keeps playing with it, holding it up to his collar in the vicinity of mirrors and rearranging his chin in a way that might imply boldness. He laughs at himself when he knows you've seen him, and then he hands the tie over to be put in a bag while you're signing the MasterCard form.

'Do you want to have coffee, or something?' he says. 'Do you think we've got time?'

'Sure.'

And you're awake enough now to notice people noticing you, as Alex pushes you into the coffee shop. It's been months since you worked in town. And it's now so obvious how unnoticed you were then, how neatly you could slip into places like this and pick up a muffin and a long black. You and your golden hair.

'God, now that I've gone a bit Sex Pistols on top, they're all looking at me,' you say, meaning to keep it in, but letting it out like a piece of narration. But fortunately, not too loudly.

'Do you want to go?' Alex says.

'No. No. Not till it's time.'

'Do you want something to eat, then? Or a coffee?'

'No, you just get whatever you want.'

'Nothing?'

'Water. Water would be good. And a short black. Is it okay if I don't drink it all, though? I'd quite like to smell it. It's been a while.'

'Sure.'

He goes to the counter and comes back with a cappuccino for himself and a glass of water and a short black for you.

'For smelling purposes,' he says, as he hands it over.

'The smelling salts of the cafe society,' you tell him, as though it means anything. 'I feel better already.'

You sip your water, and a bagel arrives for Alex.

'We might talk about the eating again, when we're back at work,' he says.

'I'm so bored with talking about the eating, Alex. You know there's really not much point. We should talk more about that cappuccino.'

'I should have figured there'd be a problem with the cappuccino.'

'Okay, let's just say, time to get over the eighties, Alex, and leave it at that. If you must have dairy with your coffee product, the choice this decade is latte.'

'What is the difference? What have you got against this quite attractive bit of froth on the top?'

'Oh, Alex. So much to do, so little time. I will never stop worrying about you. And don't you dare, don't you dare,' twice for emphasis, 'do that daggy eating the froth with a spoon thing.'

'What is the problem with that?'

'Oh god, Alex, go home and listen to Flock of Seagulls or something.'

'Stop playing with your hair.'

'Hey, rack off.'

'No wonder you don't need to eat. All those hair-sucking calories you must be getting.'

Damn. He's got you. He smiles smugly, spoons at his froth. And you don't mind that he wins sometimes.

Back in the ward you sleep all afternoon, starting in the middle of a sentence. Telling your baffled mother about your necessary trip out, your tie for Alex, and then waking again when it's getting cool and the shadows are long outside.

There's a note next to your bed. It says, 'And I meant to say thanks for the tie. A.'

Your mother's still there, standing facing away from you, fiddling with your window again.

'Do you know how little my day will improve when you optimise the position of that window?' you say to her, as though you're the parent.

You realise you're shitty, and it's because you're still sore. You up the morphine. You lie there waiting for it to work. Your mother pats the arm of the seat and wants very much to tell you to stop sucking your hair. Suddenly that's a big thing for you again. She always had this theory that when you sucked your hair it meant you were tense or afraid, but that was always wrong. It was just something that happened, and it had no meaning.

'Don't worry,' you tell her. 'You can do what you like with the window. I don't want to spoil your fun.'

'There's a bit of a breeze. I thought we could do with some air in here.'

'I'm sure you're right. Thank you.'

You're halfway through your novel and you try to read it, but it doesn't work. You don't remember enough. You slept and lost the plot (yes, literally) and you can't find your way back in. And the last two hundred pages, all of a sudden, look so burdensome.

Oh, shit, you're never going to finish this novel. Shit. You've read a novel all the way through for the last time. The only way you'll ever know what happens with this one is if you concentrate really hard and focus your attention on the last couple of pages and skip the rest of it. But that's no way to read anything.

This is so strange. You seem to have taken it for granted that you would die between novels, not during one. But you're the kind of person who always has a novel on the go. It was never likely to work out the way you'd thought.

It's crazy that you have to accept that that's too much to hope for. To read a book to the end without feeling that there's a hurry, and a genuine chance you won't make it. Crazy that you might have tasted something as rich as butter for the last time, seen Monday night sitcoms for the last time. Crazy that you bought Alex's tie with your MasterCard, without working out that you won't last to be billed. Crazy that you might never get to see him wear it, and know it was a good choice. And the list of these crazy things is almost endless, and very tiring.

'Have you read this book?' you ask your mother.

'Um, don't think so.'

'Oh.'

'Should I?'

'I don't know.'

And then the morphine works, and the day is warm and quiet and over.

And you're drifting. Leaving. Practising leaving. You'd like to leave now. Everything's done. With the exception of the novel, but that's okay.

And you're leaving by hovering over your bed, but only because of how warm it is tonight and hovering might aid ventilation. And there's a puff of that talked-about breeze, and you're off. Leaving to go shopping, and not really coming back. Leaving on a water slide. It's almost summer.

Alex wears the tie for the first time the next day.

You've had a shitty night. All that gut pain and a couple of vomits (but only bringing up bile) and that stupid, hazy mess of dreams.

'You're actually quite sick now, aren't you?' he says. 'Your morphine levels have really increased. Barbara thinks you might have some kind of gut obstruction, and I think she's right. It's probably tumour. You could just be really constipated with the morphine and from not eating and not moving round much, but I think it might be more than that.'

'And I'm taking the lactulose, anyway. Well, I was.'

'Yeah. I think it might be a bigger issue than that

now. Like, bigger than just one of those things where we up the anti-constipation treatment. We should probably investigate.'

'Why?'

'Well, to find out.'

'Oh, let's not. Can't I just stay here?'

'Well, of course you can. I just need to know you've thought it through.'

'Hmmm. I have.'

'If it's gut obstruction, it could all progress pretty rapidly.'

'Well, I hope so. Slowly would really suck.'

'Yeah.'

He pulls the curtain along, sits on the edge of the bed. Carefully, but it still hurts you. You keep the hurt in. You don't want him knowing.

'I've talked about it with Barbara,' you tell him. 'So I know what I'm doing. And I've really had enough. This way, there's no more messing round. I'm completely fed up with messing round. The only reason to leave this ward is to go shopping, or some other time when it's on my own terms. So no X-rays, no tubes, no operations.'

'Okay.'

'This'll be all right, you know.'

'Let's make it as all right as we can, anyway. I want you to tell me if there's anything you need.'

'Not much. Not really. I was going to go out tonight but I'm tired, so I'll just stay home. You'll have to handle the socialising for me.'

'Me and my new tie?'

'That's right.'

'Kelly was kind of surprised by the new tie.'

'Surprised? What did she say?'

'Oh, "There's hope for you yet." One of those kinds of remarks.'

'Well, that's not so bad. She might be right. Does she read much?'

'Yeah, she reads a lot.'

'I thought she might, from what you've said about her. She might like this. I've finished it.'

You hand him yesterday's novel.

'Are you sure?'

'Yeah. Look, I'm a bit tired, and I was going to do some reading now, but it could be easier if you . . . Could you do this? Could you read something to me?'

'Um, yeah, sure.'

And you make him read you some of *Pride and Prejudice* – no bit in particular, since you know how it all goes, and it's not as though you'll miss out on the ending.

He's a really shitty reader, but that makes it even nicer. He pulls the curtain all the way round first, as though reading, as far its embarrassment value goes, is on a par with patient nudity or jokes requiring repeated references to butt fucking. But when he reads, you know why. Plenty of throat clearing, and his eyes never leave the page. Maybe it wasn't the right thing to ask him to do, but he sticks with it.

Afterwards, you ask him if he's all right, and he says, 'Yeah.'

'This is going to sound kind of tacky, but remember that post-mortem thing we discussed?'

'What?'

'How I was okay with that? You know? Teaching hospital, and all that kind of thing.'

'Yeah. It's in your file. Do want to change your mind?'

'No.'

'You could, if you wanted to.'

'No. I just wanted to check that it was all still on.'

'Okay.'

'Do you think you'll come?'

'What?'

'To the post-mortem.'

'No. Jesus, Shell,' he says, and then moves into a mock-stern tone. 'You've got no idea of boundaries, have you?'

'No. But I never did.'

'Well, I don't think I'm going. No, I'm not going. I don't want to. If that's okay.'

'Yeah. Sure it's okay. Listen, thanks.'

'That's all right. It's always been a pleasure.'

'I think I might have a sleep now. So thanks for coming along today.'

'Well, I wanted you to see the tie on,' he says. 'I like it a lot, you know.'

And you didn't play draughts. Not today, not for a few days. That's the last thing that occurs to you when he goes. Another thing finished, all without ceremony.

So you're leaving. You are leaving with a stash of morphine in both bags, the toiletries you lost in Paris and one change of underwear. You are leaving with the world a little better dressed than when you arrived. You are leaving one foggy dawn, while the nurses are doing handover. You are leaving with the laundry, pale and twisted among white sheets, holding your breath all the way out of the ward. You are leaving on wings. They were always there, but you didn't know, and you feel pretty foolish when they're pointed out to you. You are leaving by the window, by a golden rope.

Gold because your best hair was gold. Gold because bile is gold before it spoils. Gold because you need a golden rope to get you out of here when you run out of all those other ways of leaving.

There's an argument about this, but it doesn't last. Why gold? Why gold, really? And, sure the wings were clichéd, but you kind of liked them, however fanciful they turned out to be.

You've waited enough here. It's time to up and leave. You and your rope. And that window, left open just a crack.

And they do the post-mortem, because your mother says it's fine to go ahead. Alex says she doesn't have to, but she tells him it's what you wanted.

And Barbara puts '? gut obstruction secondary to malignancy' on the form, and she's not quite right.

They find malignancy, and all over the place, but when they open your intestine, there's only golden hair. All your best hair. Taken and twisted into a long, sly, golden rope, the length of your bowel, the height of your window from the ground.

And the pathology registrar calls Alex and says, 'Mate, it's Rapunzel Syndrome,' and he sounds quite excited. 'She's full of the cancer, of course, but the obstruction looks like Rapunzel Syndrome. There's hair matted everywhere in her bowel. Thought you might want to take a look.'

And Alex says no. He remembers it from uni, the syndrome, from a pathology specimen or something, a mention once in lectures. It's rare, but he doesn't need to see it. And rare seems right, somehow. It occurs to him that there was nothing obvious about you. Nothing in the last however-many weeks of knowing you that was like much else.

And you left in the night on your own terms. Sized up all those other ways of leaving, did what you could, fixed what you could, said no when you still could. Worked out that some of the best unfinished things never even start, and all their possibilities don't spoil.

Jettisoned piece by piece the stuff you didn't need, made your escape, left, like all those other times, when you were ready to. Carrying this time just some weightless things that might still matter.

headgames

He swings his arms, wobbles his leg muscles, shakes his head. Goes through the very familiar rhythms of loosening up.

But this is still more than that, more than just physical. It still makes him focus clearly on the water, on the task. And he can still hear their voices, or at least remember them vividly.

That's where you'll win it or lose it. In your head, behind the blocks, before the race.

If you don't win it then, you won't win it in the water.

You've got to win it in your head.

In your head. That's where your toughest competition is.

Even if Matt Biondi looked like the toughest competition, since he was the fastest swimmer in the world.

But today, Biondi doesn't matter. That's what he tells himself.

He dives and swims, swims just at cruising speed with no-one shouting at him now, or showing him lap times, or telling him he can take Biondi at the Pan Pacs, or at the Olympics. Whatever's next.

There's none of that next now, nothing next but the dawn of a hot day at the end of January, maybe ten years after the two times Biondi touched him into second place.

And people will arrive to swim and he'll open the gate and take their money. Then he'll rope off half the pool for Aquarobics. Then he'll try to sort out his pH problem. In the afternoon he'll take Kids Learn to Swim at three-thirty. And today the gate doesn't shut till nine. Thursdays are always Late Night Swimming.

He's watching the map of this simple day as the black line ends and he tumbleturns.

And he imagines all kinds of things when he's swimming. Dreams and sings songs. Even Tracey Wickham sang songs, but she sang something by Chicago. He's much cooler than that. Of course, Tracey Wickham sang Chicago seventeen years ago, so maybe it was okay then. Maybe she, too, now laps a pool somewhere in town singing whatever's on her mind from *Nirvana Unplugged*. Maybe just like this. And dreams and sings and thinks of things. Rolls over lap after lap, all without a race plan, like free-falling. But maybe Tracey Wickham still sings the same Chicago song.

Sometimes he thinks about the swimming, about how his name must sit pretty high on a lot of well-informed people's lists of Coulda Beens. The problem was he should have been, he expected to be. They all told him he would be. That he would be a champion and that to get there all he had to do was give it 100 per cent. That's what they said.

They being the coaches and motivators and administrators and journalists who all, it turned out in the end, had nothing to lose.

He gave it 100 per cent. He shaved his head, and became perhaps the sixth most famous Australian swimmer of the time to do so. And inside his head he was getting it right. Working it out. Putting together a picture of victory and keeping it in his mind.

You've got to see it. You've got to believe it.

And he did. These were games he could play. And they said he'd got it all together. He was big and drug-free and fast and smart, and that should be all he needed to be.

And his two silvers from the Pan Pacs are in blue velvet boxes in his second drawer.

Some mornings in the water he's angry. Not today.

He swims, still at the same speed, probably not more than half a second different lap after lap. It's actually much better now, the swimming, with no-one shouting, no expectations.

At night, in his room, he reads. Last night he started *Robinson Crusoe* and in the early hours of the morning he finished it. Some books work like that. They're best read in one sitting, and that way they stay with you with some clarity.

And it's quite a book, *The Life and Strange Surprizing Adventures of Robinson Crusoe, of York, Mariner.* Twenty-eight years on an island, and all the practicalities and periods of questioning.

He rolls through another tumbleturn and tells himself not to get into all of that now. It must be close to six, and he'll have to open the gate soon.

He climbs out onto the side and lifts his towel from the block.

Hello, he hears someone say.

He sees a young woman at the fence, a regular six o'clock starter.

Hi, he says.

I thought you'd be swimming, so I thought I might have a chance of getting in early.

Sure.

He lifts the keys from the hook inside the kiosk door and he undoes the padlock.

I've got to be at work early, she says, *and I wanted to get all my laps in.*

Work. He imagines her work. He looks at her and he tries to place her at work. Something in town, probably.

He draws the bolt back and swings the gate open, and she smiles and steps through and drops a dollar-fifty into his hand. And she does this almost awkwardly, as though it's happened so many times they almost know each other and it's wrong to keep giving him money.

He shakes it in his hand, jiggles it in time with his ambling walking as he goes inside to put it in a tin.

For twenty minutes it's just the two of them, and he watches her swim up and down. She swims comfortably. She's fit. He wonders if anyone ever told her she could be a champion. But she's not that good. It probably never came up, and she was told other things. And the different things they were told mean that he lives at the pool in the flat above the kiosk, and she lives somewhere nearby in St Lucia and five or six times a week she pays a dollar-fifty to swim. And she probably fills Monday to Friday with a town job of middling importance, lunch at a coffee shop, evenings with the man she loves. And no pH problems, all day.

She's wearing black, one-piece Speedos, like she usually does, and he watches her swim away from him and towards him, away from him and towards him, her churning feet, her neat, black-Speedoed buttocks, her brown shoulders.

He doesn't know her name. It would be nice to know her name, but he can't ask now. Not after months of small exchanges over a dollar-fifty. Repetition establishes a certain etiquette. So perhaps he knows her now as much as he ever will.

Other people arrive, pay their money, drop their towels and swim.

At about six-forty she gets out and comes over to the kiosk window with her towel around her shoulders.

Um, Frosty Fruit, thanks, she says, and puts seventy wet cents on the sky-blue counter.

She stands there eating the ice-block and looking as though she's watching the swimmers. Water drips from the ends of her hair, trickles down her legs and pools at her feet.

She doesn't usually buy an ice-block, he thinks.

She is standing quite close, close enough for him to see the slight breeze bring goose bumps up across her shoulders.

So, you work in town, do you? he says, with the words all the time threatening to dry up in his mouth.

Yeah. I've got a seven-thirty meeting today, she says, glancing at him and then looking away. *So I'd better go.*

At five to seven he ropes off half the pool for Aquarobics and he eats a bowl of Weetbix.

And the day proceeds according to his expectations. The traffic increases and while he's gazing out at the road he thinks he sees the swimming woman on a bus, just a glimpse of her. Or at least a glimpse of a mid-twenties woman with her dark hair back and sunglasses, looking out at the pool as the bus accelerates past down the hill, blowing blue exhaust and pushing its way across the lanes of commuter cars. He should have paid more attention.

In the pool, people come and go, more of them than usual today. By mid-morning it's disgustingly hot and the ceiling fan in the kiosk does nothing but swirl the hot air. He sells ice-blocks and drinks in large numbers.

He checks the pH and he hasn't quite got it right yet, but it's a fine line. Too harsh and everyone complains about sore eyes; too light and it's bug soup in there. He documents the slightly too harsh pH so the council can show people no-one could catch anything in its pool. Of course, if no-one pissed in swimming pools it'd be no problem at all.

He expects that every day several people well over the age of five piss in his pool, and he has no idea why. Here in a suburb where the houses are the most expensive in town, a suburb populated by university professors, barristers, vascular surgeons, captains of industry, and still he is sure his pool is pissed in on a regular basis. He wonders if they are as casual with their bladder control in board meetings, all the directors sitting round an imported marble table weeing secretly into the plush upholstery of their seats. But no, they probably all swim first, and all of them probably in his pool.

He skims a few leaves and contemplates notions of civilised behaviour. With some topicality, he thinks, having just read *Robinson Crusoe*. And why, he wonders, should he expect the people of St Lucia not to piss in his pool? Why does he think pool-pissing is governed by some arbitrary notion of class? He reflects upon the socialisation that has led him to make such assumptions.

Lunchtime passes and he's still thinking about the woman. She's somewhere in air-conditioning in town and he's here sliding off his sky-blue counter with sweat. Outside, the traffic keeps passing. People come and swim and go. But he stays, inside the three-metre fence that stops people sneaking in during the hours of darkness to swim without paying their dollar-fifty. Sometimes he goes out to shop, but today he stays on his side of the fence all day. He wonders how long he could last, just within this compound. How long he could last without the city that surrounds the fence. He wonders if he could go all day just fiddling with the pool and handling small amounts of money and talking to no-one. He thinks he could do his job without saying a thing, that people would look at him and think him big and stupid and wordless and hand the money over slowly. And check their change before they roll it in their towels.

Some days he hates his big swimmer's body and it would suit him to be lithe and intellectual. People would talk to him then, and maybe he could discuss Defoe with someone from the English Department at the uni. He wants to discuss the idea that, although its allegory is undeniable, the book might be the beginning of some kind of popular fiction. And it would be fine to do that with someone from the English Department at the uni, or with the morning swimming woman. It's probably the sort of thing she'd like.

He goes from the circular kiosk up the spiral stairs to his circular flat. He has questioned the obscure circularity of the structure more than once. Sometimes he thinks the building was surely the work of a designer of lighthouses and would be better placed on a headland, guarding some remote shoal of rock from the soft skins of ships. And he imagines himself, still here at his bend in the road, as the keeper of a low suburban light, rotating its beam in circle after circle in a lonely endless vigil to keep cars from coming to grief in the pool. But he knows the council better than this. He knows it has little interest in the keeping of lights, and maybe a round yellow brick building just seemed like a really groovy idea back when the pool was being put in.

Upstairs is even warmer than downstairs, and he picks up his copy of *Robinson Crusoe* and goes back down to the kiosk. He reads through bits of it, checks a few things. The heat makes him drowsy. He shuts his eyes and sees a beach with a footprint that isn't his size. Someone wakes him to give him a dollar-fifty, and fifty cents for each of the kids.

If they're under two, it's free, he says.

Yeah, they're over two.

Righto then.

At three-thirty Kids Learn to Swim is under-attended, perhaps since it's the first week back at school, or because it's too hot to learn to do anything, even in water.

In the late afternoon the pool crowds with people escaping the heat, and he ropes off only two lanes for laps. He has a pizza voucher that gives him a free garlic bread and Coke, so working out what to do for dinner isn't hard. He eats six of the eight pieces and throws the other two in the bin.

By seven it's dark, and by eight the pool is emptying. At eight-thirty he starts turning people away, telling them the gate closes in half an hour.

At eight forty-five the morning swimming woman arrives.

Any chance of a swim? she says. *Just to get cool. I know you're about to shut. I wouldn't be long.*

He can't turn her down. He realised about mid-morning that if she ever asked him for anything he couldn't turn her down, and that was that. He holds his big hand out and offers her the pool. She smiles and offers him a dollar-fifty.

It's on the house, he says, with a smile that's supposed to be relaxed, but probably looks spring-loaded.

Oh, she says, and looks up momentarily, perhaps in the direction of his flat. But perhaps not, perhaps just up. *Right.*

Thanks. She smiles again, having realised she should. *I'll swim, then.*

She swims laps, perhaps instinctively. He knows what that's like. It's all he can do in a pool. It all he's ever done in a pool since he started training maybe seventeen years ago.

Everyone else goes and he leaves the lights on for her, leans on his forearms on his sky-blue counter watching her do laps and hoping she won't hurry. He times her by the pool clock, and she's not fast but she's not slow either. And her lap times are within a second of each other.

And he wonders what's going on in her head. If she hears the snap of a starting pistol, the roar of the crowd between then and when you hit the water, the long years of quiet when it's all gone wrong, come to nothing. He watches each lap so closely he's almost doing her thinking for her, he's seeing Biondi just ahead, but always just ahead. He feels the tears in her eyes when the silver medal loops around her neck, and Biondi shakes her hand and says, *Good swim,* but in a way that, without even meaning to, lets her know she'll never beat him. And with that one gesture the head game is lost.

And two days later there's another silver, also second to Biondi, who again shakes her hand, and says, *Good swim.* And she smiles because maybe by then second is all she was hoping for.

And Matt Biondi's probably a rich man now. A rich, happy man, guest commentating when he chooses to for some sports network, a swimmer's swimmer, with no more than a twentieth of a second up his sleeve.

Fuck him.

She swims laps until nine-thirty.

I'm sorry, she says. I lost track of time. I hope it hasn't put you out.

No, it's fine, really.

I suppose everyone else left a while ago.

Well, yeah.

I hope you weren't in a hurry to go somewhere.

No, I just live upstairs.

Really?

Yeah.

Um, the chlorine's made me really thirsty. Are you still able to sell me a drink?

Sure. My stocks aren't great though. It's been a big day. I've got some beer upstairs. If you'd like a beer that is. Of course, we're not licensed, so I'd have to just give it to you.

Already this sounds foolish, fumbling, inept. And she may not be a beer kind of girl. She may now be only a sophisticated woman who thinks she's about to walk away from a big stupid loser and back to the man she loves. Leaving the oaf with the beer to his own dull devices. Swimming elsewhere tomorrow morning and ever after.

That sounds like an offer too good to refuse, she says, and immediately looks as though she regrets saying it. As though beer is ever an offer too good to refuse.

This mutual discomfort gives him surprisingly little relief. He turns off the pool lights and lifts the counter flap and she follows him in and up the spiral stairs.

Wow, she says, as though on some adventure. You live here?

Well, yeah, he says. This is it.

This is his place. The place where he lies on his bed and reads or lies on his bed and watches TV. Or lies on his bed listening to cars passing beyond the fence until he goes to sleep.

He takes two beers from the fridge and flips the tops off.

She drinks a few mouthfuls, and says, *I suppose you have women up here all the time.*

No.

And I suppose you say that to all of them.

No, I don't have women up here. It just doesn't seem to happen.

Chlorine makes me itch, she says, *if I don't wash it off.*

Yeah I haven't quite got it right, have I? In the pool, the chlorine. You'll get no diseases in there though, that's for sure.

She puts her beer down on the table and looks at him, and it's a look that suggests a degree of frustration. That suggests at least one of them might be missing the point.

To be honest, that never crossed my mind, she says. She takes a step towards him. *I could do with a shower.*

And he feels her right hand place itself on his left flank.

What?

A shower. I could do with a shower. You've got a shower, haven't you?

And her hands move under his shirt, gently squeezing the muscles of his abdomen.

Yeah.

Well, we could use it maybe, in a little while.

And she leads him to the bed, his own bed, and she slips her thumbs under the shoulder straps of her black, one-piece Speedos and draws them down until her breasts are completely bare. He kisses her cool, firm nipples, cups her breasts in his hands, feels her body under his hands, her skin still damp as he peels the Speedos away. She lifts his drawstring shorts over his firm penis and past his knees and she takes the penis in her hand and rubs it up against her thigh.

He realises he doesn't even know her name.

Look, he says, *I don't even know your name.*

As he lies quite still and his firm penis moves faster and faster up against her thigh.

What? she says.

I don't even know your name.

I know. I didn't tell you.

I don't know anything about you.

Shut up. She closes her eyes and works harder with the penis.

You don't know anything about me.

Shut up. More emphatic this time.

You don't.

Any harder with that penis and she could make fire, he thinks.

You swam for Australia once. Someone told me that. And there's not much since then.

There's ten years. More than ten years.

She stops the penis work and looks at him, far from impressed. *And what? What in ten years?*

And there is a difficult pause, a pause he cannot fill with tales of conventional distinction.

I'm not some mindless fuck, you know, he says, but maybe too quietly, as though it's almost an apology. It should have sounded angry.

She gives him a look, just for a moment, that suggests bewilderment, that says that as far as she was aware he was, in fact, a mindless fuck.

Oh, she says.

And that's all she says as she takes the look away, turns away and stares out of the window at the dark and unspectacular suburb.

Look, he says, I do things. There are things that matter to me. I don't invite everyone up here you know. This is the only place I've got. I don't let everyone in.

I'm sorry.

She sits on the edge of the bed, naked, looking down at the lino.

I read, he says. I read up here. Robinson Crusoe. I just read Robinson Crusoe last night. Twenty-eight years on an island. That's my whole life. I'm twenty-eight years old. And this man was so alone that when he saw a footprint in the sand he spent two years building fortifications. I've wanted to talk to someone about Robinson Crusoe all day, and all they all do is give me a buck-fifty and buy fucking drinks and ice-blocks.

So tell me about Robinson Crusoe, she says quietly, still looking down at the lino.

So he tells her about *Robinson Crusoe*, a good couple of hours of theories about *Robinson Crusoe*, but mainly the part about allegory and popular fiction. And sometimes she laughs and sometimes she interrupts to dispute something or to tell him he's an idiot, but just for the hell of it (even though she's pretty sure women began popular culture due to their exclusion from a classical education). And sometimes she just lies back on his pillows totally naked and drinking mouthfuls of beer and listening.

And he's moving, always moving at some pace with the momentum of his argument. Lying next to her, loud and wide-eyed. Sitting up on the edge of the bed. On his feet, striding about with his detumescent penis swinging round after him whenever he turns back to her to make a point.

Lectures at uni were never like this, she says.

And he tells her about his swimming, more about his swimming and how it all went wrong. Losing the head game at the Pan Pacs, fighting to get it back together, doing the fourth-fastest time in history, winning a scholarship to a college in America, being told by the Australian administrators he didn't need to go to the nationals because he'd already done the second fastest time in the world that year.

Missing the nationals and being dropped from the squad for the Olympics as an example to others. Losing his college scholarship because he was out of the national team. Being offered a half academic scholarship, but being unable to afford the rest.

Coming home, training alone, but really just swimming up and down the pool because he couldn't stop himself. Watching the Olympics on TV. Retiring without anyone noticing. Trying to get his head together. These past ten years.

Let's go for a swim, he says.

And he leads her down the spiral stairs, both of them still naked, and out to the unlit pool. Cars pass just beyond the nearby trees, braking at the bottom of the hill and curving away to the right.

He walks up to the blocks, swings his arms, flaps to loosen his muscles, shakes his head, laughs.

And he dives and he hits the water like a dark bird, swims with the grace of a big, slow bat, out in this summer for mangoes, unhurried in the warm night sky.

the ekka job

It's not my idea. But, then, it never is. Of course I'm bored with having no money at all, but that's usually where TV comes in. That's what I tell Frank, as we're stagnating at the start of the August uni holidays for the third year in a row.

'Twenty bucks,' he says. 'That's all it'd take. Twenty bucks.'

'Twenty bucks and what?'

'Twenty bucks between boredom and glory, between a fucked TV holiday and who knows what. Twenty bucks and I'd be at the Ekka. A couple of beers at the Cattlemen's Bar, a go on the Zipper, a big bag of fairy floss, a few pot-shots at some metal ducks. Girls. Mate, girls love a guy who can ping a few ducks for them and win them something big and furry. It's kind of primitive.'

'Much like yourself.'

'Shit, yeah. It's like, "I shot this for you, honey," and then they owe ya.'

Sabre-toothed tiger, big furry toy. Not much has changed in Frank's world these past million years. I try telling him about how much daytime TV can offer, if you're prepared to give it a while to work its magic on you, but he's never been patient. Neither have I, really, but Frank's so bored he takes the trouble to get analytical about the plot holes in Days of Our Lives, so it's inevitable he'll crack first. And when he does, he gets us Ekka jobs.

'Mate,' he says. 'Mate, the Ekka, the show, think about it. This is the solution. This gets us in there, and it gets us cash. A holiday job, right there, right under the mighty Ferris wheel in sideshow alley.'

'Yeah, but . . .'

'Cash, uniforms, chicks,' he says, counting them on his fingers like an inventory of a lifetime's best ideas, as though, just over the old broken-glass-topped showground wall there's a land of plenty waiting for us to plunder like conquistadors.

Which I have to spell for him of course, and no simile is well served by that.

'I thought it was pronounced con-kwis-tador, anyway,' he says. 'But fucked if I know what bullfighting's got to do with all this.'

Frank does the talk on the phone, puts in quite a few calls that get nowhere. I leave him to it and get back to the TV.

'Hey, pay dirt,' he calls out a while later, as Days of Our Lives stages something threateningly climactic and the theme music swells. 'I'm on hold at the Whipster ice-cream people and they're checking their rosters.'

I mute the TV. I hadn't expected we'd actually be contenders. They get back to him and I hear all kinds of lies about experience, the holidays we've spent travelling the eastern seaboard as itinerant soft-serve squirters. I think I hear him say, 'Mate, your stall'l be nothing without us,' and that's when I have to unmute.

'But we don't know what we're doing,' I tell him when he comes back into the room, both thumbs up and a big, stupid grin on his face.

'It'll be fine,' he says, doing a levering motion with his right arm and something swirly and soft-servish with his left.

'But I've got no idea how you get that right. How you squirt the soft serve into that neat coil.'

'Mate, dogs just have to bend their knees to do it. It can't be hard.'

'Did you say that on the phone?'

'Nuh, it just came to me then. Pretty good, hey?'

'When they go to show you how to operate the soft-serve machine . . .'

'Actually, you're the one who'll be doing most of that.'

'What?'

'The soft-serve part of things. And they probably won't be showing you.'

'What?'

'The soft-serve stuff. I said you were the boy for that. I sort of had to to get us the jobs. Their star soft-server's done his wrist, apparently. So I said you could pretty much guarantee height, consistency and speed. And that I was more your hard ice-cream man. Your tough scooper. Maybe a squirt of cream on top. Maybe stretch to a spider.'

'A spider?'

'Yeah, the ice-cream and soft-drink combo. It's pretty much a chick thing. You know the spider. Daytime drink. Low-key aperitif.'

'Sophisticated chicks, obviously.'

'Yeah? I'd never really thought of it that way. Sophisticated chicks? This just gets better.'

We go in early on our first day.

'They mainly come in large,' Noela, the manager, says, when she hands us our white Whipster overalls. 'And you're not particularly large, so you might have to roll some bits up. Like, the sleeves and legs.'

Which I do, and somehow this makes the crotch seem even lower, down about knee height.

'Frank, I don't feel very attractive in this,' I can't help but say in the decompensation of the moment. 'I'll never do justice to these pants.'

'You haven't got the cap on yet. I wouldn't worry.'

'And your name tags,' Noela says. 'Have we sorted that out yet?'

'I phoned up yesterday about it,' Frank tells her.

And she says, 'Oh, yeah, that was you, Green,' and she pulls an envelope out of her pocket and hands it to him. 'There you go.'

And Frank opens the envelope, tips the tags into his hand, smirks. And mine says Philby, which makes me really shitty, the way he knew it would. But what really surprises me is that his says Juan.

When I ask him why, he shakes his head as though I know nothing at all about life, and he says, 'New chicks. Totally new chicks, right? Possibility of sophistication?' And he taps the white and pink Whipster name tag with a worldly, knowing finger and says, 'Get this. Latin lover. Frank hasn't been getting much lately, but Joo-ahn? For Joo-ahn, it'll be another story.'

'Wouldn't that be Juan? Like, no 'J' sound. And a bit less like Joanne?'

'Joo-ahn, Joo-ahn,' he says as though I have a hearing problem, a small brain and no sense of the exotic. 'Juan is like the Spanish for Wayne. W. Get it? I think they don't have an 'ay' sound in Spanish, or something. And there'd be a problem if you spelt Wayne with a 'J', hey?'

So Joo-ahn it is, clearly. And already, as we stand here in our big-man's parachute gear and our Juan and Philby Whipster name tags, I know the Ekka will be so bad (and in a way that will take Frank completely by surprise) that I'm regretting how weakly I defended the safe tedium of daytime TV. And I'm thinking I might be the kind of person who gets talked into things too easily.

'Does my arse look big in this?' Frank says, his mind fixed permanently on the science of chick magnetism.

'Frank, no-one's arse could look big in that. An inflatable boat couldn't look big in that.'

'But you can see my arse?'

'You can't see anything.'

Actually, he looks like an unmade bed with hands, and a head sticking out the top. Somewhere in there, there is probably an arse, but there's no way it's going to get to be the love-feature Frank would like. So it looks as though it'll all be down to personality.

'You were hoping for something a little more fitted, weren't you?' I say to him, realising that his disappointment needs acknowledgment.

'Yeah. More like a uniform. You know how uniforms have that thing about them?'

'You haven't got the cap on, yet,' I tell him. 'I wouldn't worry. And you can tell them about your arse, anyway. They don't all have to see it first up.'

'Yeah, I guess.'

'Okay, Joo-ahn, let's do it.'

'Joo-ahn,' he says slowly, and the smile is back. 'Yeah. Si. Si, señor.'

'You've been practising, haven't you?'

'Nuh. I think I just know this shit,' he says in a way that sounds dangerously proud.

As planned, he gets the hard ice-cream end, and a guy called Leon leads me to the soft-serve machine.

'You'd 've used one of these before, hey?' he says.

'Maybe not this model,' I tell him, going with my plan but hoping all the rehearsal doesn't show.

'Not this model? Not the Ultraserve 480?'

'I would've spent more time recently on the 485.' And it was a good plan, but it might be getting too fancy now.

'There's a 485?'

'Yeah, but not everyone's got one, I suppose. It's no big deal.'

'We've only had this a couple of years. You reckon it's out of date already?'

'No, I'm sure it's fine. The 485's just different. Actually, surprisingly different but, you know, I've heard plenty of good things about the 480, so . . .'

'Yeah, it's a good machine, the 480. A fine machine. Drop ten thousand softies between services.' And he gives it the kind of pat usually saved for a reliable working dog. 'Better show you the ropes then, hey?'

And I get the predictable jargon-riddled run-down that lets me know I'll have to work it out for myself when his back is turned, and then he says, 'Any questions?'

'Um, yeah. Clockwise or anticlockwise with the coil? The swirl? How do you want me to do it?

'The coil? Clockwise,' he says indignantly. 'This is Australia.'

And he goes to check on Frank as I'm doing a practice clockwise coil, and uncoiling a large amount of soft-serve onto my wrist and then my left shoe, and I hear him saying, 'Hey, where the fuck have you been, pal? Not more than two strawberries in the Super Strawb, and I don't care how small they are.'

Frank apologises, and Leon says, 'I don't know what kind of fancy joints you guys have been working at before now,' and shakes his head. 'Customer loyalty's one thing but three strawberries is bloody madness.' He goes out the back, muttering something about stock levels and people 'tossing round the strawbs like there's no tomorrow.'

And Frank turns to me, and says, 'We're in,' and throws a few strawberries into his mouth.

We get working, and the crowd builds up quickly and business is good at Whipster. I'm coiling and coiling and occasionally using a lid from one of Frank's tubs to scoop the spillage onto the ground outside where, hopefully, Leon will never see it. Frank's working the scoop down firmly into the tubs and saying, 'Jeez, they freeze this stuff hard,' and rewarding himself with mouthfuls of fruit.

And he's chucking on nuts and cream and squirts of topping when he's not supposed to, and telling me it's customer loyalty (when I know it's all about girls). And he's engaging as many as possible in go-nowhere conversations about spiders and recommending lime, large, two scoops of vanilla.

'For the price of a regular,' he says, and I know his eyebrows are twitching up and down like a sleazy old showman's, and surely none of them'll go for that.

Leon comes back from one of the other Whipster outlets, takes a look at technique.

'Yeah, nice coil,' he says to me, in a one-pro-to-another kind of way. 'Good on you.' And he goes down to Frank's end and I hear him saying, 'Balls. I said *balls*. Good, firm balls. People aren't paying you for those little scruffy bits of ice-cream. They can do that at home. Put a bit of wrist into it. Here.'

And he takes the scoop and does a couple before striding out again.

'He's tough,' Frank says. 'But he's fair. He can scoop, you know.'

And we start getting queues, and there's some pressure on my coiling and I'm going as fast as I can, bunging in Flakes, losing lumps of ice-cream in the choc dip. But mostly getting away with it, mostly keeping them happy. Hardly noticing any girls, though. This is too much like hard work.

At lunchtime a guy called Steve comes to help out and he says, 'So you're the pros, hey?' and Frank says, 'Yeah.'

'Yeah, Leon's been talking about you. The one of youse on the 480, mainly. Reckons you're good. Reckons that's why you're up in this one.'

'What do you mean, this one?' I ask him.

'This one. This stall. The flagship. Noela's pride and joy. Whipster Central. You didn't think you blokes got the stall at the entrance to sideshow alley for nothing, did you?'

This gives Frank confidence, even though he's never been near a 480 in his life. He bosses Steve around and Steve's happy to go with it, figuring he might learn something. Steve likes Frank, mainly because Frank's rude to him and because he's called Joo-ahn. Steve's impressed by both of those things.

Most of the time I've got my back to them, and my day's becoming a blur of slow, white clockwise swirls. Sometimes Steve appears next to my elbow, staring down at the nozzle of the 480 at another perfect coil, and then saying something like, 'Joo-ahn wants another two up our end. One choc top, complimentary choc.'

'Is she good looking?'

'Nuh. He's got Spanish blood, but. Remember?'

Our own late lunchbreak gets closer. I'm missing daytime TV. The morning bottoms out when my mother visits, dressed semi-formally, wearing sunglasses and speaking in the accent she used for her much-misunderstood Edith Piaf tribute at her last office Christmas party.

'If you sing you are dead, all right?' I manage to say quietly to her before any real trouble starts.

'But Monsieur Philby. I am 'ere only for your wonderful ice-cream. All around the world they are saying about it, *c'est magnifique.*'

'Go away.'

'Ah, Monsieur Philby,' she says, getting louder as a crowd starts to gather, 'they are saying about you that you are lovely, attractive young man.'

'Go away.'

'And that all the daughters, they should be being the locked up when Monsieur Philby is about and on the look for lurve.'

'That's it. I'm going to kill myself if you don't go away,' I say to her in the most forceful, quiet voice I can manage. 'There'll be blood on your hands.'

'But no, Philby,' she whispers back in her regular voice. 'I think we're just getting some interest. And Frank did say you were both doing this to meet girls. So I thought it'd help if I talked you up a bit.'

'Frank only ever does anything to meet girls. Now, thank you, but I think I'm probably as talked-up as I need to be now. I really think I have to take it from here myself.'

'Well, if you're sure . . .'

'Oh, I'm so sure.'

'All right, then. Now, you give me one of those cones and I'll go off saying some good things about it.'

'But restrained.'

'Restraint, Philby, is my watchword.'

I hand her an average-looking ice-cream. She tips me generously, backs away through the queue, giving them all a good look.

'Such style,' she's saying, that French accent more outrageous than ever. 'Such form. Surely there is genius in the young soft 'ands of Monsieur Philby.'

And the girls in the queue now treat me as though I, too, am touched by madness, give me their simple orders carefully, hand over exact change where possible, back away before I try to get interactive.

I keep squirting, keep coiling, keep up the young, soft genius and keep trying to ignore Frank, hard at work up the other end. Cruising into Latin-lover win-on mode.

He's got someone interested in his name, and he's handling it like clumsy fishing, trying to reel her in as quickly as possible. But so far it's working, and it's the results Frank seems to get that have always made me hate his patter most.

'So. Joo-ahn,' a girl's voice is saying. 'Where's that from, exactly?'

'Spain,' he says, with an exotic kind of confidence.

'Spain? Wow. What part of Spain?'

'Part of Spain?' Less confidence now. 'Spain generally. We travelled a lot when I was young.'

He thinks it's a slick save, and I'm about to laugh at him when she says, 'Hey, cool,' and it's looking as slick as it needs to be.

'Hey, Leanne, how long are you going to be with that?' a guy says as he comes up to her, chomping at the end of a Dagwood Dog.

And she takes the large lime spider with two complimentary Flakes and says, 'See you, Joo-ahn,' and the two of them leave, starting an argument that begins with, 'Hey, did you know that guy?'

'Fuck,' Frank says, but quietly, so it's not bad for business. 'Fuck, I was in there. Thirty seconds more . . . Hey, what part of Spain do you reckon I should be from?'

'Portugal. Portugal could be good.'

'Okay. Portugal. Is that still actually part of Spain? Didn't it become independent, like, in the seventies, or something?'

'Yeah, good point. Still be a few Joo-ahns there, though, I'd think. But maybe Madrid. Maybe go for Madrid.'

'Madrid. Okay. So what do I need to know about Madrid?'

'No details, Joanne. It'll only get you in trouble. You came out here when you were a baby.'

'Joo-ahn,' he says. 'Joo-ahn. There's an inflection involved. And I'd stop putting shit on this if I were you. People are getting into it, you know.'

Leon turns up again at two, and tells us we're on lunch.

'I'll look after things with young Steve,' he says. 'And I'll see you at quarter to three.'

We go out the back and I'm about take my overalls off when Frank says, 'What are you doing? Men in uniform, remember? Don't even touch the cap.'

So we head out into the Ekka crowd, men in uniform, and pass conspicuously unnoticed by girls. I'm not sure what Frank expected would happen, but it doesn't happen.

We're leaning against the railings near the Zipper, taking stock, when a twenty-cent piece falls from high-up on the ride and lands near Frank.

A guy in the queue is about to pick it up when he notices the uniforms.

'Oh, sorry,' he says. 'I guess that's why you guys are there.'

'Yeah,' Frank says. 'That belongs to someone.' He picks it up and pockets it. 'And I'll be minding it for them till they get off.'

'Sure. But do you actually work here? Doesn't that say *Whipster* on your name tag?'

'Yeah, but it's like . . . a conglomerate.'

'And we're multiskilling,' I toss in, in case it helps, particularly now that a few people in the queue are taking an interest. 'So if you could all get back a bit, that'd be great. We're actually here on safety duty. You know, Safety Regs? It's a government thing. We need a perimeter.'

'No untrained people directly under the Zipper is pretty much what we're looking at,' Frank says. 'Some stuff comes out of these things, you know. And we can't have any of it landing on anybody. Plus, it's all got to go to its rightful owners.'

And at that, a cigarette lighter drops onto the grass, followed by some more loose change and, a matter of seconds later, two Iced Vovo biscuits. We pocket the change, begin a responsible-looking pile of other items. And we usher the crowd along carefully, keeping it all low-key so that the Zipper staff round at the booth don't see what's going on.

A fifty-cent piece pings Frank in the shoulder, and someone laughs.

'Hey, that'll be enough of that,' he tells them. 'This is a serious issue.' And then he turns to me and says, 'I reckon that just about puts me up to a whole beer.'

And that's when one of the Zipper crew comes around from behind the generator.

'Something going on here?' he says, knowing there's something going on.

Frank's tell him everything's fine, under control. He looks unconvinced, but he goes, and I sense grudging respect from the people in the queue, as though they realise the conglomerate's got their interests at heart, with this close attention to safety issues.

We keep collecting change, and the whole Ekka-job idea is starting to seem as though it might be worthwhile. We haven't made the girl side of things fire yet, but we've got the uniforms, and cash is coming our way.

And that's when Frank says, 'Fuck, mate, look up.'

And I look up and see, fluttering slowly down to us, a

twenty-dollar note. Frank secures the perimeter. I catch it before it lands. But I can't bring myself to put it in my pocket.

'So what do we do with this?' I say to him.

'What do we do with it? It's twenty bucks. Plenty.'

'Yeah, but it belongs to someone.'

'Yeah, right. And we go up to them at the end of the ride and go "anyone lose a twenty?" We'll never know whose it was. What are we going to do? Ask them the serial number?'

'I think we've got to give it back.'

'Yeah, and then the Zipper people are onto us.'

'Hey,' the guy from the generator shouts. 'What have you got there?'

'Nothing,' Frank says.

'Nothing, hey? Doesn't look like nothing.'

Frank takes the twenty, puts it in his pocket, shows the guy empty hands.

'You give that back,' the guy says.

'Yeah, who to?'

'You give it to me. That's all you've got to worry about. And then you piss off, all right?'

'And what are you going to do with it?'

'None of your fucking business.'

'Are you giving it back to the person who lost it?'

'Just give it to me, prick.'

'No.'

And he's coming closer, glaring at both of us, and he looks at Frank's name tag and says, 'Give it to me, you fuckin' wog.'

And Frank says, 'Hey, I've got friends who are wogs. Arsehole.'

'Frank didn't mean that,' I say, and then come over all foolishly brave. 'You've probably got friends who are arse-holes, and he's not normally that insensitive.'

The guy doesn't have the verbals to deal with that, so he goes for menace instead. Lifts his fist, takes a swing at Frank. But Frank ducks and flails his own fist around, just to get the guy away, but it connects and sends him stagger-ing backwards.

'Shit, run,' Franks says.

And we go, off through the queue with the guy run-ning after us, swearing away about what he's going to do when he catches us. The two of us running like hell in our bright white Whipster overalls, like some remake of a knock-em-down silent movie classic, but one in which both of us could end up in actual pain if the wrong ending comes about.

We keep running, probably long after we've lost him, past the Hall of Mirrors, round the Ferris wheel, past the woodchop and up into the animal pavilions.

'Department of Agriculture,' Frank shouts to someone who tries to stop us, and we hide among some pigs.

The pigs snuffle round, make room. Frank's eyes water with the straw and he pinches his nose hard, tries not to sneeze. A tear rolls down one cheek.

'Well, Joanne, that got a bit dicey,' I say, when I realise we've got away with it. 'And I don't think we can go back there now, can we?'

'What do you mean?' he says, in a pig-snuffly way.

'Well, I don't think we give the twenty back to its rightful owner. They'll be long gone.'

'Yeah. Must be finders keepers then.'

'Must be.'

'And Jesus it hurts, hitting someone,' he says, shaking his right hand. 'I'm a lover, not a fighter, mate. A lover, not a fighter.'

'And a Latin lover at that.'

'Shit, yeah. Now, we should probably get back to work. And roll on the arvo break, hey?' He takes the note from his pocket and unfolds it. 'When we can blow this twenty on lime spiders and loose women.'

And with the wild allergic response his face is mounting, it comes out as 'libe spiders ad loose wibbid,' but I know what he means. We're cashed up, we're men in uniform, we're ready.

'Twenty bucks between boredom and glory,' I say to him, and he lets out a big solid sneeze that he moves to block, but all that gets in the way is the twenty-dollar note.

'No worries,' he says, and wipes it in the straw. 'We can swap it back at Whipster. We'll tell Leon it's ice-cream.'

the goatflap brothers and
the house of names

It wasn't easy becoming Cleveland Goatflap. And who would have thought it could lead to the discovery of a brother? I had tired of many things and determined that I could change few. So much in life, I realised, is fixed.

But I could change my name. I could change my name, and from this straightforward but fundamental change I could then make others, as time permitted. Of course, this should not be a change to just any name. It should be a name with flourish, a name with which to embark on a new journey. A name with boldness, a name from which there could be no retreat. And change could then proceed, perhaps in small measures, perhaps at a charge. And perhaps the speed depended on the name itself. So the business of the name was clearly the most important of choices.

This took thought. Weeks, months of thought, list after list of names, and suddenly my life was filled with possibility. And I pinned the lists to my noticeboard at home, then Blu-Tacked them to the walls when the noticeboard was full. On my computer at work I alphabetised them and cut and pasted and printed in seven point so I could fit more to a page.

At home my walls filled till I lived in a house of names, where every conceivable surface was clad in Reflex 80 A4 paper, each sheet crammed to bursting with delightful proper and improper nouns. Names under my bare feet when I walked, names on the ceiling when I lay in bed, sheets of names crinkling attractively as I pulled my doona up over me. Comfortable soft noises like whispering voices as I rolled over in my bed filled with balled-up lists of names.

And I lived with the windows shut all this time, fearing that the slightest breeze would blow down my walls. But this was not a time for fear. There was no turning back, barely a thought of the old name my parents had given me, and which I would never speak again.

I lay awake most nights in the silent, airless house. The Blu-Tack held. No pages fell.

I pressed on, and I experimented with all kinds of things that might be names fit for journeying – old names and new names, the names of objects and countries and American states and unexpected species of flower and insect. I had a list of actual words so that I could, if I chose, compose names that would never be picked up by a computer spellchecker: Cliff Carpenter, Dane Tailor and the concise but elusive Book Smith.

But in the end there was no name that rolled off the

tongue with quite the finesse of Cleveland Goatflap.

I was ready.

In my lunch hour I left work, work where they still called me by the name I was now forgetting, the name I found it harder and harder to remember to answer to. And when I returned I would be informing them I would answer to it no more. But for now, in the interests of safety, I feigned purposelessness, and I headed in the wrong direction. I walked into an arcade and bought a hat and walked out of the other end of the arcade wearing it. I bought very dark glasses and a ferocious tie at Crazy Clark's, and I put them on. I walked the streets and no-one knew me. And already I walked with a more deliberate stride, the stride of a man who was going places.

The security guard watched me pass as I walked into the building, but he said nothing. I expect he could recognise I was involved in something of importance. I took the lift to the appropriate floor, took a number, filled in my form, checked the proof of identity documentation that bore the name I was about to cast off like an old skin. And I waited.

Around me others were doing the same, carrying proof of something, holding papers to carry out some act of registration.

My number was called.

I explained my purpose to the man behind the counter. He looked at my form, looked at me, looked at my passport with its photo of a younger, less distinguished man than someone who was almost Cleveland Goatflap.

He said to me, *I might have to see you without the hat and glasses.*

But I wear them now, I told him, and he thought about it for a while and said, *Righto,* but not with any certainty.

He read my form again. He looked up.

Might be a problem with the name, sir.

I told him I couldn't see it.

Some people might think it's frivolous.

I told him I found the very notion offensive. He apologised. I told him they were old family names, both of them, that my mother's mother had been a Cleveland and my father's grandmother a Goatflap. But here I outwitted him. I told him that the word he might presently be reading as Goatflap – an obvious choice for which I could forgive him – was actually a very old and distinguished French name, and should be pronounced *Gofla.* I told him that when I was very young my father's grandmother, to whom I had been close, had suggested it derived from a Basque name, from a family who made terracotta roof tiles and moved to Toulouse in the twelfth century, and that there had most certainly been Goflas on the French side during the Hundred Years' War, and that they had, sir, served with distinction.

He told me he would have a word with his supervisor.

He was gone for several minutes and he returned with an older man who studied me carefully as he approached.

Never heard of this Goatflap, sir, he said. *Heard of a lot of French names in my time, but never Goatflap.*

It's pronounced *Gofla,* I told him, and it may have been curiously translated from the Basque.

I was becoming concerned. Becoming concerned and starting to sweat more than a little. Clearly this man was an expert in the business of names and would not easily be bluffed with bluster and stories of roof tiles. But I had put months into this name. I couldn't imagine living a moment longer without living as Cleveland Goatflap.

Excuse me, a voice said beside me. *Excuse me.*

It was a voice of very individual intonation. A voice that spoke perhaps the way a chicken would speak if it could speak actual words. A chicken's voice, if chickens had lips.

I can confirm that Gofla, he said, with such a flourish that his head snapped back, *is in fact a very old French name, very old indeed. And I can confirm this*, he went on sternly to the supervisor, *for I, monsieur, am this man's brother. I too carry the blood of Goflas in my veins.*

And with this, he rolled up a sleeve and shook his fist around till the veins stood out like ropes, and he pointed to them as proof positive of his Goatflap origins.

We embraced, despite his problem with personal hygiene, and I felt tears well in my eyes, for my parents had always told me I was their only son.

He slapped his form defiantly down on the counter and I could see he had crossed out his previous choice of a new name and replaced it with Eleanor Goatflap in bold, black capitals.

He pushed the form to the more junior officer who read it and looked up at him.

So you, sir, are at present Eduardo Saliva, wishing to change your name to Eleanor Gofla.

That's correct.

You've been here before, haven't you sir?

Regularly.

The Eleanor, sir. Are you aware that that is a woman's name?

Sounds like discrimination to me, son.

And I liked Eleanor already. I liked his feistiness. He was a good man to have on your team.

The supervisor interrupted and said, *Geoff, I don't think the department would like to see itself standing in the way of a family reunion.*

And the junior officer smiled, and said, *No George, I guess not.*

So we left the building arm in arm as brothers, my eyes still misting over periodically as we walked through the mall.

Let's have a drink, young Cleveland, Eleanor said. *To family, and to the great days of France.*

So Eleanor took me to a pub where he asked if they had French beer so we could celebrate appropriately. They told him they were all out of French beer, and he said, *Not to worry. Vive le Fourex, eh?*

So we drank toast after toast in Fourex. We toasted the family and the great days of France. We swapped sides and toasted Blenheim, Ramillies, Oudenarde and Malplaquet. We even toasted Waterloo though, as Eleanor said, it's not really our time.

And suddenly all the changes I could ever need were mine.

We went home to my house, the House of Names, and Eleanor said, *It looks like heaven to me, a place like this. You've done well for yourself, young Cleveland. All these names. All these possibilities.*

And I felt proud. Proud as he spent hours just reading my walls, exploring all my surfaces, marking his favourites with a highlighter.

We enrolled in French classes together and practised during all our spare time.

I even took him along to confront the parents who had abandoned him years before, though he was quite hesitant about such a meeting and could barely remember them. I parked outside their house and we spoke in the car and he said he was a bit tense, but I told him he'd be fine.

He took a deep breath and hugged my father and addressed him as *mon père*.

And the last words I recall my father saying, were him shouting after us, *This is madness,* as we left. *He's bloody older than I am.*

But we talked in the car and decided we would let no-one come between us. And my parents can make their own choices. I told Eleanor that, and I told him not to worry. I said we'd be okay.

So we live in the same house now, our house, the House of Names. We speak only French there. We pal around. We share the same dreams, Eleanor and I.

pe

Mr Lewis is only physical, only muscle and bone, hard muscle binding big bones into a bad machine. Old and mean, standing over us, stooping over us ox-shouldered, pounding his left hand with his right fist, compact, impacted violence, brute force punched into his hard palm, always too near us, always as though it's only just contained. Flinty old fist into scuffed-leather skin, pounding to make some point, pounding for the sake of pounding, pounding as though it gives him more power, more menace, builds up a charge.

Age has not wearied Mr Lewis, just made him very nasty, set his face in a scowl, pushed his eyes back under the bone shelf of his forehead, silvered the cropped rim of hair around his balding head, only making it look more like a missile.

Mr Lewis does PE all day, has done PE for thirty years. Mr Lewis thinks that anyone who isn't fit isn't trying, and that anyone who isn't trying will change if shouted at loud enough and often enough, if degraded sufficiently. Mr Lewis has a very small non-mammalian brain and understands only this. Running and push-ups, running and push-ups, running and push-ups and no poofters.

Poofters, shirkers, wimps, girls, nancies and everyone else not entirely fascinated by five laps of Ovals One and Two and five sets of ten push-ups just won't cut it with Mr Lewis.

I don't cut it with Mr Lewis. I am, in the engaging vernacular of Mr Lewis, all of the above. A poofter, a shirker, a wimp, a girl, a nancy, that is, a person not particularly disposed to the physical.

You're a wimp, boy. What are you?

Wimp, sir.

Louder, boy. I can't hear you.

I'm a wimp, sir.

What does he think we are? Paratroopers? Mr Lewis should have been killed in a war.

PE. Physical education. Sure it's physical, but where's the education? What am I learning from running and push-ups?

These things I can't say. There is no room for questions in PE. There is no answering back, no discussion, no room for negotiation of any kind. Room only for fear. Fear of Mr Lewis.

On his good days, days when nothing stirs him up, we do our five laps and our five sets of ten and that's that. On the bad days he just keeps us going till he's had enough. You *don't stop till you're told to stop*, he shouts at us and waves us on, another lap. *It's not your bell, it's my bell and I can ignore it as long as I like. I don't have to let you go until I'm ready to let you go.* And this is what he does, day after day, week after week. This is his life. Six classes a day, thirty boys. A bare minimum of four and a half thousand laps of the oval and forty-five thousand push-ups a week.

In our class of thirty I am, as far as Mr Lewis goes, the twenty-eighth most highly regarded athlete. I am the second worst asthmatic in the class. The worst asthmatic, Hall, is ranked behind me specifically because of the time when Mr Lewis called him soft and told him to work through it and Hall, in the process of working through it, fell to the ground pasty-faced and wheezing and with strings of green mucus coming from his nose and mouth. Mr Lewis thinks that asthma is a kind of stitch. Nice one, Mr Lewis. Nice little non-mammalian brain you've got there, Mr Lewis.

Ranked just behind Hall is Faulkner, who has a significant weight problem and cried once when Mr Lewis called him a *good-for-nothing lard bucket* and made him do push-up after push-up in front of the whole class until his arms could push nothing more (particularly not the many kilos of lard they were required to). And Mr Lewis stood with a foot on either side of Faulkner's head, so close that his head couldn't turn and he stayed face down in the grass, the big humps of his shoulders shuddering with each gasp of breath.

Good-for-nothing lard bucket. There's some physical education for you, Faulkner.

But tears mean nothing to Mr Lewis, nothing but weakness, so Faulkner is his thirtieth-most-favoured class member, and he got another ten push-ups for crying. Which is typical. Usually if you're physically unable to run five laps Mr Lewis makes you run at least six. And if you show any signs of being unable to run the last you get another. And only in the none-too-complicated brain of Mr Lewis does this make sense.

Any transgression, however non-transgressive, however marginal or mundane or pointless, is met with that small-brained, big-throated breathy bellow, flecks of spit flicking from the lips. And it helps if you don't listen, or if you just listen to the last words, since you'll have to repeat them when he shouts, *What are you?*

So you just stay stiff-lipped and go with it and hope it'll be over soon. You just stand there and look into his soulless blue eyes and say to yourself, This'll be over soon, this means nothing to me, one day I'll leave here and get a life, and this is all he knows, this is where he'll be forever.

And you stare blankly into his eyes, echo when you need to, take it impassively since that's something he almost respects. And you're consoling yourself with the numbers, because you aren't the one with four and a half thousand laps a week, one hundred and eighty thousand laps a year, seven-point-two million laps of Ovals One and Two in your career. That's your life, Mr Lewis, seven-point-two million rings run around nothing. Kids running nowhere, eighteen times to the moon and back and nowhere but away from you. Seventy-two million push-ups, each one counted aloud on the way to ten, one to ten, one to ten, seven-point-two million times. Shirker, sir. I'm a good-for-nothing shirker, sir.

And I tell Faulkner, Don't listen, don't let it get to you, but Faulkner doesn't operate that way.

Faulkner, chess champion, master of both Space Invaders and haiku, numismatist. All of this and not yet fifteen. Fourteen and in the company of other fourteen-year-olds who are built quite differently, built of limbs while he's all bulged up with family fat, with the lard his parents gave him. Faulkner whose knees haven't touched since he was eight. *Good-for-nothing lard bucket, sir.*

PE is two hours a week and it comes in three parts, Health, Fitness and Games (but 'HF&G' has never taken off, so it's still 'PE'). Mr Milson takes us for Health, an hour every second week, and he tells us in a very soft voice about safe sex and not using drugs. Given five laps of the ovals, Mr Milson would be dead on lap two. And he'd still have to run at least another three, with Mr Lewis bellowing, *You don't stop till I say you stop.*

On alternate weeks we have Games for the first hour. Games is excellent. In summer we go down to the nets and practice cricket. In winter we play touch football. Games is so good it's almost better than lunchtime.

Fitness. Fitness is the second hour every week. Fitness is Mr Lewis. Mr Lewis in his neatly pressed white short-sleeved shirt and shorts and his black boots, sending us out in pursuit of fitness through five laps of the ovals and fifty push-ups, running and push-ups, week after week. Roaring mercilessly at the back-markers, but we go no faster. Sometimes, certainly, we end up doing more laps but it doesn't seem to help us. Sometimes the whole class does more laps, but the others don't blame us since we suffer from the extra more than they do.

And in winter my asthma's worse. I'm not good in cold air, so on the second Tuesday in June I'm sucking on a lot of Ventolin on my way down from Health.

I change to run and the Ventolin's making me dizzy. We set off on the first lap, and I'm in trouble before we get to the rifle range, lagging behind. I'm working with the breathing, trying to stay calm, but it would be easier trying to breathe through my shirt than using these lungs.

I'm last when we finish, last to drop to the grass for the first ten push-ups. And today I have the breath to either count aloud or do the push-ups, but not both. I stay quiet, I do my ten. Some of the others are far ahead on the second lap when I stand.

I didn't hear you counting, Mr Lewis says.

It's the asthma, sir.

Round here we count when we do push-ups. Give me another ten, and this time I want to hear it.

So I'm back on the grass, half-wishing he'd had a bigger go at me and given me more of a break. He paces round me. I can see his high-gloss black shoes pressing down into the neat grass as he passes. And I know he's listening to every number and I'm telling myself this is okay. That I'm the one who can count to ten without assistance.

Very small non-mammalian brain, I tell myself, very small non-mammalian brain.

Now get back out there. Get back out there and start trying for once.

And this lap is worse. And I do try. Even the stragglers from the pack are well ahead of me when I start and further ahead when I finish. I'm a hundred metres out when some of them are standing from their push-ups and beginning their third lap.

And the asthma isn't good. It occurs to me, as I run into the glare Mr Lewis is sending me down the last hundred metres (and something has to occur to me to take my mind from this), it occurs to me that it would be easier to suck yoghurt through a cheese grater than to breathe this way. And I know he's going to shout at me, but that's okay. I'm ready, I'll be ready. This will not be a good day.

I stand in front of Mr Lewis and think of sucking yoghurt through a cheese grater as he goes on at me and he's making me repeat things. Wimp. Girl. Easy words, so that's fine. But his voice is harsh, rough, and I'm looking beyond him, looking at the ground, hoping this will pass. And he's shouting at me, *You'll keep going till I think you've done enough* and I notice, when I think I should make eye contact, that one of his eyes seems to be looking out to the side. Just one. And his words are starting to slur, thickening up like my breathing. But I don't think he'd appreciate the yoghurt and cheese grater analogy.

I do my ten push-ups. I set off on the next lap, doing something that looks like running but isn't much faster than walking. But it's all I can do. People are starting to lap me. I'm thinking about breathing, thinking about being calm and breathing, getting ready. Ready to be shouted at. Focussing on getting through this, however many laps it takes.

And when I run into the straight I can see that Mr Lewis is listing to one side. And he shouts at me and spits and his tongue flaps in his mouth like a piece of loose meat, like the tongue of another animal, hanging there like some bad joke. And his voice is husky, nasty, imprecise as he hurls abuse my way, rages on about my slackness and scowls his face up and drools. Swings his left arm round as though it's come loose at the shoulder, drags one of his feet while I do my push-ups. Scrapes one shiny shoe past me, carries his weight heavily on the other leg. *Get going, get going, get on with you*, he shouts, sending me off on the next lap.

When I get back he's on the ground. He's propped against the low white perimeter fence of Number One Oval and he's angry and incoherent, raging against something we can't see, grunting and ranting at everyone, sending them off on more laps, however many they've done. And a slick of murky saliva is now making its way down the front of his pressed white shirt, getting the hell out of that bad mouth.

I stop and he makes fierce noises and points at the ground and I do my push-ups. When I stand I ask him if everything's all right. And my voice sounds very small and neat and horribly, dangerously out of place. Is everything all right, sir? The voice of someone who knows it's about the least appropriate thing he could ever say, someone who knows you just don't ask Mr Lewis something like that.

And Mr Lewis's one straight-ahead eye looks right into mine and his neck and facial muscles move frantically to give his voice as much noise as they can and he waves his arm to send me off on another lap.

And as I run the lap, or at least run some parts and walk others, I know something very bad is happening in his brain, his very small non-mammalian brain that knows only running and push-ups and fear. Some imploding noiseless violence that his big slack body can't fight, that cuts him down to fence height, bends his glare, folds up his shouting voice and lets only the edge of it out.

And when I get back, some of the others have stopped doing laps and are standing around him, but a safe distance away, and he's lying on his side and his face is grey and his tongue hangs down into grass, bitten and bloodied.

As someone goes for help, help that will surely be futile, I look out across the oval. From here I can count at least six people, and then eight or ten, half the class in fact, still out running. Running till they're told to stop.

there must be lions

When the night is quiet, you are visited by lions.

You are sure of this because they give you babies, sure of it because they are there swinging disconsolately in your lion nets until, foolishly and still half-asleep, you let them go, and tuck the nets away. And the room in the morning is small and pale blue and quiet as all the others when the sun comes in, when you hear the clatter of breakfast trolleys, when the first nurse visits to ask about the night.

There must be lions because otherwise there would be rats. (There used to be until the lions came.) There must be lions because who else eats the left-over cheese-cake you occasionally leave under the bed? Only on Christmas Eve might there be another, more universally acceptable, explanation. And it's not as though all your Christmases are coming at once and you hear reindeer or fat-bellied laughter all these nights that the cheesecake goes. It's not as though you've even got a chimney.

There must be lions because what other species would be so sly as to hide their crawl through the long grass by faking the noise of passing traffic?

The disappearance of rats, the frequently disappearing cheesecake remnants, the traffic noises: all these became apparent to you around the same time. Not that days didn't pass (lions aren't that transparent), but in a small, pale-blue room one adds things up. And time in the room is not the issue it might be, so when you evaluate the evidence it might all have arrived between lunch (mixed sandwiches) and dinner (chicken à la king) on the same day, or it might have taken years. But so little else of consequence has happened that it only makes sense to view the events (rats, cheesecake, traffic) as synchronous and, indeed, causally related. And the implication of lions is therefore overwhelming.

There could be other ways, no doubt, to account for some of the happenings in your room but, to be fair to your lion theory, not many could accommodate the various maulings and the offspring. These incidents are among the more challenging to explain without invoking the presence of a large, carnivorous and fertile species. Unfortunately, slabs of lost tissue regenerate by dawn and babies climb out of the windows and run away through the trees. And while the lions might be ravaging absolutely everyone, they leave only you with the memories.

If only you had evidence, something to show the nursing supervisor, the doctor, the tribunal. These are people of science and they will not be easily persuaded by a plate messed with crumbs, an absence of visible vermin. You have put your hypothesis to them and they have smiled, nodded, thanked you for your time. And you have gone back to your room in a state of some embarrassment, feeling foolish that you might have made such a claim without supporting evidence, without so much as a tooth or a fur sample. To be fair, though, specimen collection is far from easy. And it is hard to think when you're being devoured by a lion.

And they bring students, six at a time, but they're no help at all. The only place they probe for lions is your past, as though you and the lions have some deal going. And during your childhood at Sandgate did you ever see a circus? Transparent, clumsy children. What do you think of elephants, do you have any views on elephants? As if elephants could fit through these small windows! So they ignore the cupboards, the corners, the potential spaces behind curtains and they strangle themselves with wheezy coughs as you tell them about the various outcomes of a visit by lions. Yes, that's right. By lions. Not to lions, not to a circus, not in the imaginative realm of childhood, but a visit by lions to this particular room last night, damn it.

Anyway, it's not as if you haven't thought about elephants yourself, what with their well-documented fondness for sweet things, but beyond that the idea is close to ridiculous. Monkeys, now monkeys might be a possibility, but they would be unlikely to eat whole limbs. These limbs (you know from the great number of your own bleeding stumps that you've examined) are taken cleanly and by a large mouth, not nibbled to nothing by a family of smaller beasts. The suggestion is also there in their regeneration, because something is surely more likely to regenerate, at least in this short period of time, from a tidily fashioned stump. Otherwise you'd be hobbling round for weeks saying, Look what the bloody monkeys did. Everyone would. But all is well by morning, every morning. So there goes another hypothesis.

Of course, people scoff, but people scoffed at Columbus, at Copernicus, at Darwin, so you are in fine company. And you watch the others leave their rooms and slouch their way to breakfast, stretching the stiffness out of their fresh-healed injuries, sending away the last moments of amnestic lion-sleep.

And then they hang around all day, docile as old house pets, and night comes back and their viscera are torn from them by powerful jaws, their blood is lapped by tongues like big, pink dinner plates and their wounds knit like neat flesh long before they wake, their new kidneys, liver, spleen clad in a fresh sheath of skin.

You meet them over cereal and you tell them to get some spirit about them, get involved. You tell them to leave cheesecake under their beds and they will see. You tell them this is the best you can do at the moment, but when you hold a lion in your nets till morning they shall be among the first to know.

And they tell you they shall wait for your call with a whip and a wooden stool, ready to teach your lion a thing or two, should it be required. You make a note of this as it could be useful if a lion becomes difficult to control in the very limited space of your room. Expressions involving caged lions come to mind, and caged lions are clearly not to be treated lightly.

Some, you know, will not be persuaded by talk. They will wait for incontrovertible proof. And proof is taking time, not that you aren't trying. Since your first actual sighting, a slip-up on the part of an old and clumsy lion, you have gone through the various stages that are likely to be necessary to achieve something conclusive. You have mastered the steps of luring, trapping and holding (an open window, a tempting whiff of cheesecake, a spring-loaded net), but so far success has been short-lived, as you keep letting the damn things go before you can think to stop yourself.

It is not, you assure yourself, in your nature to do this, to be so careless, so it must be some trick of the lions, some subliminal influence they exert on you while you are not yet awake. The next strategy you evolve must be designed to overcome this. You wear ear plugs to bed, then a blindfold. But each time you let the lions go. You put a bag over your head and play background music and still you let the lions go.

You feel their influence must be exerted through your pores, must infuse into you while you sleep, trickle into your smaller blood vessels till it pounds in your fuzzy, dream-ridden head, insisting that you let them go. So you tell one of the staff you have scabies again and you coat yourself with lotion and go to bed like a powdery ghost, with the last remaining conduit for the influence of lions surely stifled.

And shortly before dawn, lightly dusted in off-white, with a bag over your head, ear plugs and a blindfold and Metallica playing as loudly as the night staff will permit, you rise and let the lions go.

Is there no defeating the wiles of lions?

Every night you catch them. You're good at catching them now. Every night you hold them for hours and they hang high in the nets in the distant shadowy corners of the room, struggling frantically but only becoming more entangled until all they can do is rock gently and send out the subliminal signals that will force you to release them. You've had about enough of this.

You read every book about lions in the limited library available to you and, while nothing you learn in any way contradicts your hypothesis, it teaches you little about lion trapping. The issue, in fact, seems quite unfashionable.

You write to the Zoology Department at the university, but the person who posts your letters says they tend to be very busy there. And sure enough there's no reply, even several weeks later.

Sometimes it's hard not to become despondent like most of the others. The others who have given up dreams, given up accumulating evidence, given up searching for proof, whatever propels people through the years. But perhaps you've got it backwards and they've found all the answers they need and are untroubled by the riddle of the lions. Perhaps they all know, about rats, about lions, about everything, and part of their omniscient knowing is an understanding that you should be allowed to learn for yourself. So they encourage you with blank faces, weary smiles, a shrug of weightless shoulders and a few words of doubt. Giving you a nudge to think again, examine from another perspective. Search further for truth and come a little closer.

So in each conversation their apathy invigorates you, and the more apathetic, the more scornful, the less knowing they make themselves, the more you are invigorated. The less credibility they give the lion hypothesis, the more credible it becomes.

You order several university zoology textbooks and when they arrive you read all about lions, learning a good amount about their biology and behaviour. Nothing directly useful, but given time and some productive thought, who knows?

You keep writing, to more and more people who might have something to offer on the matter of lions. You keep a list of your letters and they number dozens, and then more than a hundred.

And you expect correspondence in return (that is, after all, what makes it co-respondence), and in it you hope for an answer. You know that, when you are ready to know, you will find the answer, and it may well come in the form of a piece of good advice in response to all this letter writing. Someone will answer, one day. Someone will give you the one small missing piece of information you need.

Someone. The university, the CSIRO, a variety of circuses

and filmmakers, the producers and distributors of *The Lion King*, Lone Pine Koala Sanctuary (okay, so that one's a little tenuous), anyone named 'Bullen' in case they are connected with the long-defunct lion park on the way to the coast (and perhaps that's where the lions escaped from, anyway), a number of African governments and their embassies in Canberra, the companies that hold the rights to the songs 'In the jungle the mighty jungle the lion sleeps tonight' and 'You can't hide your lion eyes', the authors of the fifty-four *National Geographic* articles from the last thirty years, dealing with or mentioning lions, your old biology teachers from school, the RSPCA, local and national newspapers, members of all levels of parliament, and so on.

And if this doesn't keep you busy enough, Christmas is coming. You feign an interest in the festivities, in case you can use this to advantage. You dress in elf red and green when they ask you to, and you go with one of the admin staff around the whole facility, selling tickets in the Christmas raffle. As an elf with a cellophane-wrapped basket of goodies you have unprecedented access, and while people are taking an interest in your pointed elf shoes and your floppy pointed hat, while they're preoccupied with seasonal remarks, you're taking in everything.

Back in your room you make notes, you draw maps of offices, you record any feature you can recall in case at some point it means something to you.

And then you're out again in your elfen garb with your basket and the beige-clad admin officer, and you're count-ing the paces between buildings, scrutinising fences you don't normally get near. But no, lions don't leave holes. As if there'd be holes, lion-sized holes in the fence. That'd be too easy.

It's only when you trip on some steps while gazing up at the guttering for claw marks that you see it.

You drop the basket and the cellophane comes undone and there, below the glacé fruits and the corn chips, is a Lions' Christmas cake.

You show only calm. Despite the thrill of this, you show only calm, give nothing away, put the blame on the pointed elf shoes and stick the cellophane down again. You have an ally on the outside now, someone who is smuggling you lion traps. Someone who has received a letter and is far too clever to reply by mail. Are the lions reading your letters? Does your friend know this?

A lions' Christmas cake. A Christmas cake specifically for lions. What irresistible temptation. No wonder the cheese-cake was never quite enough. You can see the lion purring in your nets as night becomes Christmas morning, as you stand at a distance, throwing it pieces, taking its mind off sending you signals, taking its power away.

I have some correspondence to attend to, you tell the beige-clad admin officer, and on this pretext you return to your wing, to your room, wishing Merry Christmases to everyone you come across on the way (saying to yourself on the inside, Every time I want to tell someone the lion plan I'll wish them Merry Christmas).

You hide the cake under the bed, put paper in a few envelopes, scrawl addresses. You go out and put the basket on the desk, as though it's just as heavy as always, and you say, I have several letters, Christmas wishes for colleagues and others. Merry Christmas to all.

And the person who always takes your letters takes them without enthusiasm and says that these people are very busy, and you shouldn't hope for too many replies. And he puts the letters in a drawer and says he'll post them later. And when you realise he won't be posting them at all, you know you must be close now.

Merry Christmas, you say to him, Merry Christmas. And he gives you that blank look, and then a dumb, sad smile. And you want to tell him not to worry, that things'll be okay soon, that you have a plan. But you just tell him Christmas is coming, Merry Christmas, and you give nothing away but the compliments of the season.

nights at the palace

Tuesday

Clothilde is waiting for me on the stairs. We talk in a whisper.

Someone else appears, approaches, circles when he can't see we're talking. Stan from Texas, Austin, M, twenty-five. Why is he even awake? It's one or two in the morning in Texas, Tuesday morning.

Clothilde, in a way I'm beginning to quite admire, ignores him utterly.

> You really have a beach, just there?
> Sure. Yes. Nearby.
> Tell me things about your beach.
> It's a beach. What do you want me to tell?
> All.

This, too, is Clothilde. Happy to ask for all and sit while

I tell it, stopping me only to check the words she doesn't know. Sitting with her lunch on her lap and her cat on the bed and Geneva outside her window. Complaining about the cold, the intermittent snow, the walk uphill to the campus and the way some of the snow always finds its way into her boots and melts there.

So we meet in the Palace – not in any really organised way but we find each other there at this time of day, some days. Lunchtime for her, after dinner for me.

It's been a few weeks now, and the intro stats seem long ago. Clothilde, F, twenty-one, Geneva, studying languages. Andrew, M, twenty-three, Brisbane, second-year medicine (post-grad, because that's how it is now). At least the last bit of hers means we speak in English, or something that's mainly English. I tried French at first, and still do occasionally, but since I've never learned French it isn't exactly smart. On my one visit to France I could only point, even if I'd memorised the words outside the shop. Point, smile nervously, offer handfuls of francs, often for something I'd only been pointing near. You get to eat some pretty bad stuff that way.

Here in the Internet chat rooms there's none of that nervousness. It's brisk and it's mostly useless and it's unafraid. Blobs on a screen, monochrome round faces or made-up images, all talking at once, blurting out bits of text in a meaningless urgency to get to know details. Chance chat encounters that go nowhere, amount to remarkably little. And maybe because of that inspire boldness, playfulness, intolerance, flirting. It's hard to imagine playing it this way just once in the real world.

Clo was a surprise. The first time we talked it went for more than half an hour. If people came near us I tried to include them. It never worked. Clo never tried. So I suggested we find a quieter room, the Armoury. The only room I could think of and now we always meet there, on the stairs.

And she made the move that means we're still doing this. At the end of the first conversation, when she had to leave.

> I must go now. We meet here again?
>
> Yes. Is this a good time?
>
> Yes, this is a good time. Good talking time.
>
> Quelle heure est bien pour conversation?
>
> This is a good time for conversation. Ask question again if my answer is wrong. Maybe ask in English.
>
> Don't you like my French?
>
> Yes I like. But you are making it up. Aren't you? Your French?
>
> You can see right through me.
>
> But I cannot see you at all. (I am joking. Do not translate your last message.)

So tonight she asks about the beach, the beach near my house. And when I said *near* I meant within an hour's drive, almost, but I didn't say that and now she thinks it's right here.

She wants to think that, and I want to let her. And it's near enough, surely.

There is a garden first, a garden cared for by my father. Maybe the only garden in the world where every blade of grass is the same length. Beyond the garden are trees, tough, wild trees bent back to the house by the easterly wind. They grow out of sand, and there are paths among them and sometimes things that seem like paths but aren't, and take you nowhere. I've been lost there, years ago, when I was young. And there are lizards called goannas, one of them as long as a man is tall, and it's been there most of my life. It's green, dark green, black in parts. As thick as a big tree branch but darker, so it's easy to see.

What colour are the trees?

Silver-grey, with bark like paper.

Really?

Don't you believe me?

Yes, I believe. Tell me more.

Beyond the trees are vines, green creeping plants with thick leaves, all spread like a mat across the sand. Here the paths are clearer to see, and the crab holes. From this point, the dunes, the low hills of sand, rise to their highest and have the shape of waves. Then they fall away, to the long, flat beach and the sea. And the sand on the beach is white, soft, hot in summers like this and it squeaks under our feet when we run across it to the water. From the beach no nearby houses can be seen, just the trees. Far away to the north is another town, far away to the south a headland, out to sea are freighters in grey and dusty-red.

What are freighters?

Ships carrying things. Cars, electrical things.

How are they dusty?

Dusty-red. I meant their colour, the kind of red they are – not bright red.

Tell me something dusty-red.

Red dust. I don't know. I made it up. Bricks, but not as orange.

Then not bricks.

Correct. Like a red-wine stain, but also not quite.

I like your beach.

Thank you.

And it is just over the trees and the dunes. You are lucky.

I can hear the sea now. My window is open. The sky is clear and the treetops are still and I can hear the waves breaking. The stars are out.

The stars I will see tonight. Or maybe not. I wonder if we see the same stars. Do we get different stars?

Some different, but I think some the same. But I have to go now. I have to work. I have to read about an operation, a surgical operation. For tomorrow.

I leave the Palace, check for email. There's nothing new. I shut down the system. I look through the article, the stats, the failure rate. It's okay, but it needs a larger study to be anything like conclusive.

The evening traffic noises come in through the window, a train heads west just over the hill. And I told her I can hear the sea now. What a slack lie that is. I turn the light out when I leave, and from the door I can see stars, just a few.

Do we get different stars? What a question. Maybe it was simply a question about the night sky. Yes, we get some different stars, I think – the Southern Cross, Magellanic clouds, I get those. Clo gets the Pole Star, and who knows what else. I think I've seen Orion in both hemispheres, but with different orientations. But I could be fooling myself. I've never paid attention.

But perhaps it's not about stars. It seemed to be something about us. Or maybe not, but that's how it seemed. I don't quite know how. We've never met. We've exchanged lines of text maybe six times over a couple of weeks, and already I'm on the edge of thinking that we share the sky. We're not supposed to be sharing anything. That's not the Palace. I had come to rely on the Palace being junk, being a place to connect poorly, briefly, then bounce away. That's what was interesting about it.

Friday

So, the operation was good? That you saw on Wednesday?
Yes. Just like it should have been.
Did you swim today?
Yes. Today it was hot all day. It still is. Often we have afternoon storms that take the heat away, but not today. But the water was cool, perfect. Small waves, but easy to ride.

How do you ride waves?

It's in the shoulders. Imagine snow and a sled. It's a bit like that.

You have a sled? On the waves? The sled for snow is very heavy.

No, sorry. You make the shape of the sled. Take your arms, lean your shoulders forward, turn your arms in.

In to where, what?

Lean your shoulders forward, bend your arms slightly, turn your arms so that your hands face out.

Okay. I am doing it.

Bring your arms in, put your hands on your thighs, imagine leaning forward, a little like a swimmer just before the race starts.

Still doing it with no problems. Where is the waves?

You are leaning forward, and the wave is pushing you from behind. Your shape means that you skim across the water. Your arms lift you above the water, a little. So you move with the wave, with your head out. You watch everything, you hear the water rushing past you.

This is good.

If you do it well, you can catch many waves without your hair even getting wet.

I am sure I do it well. My hair is not wet. But why is wet a problem?

Wet is fine. I am talking about catching waves. If you are on the wave properly, your head is dry.

I remember learning to bodysurf when I was young. It's all in the timing. It's in the shoulders, too, but timing is critical. It's probably not helpful to tell her that. You can probably put together some semblance of the right arrangement of limbs in a bedroom in Geneva, but I really think you need water before you can conquer the timing issue. Not that Clo minds. Not that she isn't totally sure she's mastered it already.

So does she go back now, to her afternoon lectures, and tell her friends she learned to bodysurf at lunchtime? I hope so, for no good reason. I hope she shows them the arms. Tells them she's good. And what were her arms doing then? I'll never know. She could drown people if she's not careful. Send them out bodysurfing with all kinds of confidence and arms everywhere. But probably not.

I have to say she impresses me. The way she can play this game, play at learning to bodysurf without water, without anyone in the room. Play in another language. And my own accent changes when I'm writing messages to her, I can feel it happening. There's something about her that's quite contagious.

The others will be waiting for me at the restaurant, so I walk quickly. I'm still in the conversation, still listening to her, looking down at the pavement as the wind blows into my face. Trying to get my own voice back and ending up singing. The Graham Bonnet version of 'It's All Over Now, Baby Blue', for some reason. Where has that song gone?

Monday

> In my whole life, only you call me Clo.
>
> Is it okay?
>
> Yes. Very okay.
>
> Très bien.

And do I tell her that in my whole life, only she calls me An? No. It took some adjusting to, her choosing her own abbreviation of Andrew and calling me something that's essentially a woman's name. Why didn't she go for And? Because she knew it was already a conjunction? Did she think that would bother me? As if anyone ever got bothered about having their name abbreviated to a conjunction.

As if I should be thinking this, still playing some kind of game long after our conversation.

And she likes me calling her Clo, having my own name for her. As if I should be thinking that. Having to tell myself this exchange isn't life.

Wednesday

This time we describe our rooms, in more detail than we have before. It's her idea, part of her tell-me-all way. I'm beginning to see her in her room now, the colours of her walls, her small window, her grey street, the cast-off chair that she's sitting on, taken from her mother's office. Her boots on the floor, her legs tucked under her.

And then it's not enough.

It feels like a risk when I ask it, when I watch the words appearing on the screen. I wonder if I shouldn't, but already I'm hitting the return key. Telling myself it's nothing, as far as questions go. Basic information.

What colour is your hair?
Yellow.
Blond, maybe?
Why not yellow?
Like a banana or like straw?
Straw?
Straw is like dead grass.
Hair like dead grass? No, I have shampoo and conditioner, specifically for use with fine hair.
Sorry. Colour. We will try another way. Who has hair like you?
Hair like my hair?
Yes.
My sister.
Very funny. Someone I would know?
Gwyneth Paltrow, I think.
Gwyneth Paltrow?
Yes. I look very like Gwyneth Paltrow. This is what people say.
People say?
You don't believe me? What about you?
Sorry, I believe you.
Yes, but what do you look like?
Not much like Gwyneth Paltrow.
Waiting.
Okay, like this. This is me. I'm a little round green

blob, but I'm happy.
You are slightly funny or very ugly.
Or maybe both.

Friday

On the stairs next to the suit of armour is a new avatar.
A photo, run some time ago in practically every magazine
in the world. Gwyneth Paltrow and Brad Pitt.

I waited for you. Yesterday, and some more time today.
Sorry. I couldn't help it.
No, it's okay. No problem, definitely. Anyway, this is me.
The man I stand next to I do not know. Perhaps it is a man
who looks like you?
Perhaps.
Perhaps not?
Not quite. I'd like to think close. More like George
Clooney maybe?
You have bad hair, George.
It's better than it used to be. And nice eyes.
Yes, nice eyes.

Sunday

I'm cold. Tell me about the beach again.
Today the beach was hot. I swam early, and then
late. I spent the day inside, in airconditioning. Even
now the air is still thick and warm outside, and
there is no breeze coming from the sea this evening.
My hair is still wet and I'm sitting on my towel.

I have eaten a fish tonight, caught by a man at the beach, our neighbour here. A silver fish called a trevally, cooked in the ashes of a fire. It wasn't long ago. I can still smell the smoke. The sun is just setting and the insects are going crazy in the trees.

Why are they going crazy?

The sun is setting.

Yes, but why are they going crazy?

It's what they do. Making noise at twilight. Maybe they're glad the day is over, maybe they're talking, making arrangements for the evening.

Arrangements. Insects making arrangements. I like that idea. I wonder how they do it.

They have very small wrists, so their watches would have to be tiny.

I wonder if they use the stars instead. That would be a nice way. The very small insects using the big sky to make arrangements.

I wonder if we see the same stars.

Hey, me too!

I couldn't imagine a summer twilight without a ringing in my head. I hardly thought to mention the cicadas because they were so obviously there. When I was very young I'd always want to look for them. I'd follow their noises, but whenever I got close they'd stop. And, since I meant them no harm, I thought it was a game, their game that they'd taught to me.

In the distance there's a fire engine, part of the busy

night outside. Car horns, traffic, shouting. The siren coming closer, then receding, absorbed into other noises as it chases smoke somewhere across the city.

Monday

My mother thinks we talk too much sometimes. Too much talk and not enough books she says.

This is a common thought among parents.

But my house has had the Internet for only six months and my mother was twenty-one long ago (twenty-eight years), so how can she know?

So that makes it hard for her.

But I tell her how much I like talking, so she should not say there is too much. She tells me you are not a person, An, and that I should talk to people. She says you are a green ball and that is all I know about you.

I've told you other things.

I know. She does not know. That's okay. She does not understand. Did you swim today?

Not today.

Why not today?

Too busy.

Why not swim now?

It will be dark soon. It's not safe to swim when it's dark.

Okay, but go to the beach. Walk on the beach now when the dark is coming. Across the grass and the trees and the low hills of sand that make waves. Walk on the beach near the water, and I will think I am doing it too. Tomorrow tell me all about it.

When I leave I go to the beachcam site and watch night fall over Manly, Bondi, Cronulla and Narrabeen. There are clouds coming in from the sea, and the surf doesn't look like much.

And this is changing. It was a conversation once, just that. A better-than-usual version of Palace chat. Details about rooms, neighbourhoods, days spent doing regular things. But it's not that now.

Already I'm wondering what it would be like to walk on a beach with her. I'm thinking it through, Clo beside me. Her voice, all those words I've seen, finding sound in the accent I think she has. Her fine hair lit quietly by the moon.

It's all wrong, all of this.

I'll be in Geneva in two weeks, and I was thinking about calling her. I wondered if she would give me her address if I asked. And now I think she would, so I won't ask. I was telling myself it would be fun, put a face to a name, but then she made me take her to the beach. And talked as though she needed this.

And I've always wondered about this game. Speculated that she might be eight, or seventy, or nowhere near Geneva. Some zit-faced kid close to home, wasting his evenings stringing me along.

And I know that's not true now. I believe everything she's said, with the possible exception of the Gwyneth Paltrow part, and I'm telling myself not to think about that.

I don't know how to fix this. At first I didn't even

believe her name. I thought it was some medieval reference that I hadn't read enough to get. I thought it was William the Conqueror's consort, and I didn't remember that that was Mathilde until we'd been talking for two weeks. Clothilde, Clothilde, where did it come from? It's her name. Her parents gave it to her. The explanation for her name couldn't be more normal.

I try to call home on my mobile, but the number's still busy, so I email and they'll get it later. I say that I hope everyone's fine. I say I tried to call, but the line's been busy so I've been on the steps talking to my Swiss friend. I do the dad thing and I say if it's Laura on the phone talking to a boy all this time, she's been on there long enough. I know this will be groaned at and ignored. It always is.

They will have had takeaway tonight. After the usual argument about which takeaway. And the engaged phone is Laura talking to a friend, bitching about how unfair it is that Matt gets to control the TV just because she chose dinner. Lynne will have negotiated this to an uneasy truce, and will now be sitting with Matt watching something other than *Party of Five*. *Drew Carey* maybe? Indian takeaway and *Drew Carey*? That's what I'm missing. Eighteen time zones and one wide ocean from here.

And my time's up.

I put on my jacket on the way out, but I'm cold anyway. I'm cold and I shouldn't be awake at two a.m.. Pretending it's eight in the evening all the time. Cutting twenty-three years from my medical career and borrowing the beaches of my adolescence, a fish I ate thirty-one years ago, the noises of insects, the pool of smells that slump in the heat of old twilights. And I remember the fish when I opened the foil. The way it fell apart, and I lifted it out piece by piece with my fingers. The taste, all smoke and lemon and butter. As real, at least as real, as this evening.

I started this so innocently and the lie that it is has been creeping up on me for days from a long way off, and I've ignored it.

And I've had enough. Enough of San Francisco in winter. And Tokyo, and Chicago and Internet cafes and all the last few weeks. All the travelling round and demonstrating the new procedure. Enough of a life spent down a laparoscope and in a bedroom in Geneva. Continually working out when it will be eight o'clock in eastern Australia, since that's when I always talk to someone who's nowhere near there.

Who's half my age, who I've lied to a million times, who is starting to need this contact, in a way that might or might not be like the way I'm starting to need it. Whatever that is.

And the lights of Van Ness seem to go for miles and the cold numbs my face first and then works its way into my legs, and I just want to be home.

losing it least of all

Exams. End of fourth year.

Two things I've learned in the last day and a half. One: if your eyes shut while you're walking, you can fall onto the road. Two: shaving does not improve the concentration, at least, not beyond the moment you finish shaving.

The problem: neither of these things constitutes epidemiology. Neither makes me more comfortable with generating P values, or more acquainted with the subtleties of metanalysis. All I know is that metanalysis has the word 'anal' in the middle and that hasn't been funny since three-thirty this morning. But the pre-dawn hours are desperate, everyone knows that.

I'm losing it. Four years (eight semesters) into this degree and losing it. So far, a total modest kind of success story, but that's about to change.

I am at the stage of believing that milkshakes become fascinating if you add a banana. Of telling myself I can have a toilet break after every even-numbered page as a reward for work well done. Of believing that twanging a rubber band against my wrist can keep me awake and make me pass this exam. Even though, as you slip into inappropriate sleep, the first thing you don't do is twang and you end up just cutting off the blood supply to your hand.

I tell my mother it's not working, nothing's working any more and she says, 'Maybe you need a break, Philby.'

So I go right off at her, of course. Does she want me to fail?

Eight minutes ago I went to the toilet. What does she think this is? I've got plenty of breaks built into the routine. It's the bits in between that are killing me.

And she says, 'That's quite a welt you've got on your wrist, Philby,' and she confiscates the rubber band. 'Now,' she says, knowing that I don't take confiscation lightly, 'I'm going to make you a nice savoury-mince jaffle. And a milkshake.'

With the promise of an added banana, she gets the truce she wants and I don't have to go off at her about the rubber band. Besides, I've got plenty more in my room.

'Can I call this a meal?'

'Yes, you can,' she says, 'if it helps.'

'It helps, I get fifteen minutes for meals.'

I'm sure the others aren't having these problems. I tell myself that to get me going while I eat the first half of my savoury-mince jaffle. I tell myself there's a high probability ($P<0.05$) that the others aren't having these problems. That they're cruising with this stats stuff. Declining intrusive offers of jaffles so that they can squeeze in a few more analyses of variance (if there is such a thing) before tomorrow's exam.

But even that doesn't help. I can't scare myself any more with other people's study habits. I can't scare myself with the thought of a supp in the holidays, 'cause I'm expecting it now. Expecting it ever since three-thirty a.m..

I'm gone. Four years, eight semesters and very nearly two-thirds of the way through this degree and I've hit the wall and slid down it like old fruit.

Frank Green comes over. I ask him how he's going with the epidemiology.

Frank Green says he has an all-over tan, baby. Frank Green has been to the gym. Combed his hair, far too much. Bought groceries, made lasagna for eight (and eaten five portions overnight), washed and fiddled with his old Valiant so thoroughly you'd have to call it detailed.

'Definition of perfect,' he says as he shows me over it. 'Definition of way-fucking perfect, baby.'

As he shows me the customised driver's seat, runs his hands over the brand-new bed of beads in a way that looks far too close to genuine affection. And he drives with three gonks now, on different parts of the dashboard, and seven hanging airfresheners, since, he says, six proved insufficient to distract his sinuses from their problems with seasonal change.

And he paces up and down, squirting drops into his eyes as though he drinks through his corneas, burping big, salty, lemon-lime burps and turning them into words.

Frank Green has reached the edge and travelled beyond it. Frank Green is maxed-out on Gatorade. Frank Green has a Daniel Boone hat.

He is coping very badly with our end of fourth year exams. And I'm not looking good, but Frank is in a state of raging, open disrepair.

'But don't let me get in the way,' he says, and blows in my ear when I get back to my desk.

Gently, admittedly, but it's still blowing in my goddamn ear, and I already had a bit of a concentration problem. He unravels a paper clip and pokes my ear lobes with it.

'Big lobes, big lobes,' he says. 'Hey, is that a savoury-mince jaffle?'

'And it's all yours,' I tell him. 'But only as a present for quietly fucking off. Baby.'

And he dances behind me, as though there's a special dance you do when you get a jaffle and I've just never known it. And he dances out of the room, with only two brief curtain calls to mark his departure.

I hear a splash and he's in our pool. In our pool, wading up and down, arms above his head para-military style and chanting, 'I'm mad as hell and I just can't take it any more.'

And I want to tell him, no, it wasn't that kind of mad, but it wouldn't seem right. And besides, I'm studying, that's what this book's for. This book I'm gazing at. This book that refuses to infiltrate my resolutely unthinking brain.

And Frank's wading and chanting, wading and chanting, and my mother brings him a pile of savoury-mince jaffles on a plate, and a milkshake. With a cocktail umbrella bobbing around on top, pinned to a maraschino cherry. And then, a separate appearance to give him a broad-brimmed hat, and I think he sings her something from The Gondoliers. She applauds, but that's only politeness. He's doing a shocking job of it.

Meanwhile, I have an appointment with a trance to get to, and I only come back when I lean forward onto the unravelled paperclip, which I'm now holding in my hand.

And there's less noise outside, and I look out again and Frank's still wading. Still with one arm above his head, clicking his fingers, but he's got the kitchen phone in his other hand, dragged out the full length of its extension cord.

I don't know what's going on. I don't want to.

So back to the books. Back to the gazing and achievement of little. Back to the menace of the paperclip, held in front of my forehead in case I drift again. And I do drift, of course I drift, but this time into a dream involving a sharp stabbing pain that just gets worse and worse.

Then Frank's in my room. In my room with my sister's towel around his waist (which will, in time, mean trouble) and a beer in one hand.

'I've been putting in some calls,' he says, like a man with better options than he actually has.

'And drinking my beer, too.'

'Yeah, yeah. They come in sixes. You're supposed to share them. Anyway, stop the study for a sec. You'll want to hear this.'

And he tells me about the calls. Tells me Jenny Blair's

bought four tubes of toothpaste and she's already onto the second. Tells me Slats is crying so much his nose is running. Tells me Oscar Wong told him to fuck off cause he'd never had a day like this with his Pac Man before.

'Oscar Wong,' he tells me, 'is in awe of himself, and that's a quote.'

'Yeah, a Greg Norman quote.'

'Yeah, but you get it, don't you?'

'What?'

'They're gone, aren't they? I've got this exam pretty much pissed in if I can keep my cool. I made ten calls out there, and I can name three people I've got beaten already.'

'Biased sample. You picked them deliberately.'

'It'll still stack up. What do you want, a metanalysis? Slats is so gone he's losing snot over it. I've got a four sewn up unless I cop some serious sunburn. P less than point-o-five, no worries. So I only came in to borrow some suncream.'

'So what do you know about variance?' I ask him.

'Nothing,' he says.

So we split the beers and drink three each, and for hours at least it won't matter that they were my father's.

I've got four people beaten now, four out of eleven, and even though the methods are questionable, it should extrapolate just enough.

plaza

There was a Woolies on the site originally. Or perhaps a newsagent and a hairdresser and an empty bank building, with a Woolies across the road. This is of vague historical interest only, for when they built the plaza they planned for expansion and soon enough it jumped the road, a fat foot of a department store on a spindly travelator of a leg. And each time the plaza became bigger, it became twice as big again.

It ate up them all, the newsagent, the hairdresser, the empty bank building, the Woolies, a boutique, another newsagent, two video stores, a turn-of-the century post office, the service stations on two corners. It swung a broad limb over the railway station, adding eight cinemas, forty-six specialty outlets and the Second Largest Department Store in the Southern Hemisphere. It consumed the adjacent parkland, preserving its heritage-listed ANZAC memorial by encasing it in the foundation concrete of the

Third Largest Building in the World. At the far end of the park, the next railway station too was surrounded, built over, engulfed.

And in the centre, at the hub of this marvellous era of marble and gold, the plaza itself began to swell. It towered easily above the worker's cottages and soon above the office buildings. It cast shadows the length of the river flood plain and then over the mountains beyond, until dawn was coming minutes later to the farms to the west. The photos of its opening, still, in the grand scale of time, in the very recent past, were subtly faded by a team of expert degradationists, from bright contemporary colours to an impressive archival sepia. Najee suits were retouched to be plus-fours, gaiters were added to Jag jeans and porkpie hats appeared in ever increasing numbers. They toyed with the idea of painting in Captain Cook to cut the ribbon at the opening but, after consideration, settled for a late middle-aged Henry Parkes, accompanied by copies of the Tenterfield Oration and other documents relating to federation. The plaza, then, had a history and had a place in history, so that people could watch it grow and be glad that it was growing, because every millimetre that made it a Bigger, Better Place made the country a Bigger, Better Place too.

The day the plaza reached Tenterfield would be an important one, a homecoming, a time for nostalgia and pride. The specialty outlets had reached there already but, really, it would only be historic when the town, or at least the site of the town, was under the great dome of the plaza itself, joining two hundred and forty-two other Heritage

Sites that were preserved, again in the fashion of the times, by encasing them in foundation concrete and placing a small exhibition of photographs, agricultural and kitchen implements and so on, on the new ground-floor level. Such acknowledgments of our challenging pioneering past met with great public appreciation and were usually opened by a significant local figure, such as the premier of the state. Occasionally, exhibitions were, out of necessity, opened by two premiers, as state boundaries had become a little difficult to define, for however carefully they and their landmarks were preserved by the concrete, design imperatives that not too much of this could show on the surface.

Unfortunately, though well loved by all, the plaza had struck a few teething troubles. Not that the problems were with the plaza itself, far from it. They were really, in essence, People Problems. The best way to look at this is to examine it from the point of view of one of the people in particular, one of the people and, for example, the travelators.

The person in question is about seventeen when she enters the plaza. She and her friends have set the day aside for shopping, for they are on holidays from school. They live close to one of the outlying precincts of the plaza and, of course, visit that part regularly, but today they have decided to head for the dome itself.

On the third level they connect with an arterial travelator. Here, the territory becomes less familiar. They were probably last at this point during the previous school holidays. They travel for about an hour, stopping three times to browse briefly in boutiques, and then decide to have coffee. As it's the holidays, they share a chocolate croissant. When they are back on the travelator one of them points out that it's a shame they didn't buy cigarettes. The others agree.

They're not sure when they expected to reach the dome, but they still haven't two hours later. They stop to confirm that they are heading in the right direction and lunch on toasted sandwiches in the second cafe they come across. The first looked nicer but the proprietor refused to sell them cigarettes. In the second they ask only for toasted sandwiches and milkshakes.

Afterwards they look through a few adjacent specialty outlets and soon they are moving again.

In another hour, they join a much larger travelator, six lanes wide, and they know they must be nearly there. This is all new territory to them – labyrinthine arcades winding away to the sides at twenty, and now perhaps thirty levels, hanging gardens, fountains, enormous cinema complexes, a Virgin Megastore on eight floors. Two more travelators sweep in beside them, and soon another. They wonder how people leave the travelators when they have eight to the right and six to the left. But it means the dome must be close.

At home, night will fall soon. They talk about the prospect quietly among themselves, so as not to seem like adolescents with curfews. They decide to go on.

The ceiling is lifting. They notice that with each minute that passes it is higher above them, that the arcades have more floors and, just when the heights reach dizzying dimensions, the shops end, and they are under the dome. They step from the travelator and on to the tiled floor.

The roof is like a pink sky above them, a pink sky reaching far out across the plaza, sinking down eventually to the pink-tiled horizon.

The seventeen-year-old girl of particular interest to us heads for a nearby bank of price reference terminals, agreeing to meet the others in an hour. She finds an available terminal and searches for Levi 501 jeans and selects 'Best twenty ranked by price'. From the look of the location co-ordinates, there are several reasonable choices not far away, but the best price by almost twenty dollars is to be found in a department store on the other side of the plaza. She confirms her size is in stock, and hits 'hold'. The hardcopy statement tells her the item will be held for a maximum of forty-eight hours and gives her directions, which seem straightforward enough, and she folds the sheet of paper and puts it in her pocket.

She takes a lift to the eighty-second floor, and then a travelator leading north-east, high out above the centre of the plaza. She wonders how much of her day she will be on travelators. She should probably have told her parents she would be late home or, better still, that she planned to spend the night at the house of one of the friends. It is the holidays, after all.

She is briefly concerned when, after twenty minutes, she has left the home end of the plaza back over the horizon and has yet to see the side with the bargain jeans. She tells herself people ride the travelators every day, pick up jeans, take them home. Such people are all around her even now. There is no cause for concern.

She doesn't look over the edge at the floor far down below. Heights have never been her best thing. She thinks about her friends. She'll be a few minutes late, but they won't mind.

Someone tells her that just last year the travelator ended about here, but since then the plaza has expanded rapidly, so it's still a way to go. The girl wonders how long, but no-one can put a figure to it. Someone else says that about forty minutes from this point, on the same journey a week ago, he first heard the work party up ahead extending the travelator, and that the plaza came into sight five minutes later. That was the sign the girl would wait for, the noise of the work party.

It crosses her mind that the time when she'd agreed to meet her friends has long gone, that she should head back, but she can do nothing. There is nothing around except the travelator on which she is moving at an ever-increasing speed, but, without a reference point, she is not even aware of the acceleration.

Time passes, her jeans go off hold and eventually the batteries in her watch flatten. It has been daytime in the plaza throughout, but her watch has gone through numerous days and nights. In her conversations with her fellow travellers, she has talked about the passage of time and its inherent inevitability, but within the first month they agree only on the futility of such discussions, and consensus is reached never to raise the matter again.

Gradually, the influence of time is seen on a wide range of subjects and one by one it is agreed that these will not be talked about.

Every so often someone calls for silence so they can listen for sounds of a work party. Eventually, a short man with a large nose admits that he has long ago lost any idea of what a work party might sound like. Someone tries to be helpful by mentioning electric drills and arc welders but, when pressed for the sounds that might be expected from them, says that it has been enough of a struggle to remember the names of the equipment. He says he believes that the drill will be olive green, but the others know he's faking it.

The girl meets a man and they eventually get on so well that they have two children, one of each.

It is when the boy is about twelve that something happens. It isn't olive green – the man, after all, was faking it – but it is happening, and it's up ahead.

The travelator begins to decelerate. Everybody knows something is supposed to happen next, but no-one can remember what. The sight, far ahead, of a shopping arcade eight hundred storeys high, is therefore quite a surprise.

The girl, who is now a middle-aged woman, remembers the Levi 501s she has missed out on buying. She hugs her children close to her. The boy is unimpressed by this and wonders why his mother is behaving this way. She tries to tell them about jeans and how they matter, what the right clothes can do for a person's spirits.

She watches the arcade grow bigger and bigger and,

with everyone else who is old enough to remember, starts talking excitedly about shopping and movies and ice-cream. She checks the money in her purse and wonders if she can afford something special for the children.

Ahead, they see a crowd at the end of the travelator. There is shouting, perhaps cheering.

But the clothes are different, the faces unexpected. The woman steps from the travelator and hears laughter. She looks around her, looks in the shop window, looks at herself.

Everything she is wearing is hopelessly out of date, her currency, her hard-earned money from the checkouts of Coles, is worth nothing. And noise, noise is everywhere and her children try to hide. But the crowd is after them, chasing them through the arcade, shouting unfamiliar abuse.

The woman takes her daughter's hand and her son runs beside her. But the crowds are used to this and would catch them easily if there wasn't sport to be had first.

The woman dodges around corners, through department stores, tipping displays over behind her. But the laughter is louder, and the anger. Her pursuers are yelping like dogs.

Her boy is tiring and she reaches for his hand, but he is tackled from behind and lost to the crowd. A few screams and she hears no more.

Ahead there is a travelator. She runs harder, despite the cramp in her side. Her daughter's feet drag along the ground, but she's still there, still crying. A wiry-looking man moves to bar their path.

From her handbag, the woman pulls the scissors her

mother made her carry in case of attack, and she drives the point between two of the man's ribs and into his heart.

The crowd had not expected this, and holds back momentarily. She jumps on to the travelator, drops her daughter at her feet. Now, there is no pursuit.

In a matter of hours the arcade is behind them, and they are heading back the way they came. For a long time they say nothing, comforted by the silence.

Eventually the woman tells her daughter what life is like back at the far end of the travelator, where she had spent her early years. She explains to her daughter about trees and birds and school holidays.

But the dome expands, now at exactly the same rate that the travelator accelerates, and year after year it will outrun them, growing ever bigger and then twice as big again.

twenty-minute hero

This is about Louise. Louise, it could be said, was my first love. It could be said, at least, if you used my working definition of love (1980–87), that being a wistful, mildly nauseating feeling held about a person long after a single conversation. These were eight years when I met people only once, and I don't know why. I guess they never asked for my number.

Louise was the first girl I took outside at a school dance. First of two. Same thing happened both times. Conversation. And Louise wasn't much of a talker.

I meant to ask her friend to come outside, but that's okay. I was a bit nervous, and I twitched at the critical moment and ended up looking at Louise. Looking up at Louise. Louise was much bigger than her friend, who was distinctly medium-sized. But Louise was big in a particular way, a big-across-the-shoulders way, a punching-out-sides-of-beef, winning-the-woodchop-at-the-Ekka way.

Louise, it turned out, was the eighteenth-best breast-stroker in the world over two hundred metres. And I didn't want to tell her, but I wasn't world-ranked in anything. As my mother once said to me as I stood in front of the bathroom mirror, 'No matter how many of those things you squeeze, no-one else counts theirs, so it won't be a world record.'

We walked outside, Louise and me. And next to her I felt pared-back, ultimately flimsy, not much bigger than a piece of bent wire, a little pipe-cleaner boy. Louise, though all I ever really saw were her shoulders, had muscles. Excellent muscles, in places where, all my life, I'll just have skin.

We got ourselves a couple of cups of Tang and we sat on the grass, in full view of the assembly hall, as required. And I waited for Louise to take the initiative. After all, I'd done my bit. I'd got us out here. Wasn't that enough? Minutes passed. Maybe not.

Pretty good Tang, she said eventually, hinting that she wasn't the world's greatest conversationalist.

And I said, Yeah, hinting that I wasn't, either.

Don't get to drink much Tang, she said. Training diet.

She told me she ate fourteen Weetbix for breakfast. Louise was the first person I ever met who ate fourteen Weetbix for breakfast. And still the only one. I tried it the next day and I slowed down after three, and had to lie down mid-way through five. Lying there thinking, that Louise, she's nine Weetbix and a million laps ahead of me already today, and it's only eight-thirty.

But I lay there thinking more than that. Thinking about

the dream she told me she always dreams, of a long, black line, shattered every thirty-two seconds by a tumbleturn. Thinking about her shoulders and how I wanted to dream about her shoulders, or to have her shoulders, or be near her shoulders. Any of these would have been fine, as long as I didn't get hurt. Thinking about her brown eyes and her delicate eyebrows, hinting at the Louise that might have been, had she not had that breaststroke ranking and done all those laps. The smaller, inside Louise, who didn't talk much, but who, I suspected, thought about things a lot. I liked them both – big, muscle Louise, and small, thinking Louise – the whole Louise package was fine by me.

And I thought about the time the night before when I'd said something funny, slightly funny, and she gave me a bit of a slug on the shoulder. Well, when it left her it was a pat, but when it got to me it was more of a slug and I did fall over briefly and end up with a lot of grass on my back.

And she had to go home and I went inside, inside to my friends, and I was a hero for twenty minutes, a girl outside and all that grass on my back. A hero for twenty minutes till they found Michael Morgan down by the lockers, nude and with a girl similarly clad and a mostly empty bottle of vodka. And my hero status vanished like a Weetbix at Louise's place round breakfast time.

But worse things have happened, and Louise was special. I planned to think about her for months, and I did. I knew I'd see her again. We'd gone outside together, hadn't we? And I did see her again. About twelve hundred Weetbix later, in Moscow. Well, I was in the lounge room, but Louise was in Moscow and we were together two minutes and twelve seconds. And Louise, despite the shoulders, looked much smaller than the East Germans.

And I cheered all four laps of her heat but she finished ninth-fastest overall, missing out on the final by one spot.

And it was a bad moment, a bad moment for both of us, when she got out of the pool and looked up at the board and saw her time, even though it was the best she'd ever done. And I wanted to tell her – I wanted to tell her but I wasn't in Moscow – I wanted to tell her that in the end it didn't matter. That a win would have been fine, well, great, but that what I actually liked was Louise.

And I'd been a hero myself, for about twenty minutes. I'd had my time in the spotlight but, Louise, it's so fleeting anyway, for most of us. Michael Morgan might be a hero forever, long after his suspension at least, but that's okay. That's not what it's about. It's about time on the grass, talking, Tang, minutes on end when you want to ask for her number or maybe give her yours, whatever it is you do, but you don't quite know how. Next time, maybe. Next time I'll take the chance. Because if you don't take the chance you're not even a contender. Louise took the chance, trained all those months and didn't make the final, and she was still just what I wanted.

moving

So you are moving again.

She goes to the plastic surgeon and has her nose nar-
rowed and you move. This time she wants the eyebrows
bigger. And four bedrooms. The kids shouldn't have to
share.

And they've buried you in inner suburbs, and lost you
into the mining towns of the far west. But each time she
isn't happy. Not for long. Not even in other countries.

You open the envelope and read its single sheet of paper.
You are Craig Tarrant. You are aged thirty-seven and you sell
used cars. The dealership you are about to take over hasn't
been doing well, but that, of course, is immaterial. Used
cars, you think, used cars. You sold cars once before, but
they were Buicks, when you were (Honest) John Walton.
You had the Buick dealership in Preston Falls, Idaho, and
Mrs Walton worked part-time in a local convenience store.
But even there she wasn't happy. Even in Idaho.

One night she said to you: if they wanted to look for us anywhere in America, where would they start? Right about here. We're so obvious, John. Out here where there's almost nobody. We stand out. It's all gone wrong.

So Idaho, way out in those trees and after all that work on accents, didn't work out. You moved on.

And somewhere, before or after Idaho, you were or had been Chris Lindstrom, landscape gardener in Perth. Barry Hanlon, publican in Katherine. Steven Needham, clerk in the Ministry of Education in Canberra. Adam Freeman, somewhere. But no, you never became Adam Freeman because she objected to the ridiculously transparent name and refused to even go to the new place, knowing they would be waiting. She insisted on another country.

So you went to England and you became Bernie Coulter and it was suggested you live in Earls Court because then you could keep the accents, but the bureaucrats should have realised she was keen to avoid the obvious following the Adam Freeman debacle. So they found a safe house in Camden Town and gave you a job in the local library. But every time you came home she was in the front room looking out at the street through the lace curtains with a knife in her hand.

Then one evening came the knock at the door and she had you and the kids jumping over the back fence and running after her along the alley as she hissed and waved at you to keep down. She turned left and then left again, and pushed over the boy with the money tin just as he was about to knock on another door to say Guide Dogs for the

Blind. You threw him 50 p to stop him crying and you ran off after her.

So then the UK was out. There were a couple of places in New Zealand and, of course, Preston Falls, Idaho, after which she declared the entire Untied States inappropriate, despite the offer of being Danny and Debbie Kreisler in the eastern seaboard city of their choice. And the agents, who were clearly not impressed by this, said the only option was to send you back to Australia.

There have, of course, been a number of moves since. It has been like this for years now, maybe seven years, maybe eight, maybe ten. Or perhaps those are the ages of your three children. You are not supposed to remember the original details (times, places, people) because you were not there. Not any more. That was someone with another name, another person, many persons ago. And the deal was made and seemed, at the time, the best option.

And the deal was this: that your wife would give the evidence that would put several people away for life, and for this she would receive immunity and anonymity. But as they were lead from the court they looked right into her eyes and they told her they would track her down. Even if they were inside forever they would track her down. And she could change her name and change her nose and change the way she walked and they would track her down. And they told her she had only one world to hide in, and they had friends.

So now you are Craig Tarrant, and she is Jenny. And you tell her that nose has seen more work than Michael

Jackson's, but she won't see the funny side. The eyebrows are bigger, as planned, but one of them's a little bigger than the other, so she's in no mood for jokes. Asymmetry's no disaster you tell her. Some of the nicest people are asymmetrical. It's quite normal. Quite okay. And she slams the door when she leaves, and she sends two men in to remove one of your teeth.

Craig Tarrant. Craig Tarrant. Used cars. You learn all this and more while they fit your plate. They show you slides of your new house. A renovator's delight, the agent says, playing real estate. City glimpses. Close to all amenities: schools, shops, transport. Would suit investor slash first-home owner. And most importantly, as specified by our client, four bedrooms. You ask him to cut the crap and he tells you it's twenty or thirty years old and typical of the houses in the area. No-one could possibly notice you.

Looks good, you say to Jenny. Hoping. Knowing she won't like the bit about city glimpses. You wish the agent hadn't mentioned that.

You wonder, as you have now become accustomed to wondering, who lived there before, who sold the used cars before. You wonder if there are thousands, perhaps millions, of people moving from safe house to safe house and never feeling safe, never settling down, never sleeping through a whole night without screaming and sitting up and pulling the knife from the drawer in the one motion. And you talk to her softly and she wakes, puts the knife back, sleeps again. Still seeing those eyes that looked into hers and told her there was no escape. Told her it was just a matter of time, and that people doing life have long memories.

In time, and as time goes by, less time, you notice she is concealing knives in all the rooms, looking outside only around the edges of curtains, sniffing the food you bring home from the shops, watching the cat eat pieces of it first. And she tells you that she cannot go out again, not in this neighbourhood, not in this city. That there are eyes out there only for her. That the windows of the big city buildings are tinted and she knows why. There are faces behind the windows, eyes behind the windows. The buildings are towers of eyes, sentry towers, guard towers. The eyes are the eyes of the prisoners of the towers and they track her so that she is a prisoner too, on any street, in any crowd, anywhere in this town. They follow her as though the streets are empty and she is the only feature in the landscape, and sometimes she sees herself out there, sees herself as though from a small room high in a city tower and she is running, running, but to nowhere. She tells you all of this, and you know you will be moving soon. Moving again.

And you're not ready, never ready, but you have no choice. You're never ready to end, to end and begin again. You're just settling in, recognising your own face, your own name. But you have no choice. You tell yourself, in case it does any good, that you must be far from alone in this. You know, if nothing else, that at an increasing speed you leave behind you a litter of used people, or at least identi-ties, so perhaps several dozen people have been through this, even if each of them is you. And it occurs to you that if you keep going you might eventually be everybody. Or that the world is really quite a barren place populated largely by recollections of your past persons.

When you meet people in social situations you watch them closely to see if they might struggle to remember what names they should call themselves currently. And you wonder if you will come to live in their houses, do their jobs. Remember their names, too, as your own.

But she doesn't see this future. She's too preoccupied with taking no chances, with moving. She isn't able to think that everybody's running, changing names, playing the high-speed safety game and moving on. She thinks they're chasing. Chasing her. That all around the world people are knocking on doors to sell detergent, driving slowly along tree-lined suburban streets, ambling aimlessly behind trolleys in shopping malls, sitting quietly behind newspapers on commuter trains. And all of this purposeful. All of this a careful affectation. All of this to conceal the silent bullet they are keeping for her, for the day when just one of them works her out, says, provocatively, Amway? And blows her away.

You tell her you want to put down roots for a while, actually settle in somewhere. And she looks at you with scorn and tells you you have a dangerous attitude.

You tell her you would just like something to look forward to, something to look back on, and she gives you that look that lets you know she knows you've been remembering again, despite what you've been told. She tells you

you know you are to forget, forget the past. You know that, don't you? Slowly, emphatically, like she's realised you are an idiot. Forget every other past but the past that comes with the present, the sensible past that leads from birth to school to work to marriage to this house.

But if she has forgotten every other past, why is her sleep so interrupted?

This is the quiet war between you. A war between remembering and forgetting. She must forget in order to go on, and you must remember in order to go on. You must remember in order to exist even in the present. To have any sense of existence you must know what you are, and so you must remember. Remember, if you can, right back to where you started. You the organism, and all your unavoidable consequences. Not you the recent synopsis, the computer-generated name and vocational descriptors. You must define yourself in terms of your own parents (two only), your own neighbourhood, your own school, your own time, and from this foundation, develop, move on. At a manageable speed, not at this frantic pace of moving.

But you have seen too many movies, sitcoms, advertisements, too many of your own and other synthesised pasts to distinguish the one series of events that is your life from all the images of fiction or documentary. Too often you're sifting through fragments, dissociated recollections, and it's the bright ones you find easily. Even when you're looking for slow, quiet days, one after the other, to put together some kind of history. But these are just pieces, pieces that have drummed their way into your brain, so you have to start with them. Hold onto them. Make sense of them to work out who you are. When you clean your teeth you wonder if it was in fact you who dipped the chalk into the ink and saw that it really does get in. When you bought your new Toyota you jumped in the air, but there was no Oh What a Feeling music and you went over on one ankle when you landed. You think you might be Loretta (with your high-heeled shoes and your low-necked sweater) and you endeavour to Get Back Get Back Get Back to where you once belonged. Get back home Loretta. Get back Loretta. But the journey back is not an easy one, and is fraught with forking paths and illusions.

And if you haven't ever lived in Ramsay Street or Summer Bay or Wandin Valley or Salem or Bay City or Santa Barbara, then where have you lived? In the land where the Sugar Puffs (or was it Honey Smacks) grow on trees? Surely not. And though you recall Idaho, is it your life (one of your lives) or just your own private version of a B-52's song? Or a Gus van Sant film – a long road ending in far-away dry hills, on the road a prostate body like the chalk outlines of a body. River Phoenix, but Phoenix is in Arizona and you don't know which river, which river. But you'd always wanted to live by the sea. You'd always wanted to live in a hard-working town near a body of water. Newcastle, New South Wales, or Newcastle-upon-Tyne? Or were you once a person who drank Newcastle Brown Ale or sang the Newcastle Song or lived in a new castle?

And she has not uncommonly found you trapped in this almost boundless confusion, this battle you fight where you remember facts but almost certainly remember fictions just as vividly. As you sit with your children's atlases and a number of piles of other books and video tapes and sheets of paper with your own disorganised thoughts.

She takes the books and tapes and puts them away and takes the notes and makes you eat them and she says that if you must remember, if you must have this ridiculous thing about remembering, you should just remember the piece of paper, the current piece of paper that came in the most recent envelope (and unremember that there have ever been other pieces of paper, other envelopes), remember what you have been taught about who you now are. And don't cast yourself in every life you see and get burned and beaten and lucky and reconciled to insignificance.

She tells you that the only smart thing to do is to start with this piece of paper and, if you must, if you have nothing better to do with your time, construct a few appropriate memories for yourself. Something pleasant but not inconceivable, and come up with some reasonable order. Each day should not be too unexpected in what it brings you, or clearly your construction of the present needs refining. You should wake in the morning and look in the mirror and see not surprise at the teeth, the hairline, but see only the past of the present, and live another day in the suburbs.

Okay, you tell her. And you smile.

But you remember, you remember, you fight hard to remember. And you come up with names and places and you keep them to yourself, and you fight harder but still you can't recall the name you were born with. Those details.

Once you kept a diary for a month, but she found it. And she made you eat it page by page, watched you eat each day, told you to forget it. That lives depended upon it. And as much as you tried with your eyes to photograph each page before you balled it up and put it in your mouth, as much as you tried to remember the contents and their order (even if it was for only a month of your life) the words grew soggy, mulched into something inaccessible, some sloppy, chewy, discoloured ball sludging from wall to wall in the back of your brain, slowly drying into a clumped stalactite that you cover effortlessly, silently, with the lime of other places and times. Till it sets hard and is just another shape lost high in the cavern and slowly obliterated.

For forgetting is more powerful than remembering – it soaks through the remembering and leaches it away. And you can make lists, lists of names and people, even after years of this insidious erosion, but you know the lists are intractably disordered, hopelessly incomplete. You know they will never become complete by remembering, but only by forgetting. They will become less like lists, and will become occasional names, occasional marks with many blank pages between them. And the significance of the marks, when you come across them, will be uncertain. You will forget about lists and the making of lists, and the processes of recollection, and the pictures and sounds and tastes of memories, until the sensations of the present all come as a surprise and are quite without meaning.

Even now you look at the names and you know that you must have been some of them but you can't have been all of them. You can see their faces but you can't get into their heads any more. So even some of the people you've been can probably be recalled only as people you've known and then, as the picture becomes harder to find, stories you've heard. And some events are already only words made by an agent's tongue, teeth, lips. You watch the mouth move and it tells you lives, lies. This was the irony of that Adam Freeman character. That he was always a prisoner, you heard. Even though he'd done a deal.

And she's particularly tense this time. It must be that eyebrow. The littlest things, slightest imperfections, can put her off, sometimes. Put her in a spin. She says she's tempted to do the gender change. She says she's spoken to the surgeon about it, about him making her into you and you into her. But he says it's too soon. Too soon since before.

You are pulling into the driveway of your next house at this point, preparing yourself for your next career. Too soon since before? What does too soon since before mean?

Too soon since the last time, she says. Since the last gender change. The last time you were the woman and I was the man, she says.

She tells you to talk of this no more, that you have had the talk about remembering and forgetting too many times and you should surely know better. That if you couldn't take the consequences you shouldn't have dealt in the stuff in the first place. And she slams the car door when she gets out. She knows she has said too much. You catch up with her when she is about to unlock the front door of the house.

Wait, you tell her. Wait. And you pull a camera from your bag and you say, Posterity, and take her photograph. The photograph of a woman aghast, amazed, turning towards you to strike you.

She hits the camera from your hand. Takes a stone from the garden and smashes it, pulling free the strip of film. She tells you to get in the passenger seat and she takes the wheel and backs the car out onto the road. She pushes the film into your mouth and tells you you must eat it. Tells you you should know better than this.

And you are moving again.

You keep moving, changing lives, and the rate of change only increases.

As does the level of grand disfigurement she demands from the surgeon for you both.

Your face is still wrapped in bandages when you walk up the steps. You ring the bell. A woman, probably a woman (though she has probably been many things), opens the door. She, too, is heavily bandaged. She holds a knife, just in case. You show her a packet of soap powder. You say to her, provocatively, Amway?

box shaped heart

The rain begins again, but softly. Hazing the horizon and drifting in over him. His hair is thick already with salt air so he hardly notices, and all he is aware of is the limits put on him by his short, stabbing breaths and each small step of his feet, kicking up sand. Further today, he'll go further.

This is the aim, to push a little further each time. To convalesce successfully and be back with the others again.

But that's not happening yet. It's not happening today, and it won't for some long time. He can't imagine when. Even when he's with them he's torn from them by this. They go to lectures, they go to parties, he goes to hospital, he comes home. He takes their notes and he studies, so he won't lose them, so he won't lose his place with them. They go to lectures, he gets the notes, he fills in spaces with the notes and the photocopies and the tapes they've made for him. Spaces in his inadequate learning. Spaces in these long, uneven days.

And some days he feels like shit. Dull, restless days following nights awake in pain. Quietly rocking in pain and
taking Mersyndol and sleeping for a while in the chair by
his bed. And some nights there is no comfortable position
at all. There is pain breathing, pain moving, pain staying
still. Pain where they spread his ribs, pain where the tubes
went in. This will change, he tells himself. This will start
improving soon. And the next day his brain is slow and his
body slower and the anaesthetic of a week or so before
heavy all around him, like gravity on some much larger
planet. And he dozes off at breakfast, wakes and looks at his
coffee, sitting to his left near his useable arm. But it's too
far, too far to bother. Nothing will be done today.

Other days are better. More sleep, less pain, less of the
drugs. So he walks, just as the rain begins.

He's careful over the sand. Any jolt grabs his wounds,
sends cut muscles twitching. And each breath feels as
though it's being sucked into a sick chest, feels too thick to
draw in. He walks with a stoop and watches his feet. It's
amazing how little they've changed. Same toes, same ten-
dons, sand sticking in the same way. In summer he ran on
this beach. Last summer.

The summer in the space between school and university,
that strangely detached time when you don't know what to
call yourself. When after all those years school has ended
and everyone has written all over your uniform and you've
gone to the coast, despite your parents' reservations, and
survived. And come home to wait for the offer in the mail.
It was only when he got what he wanted that he realised he

had no idea what it meant, what he would actually be doing for the next five years, what he would be doing after that.

So he ran on the beach, walked and ran in his unmarked body. Caught the last daylight waves as the sun settled into the Glasshouse Mountains in the long summer evenings, drank beer on the verandah with his father and ate pizza from Bruno's Taverna. This is a family ritual, pizzas from Bruno's, a large capriciosa and a large marguerita to feed the five of them. But the others are in Brisbane now, Owen, Tam and his father. And his mother's taken time off work to bring him to the coast to convalesce. Convalesce. It's a word from another age, he thinks, as he walks – gassed soldiers back from an old war to convalesce. He doesn't have that kind of time. He doesn't have the time to get used to this. To be unwell and be like a person who is unwell, like a person who has almost died and now probably won't. He doesn't have the time for convalescence so he's angry with his mother when she uses the word.

And sometimes this is all too much to work out and he is only the body. This useless liability of a body. Limited by pain and stiffness and heaviness. Once the cat caught a bird and chewed it as one of its killing games and his father took the bird away and it walked slowly but it couldn't fly. It had one wing bent and its chest torn and it kept falling over. His father killed it with a hammer and the cat was angry with him.

Now he walks on this beach with his slow stiffness, with every aspect of moving an intolerable effort. And he never circles far from home.

He goes down to the edge and lets the waves wet his feet,

but the sand softens and he backs away before he loses his balance. He is tiring. There is more rain now. He heads home.

Minestrone, his mother says.

A bowl of minestrone with the spoon to the left. That's his.

Your father called, she says. Just to see how you are.

And he can't find a comfortable position at the table, even taking short breaths that would usually do no harm. And he feels the steam from the soup on his face, smells it, wants to eat it, but there's no part of him moving, nothing in him right now but the pain. He can't reach for the spoon, can't make any effort to lift his arm and feed himself. He feels sweat breaking out all over him, hears his panting breathing.

I'll get you some Mersyndol, his mother says, and we'll take it slowly.

When the tablets start to work he eats. He won't let her help him, even though she hovers nearby not eating her own, wanting to help. There is a haze with the drugs, but that's okay. An enveloping haze through which he pushes the minestrone and eats, chewing slowly, needing to sleep. His mother fits pillows around him when he lies down, and he dreams crazy, anaesthetic dreams.

In the evening he's awake, sitting with coffee and studying, trying to study. His mother no longer asks him how he can study with music on. That noise, as she calls it, or used to. It's music now, and she tries to take an interest. Nirvana, she says, turning the tape over carefully, Now what do they sing that I'd know?

He sits and plays music because he can't study anyway, with or without it. Nothing goes in. It all seems to matter very little. He's not concentrating, and he doesn't know if it's the lingering pain, or the drugs, or everything else. But he wants to keep studying, to stop this drift away from normal. He wants to sit and pass the exams. And people say he should be glad just to be alive. But they aren't. They expect more. So does he. Besides, it's almost impossible to understand not being alive. He has always expected to live, without thinking about it. All of his plans rely on living.

He can't imagine being drunk for the last time, going and leaving things unsaid and undone, stepping back from his friends and watching the gap he leaves close behind him. And when they're older they look back at photos and they see him there, looking just like them, and they say, Hey there's that Aidan guy, the one who . . .

He doesn't let himself think to the end of their sentences. Doesn't let himself think about what it all means for him, other than absence. He should study now. Concentrate harder and stop the words rushing by unnoticed. Think about each sentence, each paragraph of each lecture until it makes enough sense to remember.

The sea is dark outside, invisibly dark from his bright room. He hears a car drive past. Study isn't happening, again. He turns the music up a little louder. Nirvana, 'Heart Shaped Box'. It fills the room, fills his head, and he sleeps. When the tape has long finished playing he is vaguely aware of his mother helping him into bed, easing him down among the pillows, asking him if he's okay, comfortable. She gives him something, some tablet, and he's gone again. Gone for hours.

Waking in the dark, but just at the edge of dawn. And he watches the light come over the sea, the first diffuse light and then the sun. And he's stiff with sleeping, stiff after hours spent in the twisted position of least pain.

It's cool outside, and bright, and he takes the stairs backwards, one at a time. This stretches things less, and he knows he won't fall. He can just remember when he was very young and stairs everywhere were so big they needed real climbing, and the only way to do that was to face them, and take it slowly, like today. Whether it was up or down. Big red stairs in the house in London, where he had been born while his parents had studied there. And all he remembers of London is the stairs, and the careful task of climbing, hands all around him, his mother's and father's, in case he fell. It was like that going home this time, going home from hospital. They went with him up the front steps, one in front and one behind. And their hands were still there, still ready.

But climbing stairs is not the only mundane task he has lost the right to take for granted. He has made assumptions about movement, about comfort, about putting on his own shoes, about not being constipated the way he is now by drugs and the anaesthetic. This life is so different, unbearably different. He is such an unsophisticated animal, and every simple thing such an effort. And he can see now that he didn't appreciate what he had when he was well, and he wants to recover so he can take it all for granted again. Just like the others, just like his friends who couldn't understand any of this. Who expect not only to sleep well at night but to sleep in on weekends, and resent the hot days that wake them early, resent the parents or the part-time jobs that take their sleeping-in away. And this is just how he'd like to be.

They'll be here today, his uni friends. He's not sure how he feels about that. He wants to see them, but far more than that he wants to be one of them, and that can't happen yet. They are visiting because he is ill, so they are visiting because of the thing that makes him different, not anything that makes him like them. And this will be painfully apparent all day. Matt, Jason and Kimberley. He's known them since orientation, when they met at the faculty's barbecue for new students, where everyone stood in school groups if they had one or tried to make conversation with strangers. And Aidan had taken a deep breath and walked over to Kimberley, who was standing by herself with a plastic cup of cask red wine trying to look inconspicuous. He started with some carefully inconsequential line and it all went well until the moment she said, slightly too late, I think you've got a problem with your sausage. And his hot dog emptied itself onto his shoes, splattering tomato sauce across the lino.

Well, she'll remember you, his mother said later, trying not to laugh at him too much.

Then lectures started, and with them all the adjustments. Where to find lecture theatres, how to take notes, how much and how little to study, all changed from school. And there were parties at people's houses where you stay and drink and sleep on the floor, where no-one owns up to the vomit on the parents' bed the next day.

It was just the life Aidan had hoped it would be, and then the blackouts started. Came from nowhere and struck him down, a tiny mass of malfunctioning cells in his heart, stop-starting, running quite out of control.

In some people, the cardiologist said, these things just happen. But he asked questions anyway, going back to birth and further, back to parents and aunts and uncles and beyond. As though there might be some error back there, some blunder in the genes, some small bomb left unexploded all the years till now.

But no. There was no sign of that. This thing just happened. And the first operation went well, but the machine they put near his right armpit failed, which meant trying another way, and rib spreaders and a new kind of pain.

His friends arrive in the afternoon. We come bearing gifts, they tell him. Jason hands him a magazine, rolled up and wrapped in tissue paper.

So how do I get it out? Aidan says, holding it in his one free hand and shaking it. With my teeth?

That's exactly the point, Jason says, and undoes the paper for him, lifting out a *Playboy*. Now you really can only read the articles.

Funny guy, Aidan says.

Matt gives him a small box, wrapped in the same paper. With some help he opens it and finds two double-A batteries inside.

In case yours conk out, Matt tells him. I was going to get you jumper leads but they wouldn't fit in the box.

And nothing exciting from me, Kimberley says. Last week's lectures. Photocopies of my notes, and summaries of them on disc. This is making me study you know, so don't get well too soon.

She hands him about thirty A4 pages tied up with a thin red ribbon.

They go down to the beach, the others suddenly aware how slow he is when they walk together. And they ask him how he's going and he says he's getting there and he lifts the edges of his dressings to show them the bump of his new pacemaker under the skin of his abdomen, sutures along the top like a blue fishing-line train track.

They come out the day after tomorrow, he tells them. Mum's taking me back to Brisbane to see the surgeon on Friday morning.

It's warm in the sun, even now, well into autumn. And he's tiring. They can see he's tiring. Back at the house he rests, and just as he's falling asleep he can hear the others talking his mother into a game of cards. This moves into his dreams, his mother, his friends and playing cards. But it happens hazily, as though behind frosted glass.

His mother wakes him when it's dark outside.

We thought we might have Bruno's pizza, she says. Your friends have some very dubious wine that they say would go well with pizza.

Okay, he says, before he remembers the stiffness, the pain in him. Before he remembers that the operations were real and that the card game might have been, or might not, even though he can see it more clearly.

Do you want to wash your face? You'll feel better if you wash your face.

Do you really think so? Do you really think I'd feel any different if I washed my face?

He lifts himself to a sitting position on the edge of the bed and stays there with his shoulders hunched until he is ready to stand.

It's the drugs, his mother tells the others in the living room. They make him really slow to wake up whenever he has a rest.

And he hears his own feet shuffle as he comes out of the bedroom to join them. At least he's not wearing the slippers his mother has bought him. That would be worse. As if he'd wear the slippers, ever.

He sits next to Kimberley watching the news while Matt and Jason go out for the pizzas. And he's constipated again. He feels like he's been filled up with concrete and none of it's shifting. He's sitting here next to Kimberley like some bent old man made grumpy by constipation. He can't even say, Don't worry, Kim, it's not you, I just think part of me is trying to shit a housebrick. Kimberley, who is so nearby and attractive and symptom-free and trying to pretend that everything's fine. Her eyes on the news, on some damp cat in a drain-pipe in Iowa, as though she's even slightly interested. Her neat fingers folded into each other and resting in her lap. He can't even do that.

He has no appetite for pizza when it arrives. He insists

on a glass of the wine and it makes him dizzy. His mother, for no apparent reason, chops his pizza into small pieces and gives him a fork and pushes him through each cut-up mouthful of two slices. And he only puts up with it because he's worried that if he shows any greater reluctance she will start making choo-choo train noises and saying, Come on now, one for daddy. She gives him something for the constipation and he goes to bed.

He wakes once, some time later, and hears laughter from the living room, drunk people laughing. He finds a more comfortable position and drifts back into sleep.

The morning is cold again, and overcast, and the others are still not awake when he leaves. He goes through the back door and slowly down the steps and the dew is achingly cold on his feet as he crosses the grass. With his free hand he holds his jacket closed around him and he moves onto the damp sand and down onto the beach.

This is a better morning, he tells himself, after better sleep. Things need to be improving by now. Because he's far too lonely, wrapped in all this. He is separated from everything he knows by layers of pain and layers of caring. By people's best intentions that mean they end up treating him like an alien. He has come to mean something else, so he does not fit in. They just don't see the person they saw six weeks ago when he was well, he can tell that when they look at him. He is hidden by his illness, his wounds, his pain, his brief closeness to death. He is even hidden by not giving in, by trying to keep up with them, and by becoming some symbol of courage in the face of adversity. But this courage is a hollow shell. It isn't courage at all. It is only a desperate need for normality, a desperate need to maintain some identity in the face of all this, to not give in and become the life-support system for the illness. To not give in and become part of other people's pasts. He won't let them go that easily. So maybe it's fear that keeps this bent body going. Fear of what might happen if he stops fighting.

He's thought about dying, and he still doesn't understand it, doesn't have any answers. But it's much more likely that he will live, and he doesn't have the answers for that, either. Too much has changed. There is a box just under his skin that ticks away and keeps him going and always will. And how can he put that out of his mind, and go on normally? He tries to fit the normal things back in his head, to put them all back into place, into the places from which they have been crowded out by pain and other disruptions. He wants to sit his exams and pass them. He needs to see that kind of progress, that kind of achievement. He can't bear the thought of being someone whose only achievement is to sit down and heal wounds slowly. Because that is unbearably different and inconsolably lonely.

And his friends turn up and eat pizza and drink, but more than that they move the way they do, so quickly and easily, they sit in any position without being in pain, they sleep through the night on beach-house furniture, they dress themselves, feed themselves, stay awake all day. And he can't tell them what it's like to lose all that.

But he is walking well today, relatively. Today he will

reach the old shipwreck before turning for home. He sees it in the distance and keeps his eyes on it, like a target, the clean-picked carcass of a boat that sticks out of the sand like a broken cage of ribs. He's sure there was more of it when he was a child, but perhaps that was a different ship, a different beach.

He hears a voice behind him. Kimberley calling his name.

He doesn't turn. He doesn't take his eyes from the shipwreck. He hasn't been past the shipwreck since Christmas, when he was well and it was the beginning of a run. His chest is hurting, his difficult breathing drawing at his wounds. He keeps walking. He hears his name called again, and she's closer now. He keeps moving, keeps pushing one foot out in front of the other and down onto the wet, sure sand. Even in the cold morning he feels sweat breaking out under his dressings.

And the waves are reaching in around the wreck, curling in through its rusted metal parts and slipping out again. Just like any morning of the last hundred years. And there is none of the panic of the night of the wrecking, just the clean rhythm of the waves, washing the rust, slowly, slowly turning the ship to nothing.

He hears his name again, this time spoken as Kimberley catches up beside him. He holds up his hand to keep her back, but he can't find the breath to talk. He points to the wreck, now just ahead.

The ship? she says.

He nods.

Okay.

And he pushes on. The breaths are shorter now. He is dizzy, nauseated. But he's nearly there. He keeps going, and he focuses on the bow, the black broken bow of the ship. And he reaches out for it, reaches till he can take it with his free hand, and he grips it tightly and holds himself there, bent over, fighting off dizziness. He feels Kimberley's hand on his back.

You made it, she says.

Yeah.

This has been his goal for days, the shipwreck, and he's here now. And his mother said, Don't push it, don't go too hard, there's no hurry. But she's wrong. She's wrong and he's here and he's breathing, leaning on the wreck. No-one thought he'd go so far so soon.

Slowly his breathing settles, and the dizziness, and the sweat on his face starts to cool in the light, fresh breeze. And he looks at her in her last night's clothes with her pale face and her dark hair drawn back.

I wondered where you were, she says, when I woke up.

Just walking.

You're doing well.

Yeah. I'll do better.

I thought, when you're back in Brisbane in a couple of days, I thought I could take you to get the stitches out. If you want.

Thanks.

And she frowns and looks at the sand. And looks as though she's trying to work out what to do next. I wish things weren't like this, she says.

Yeah. Me too. I'll get better, you know.

Yeah. Good.

And they walk back slowly. And the only sounds are the breaking waves and his difficult breathing, stopping him talking, stopping any conversation. Kimberley looks at the ground in front of her, or looks out to sea.

And this is another moment of unbearable contradictions, a window opened for an instant to give a glimpse of a distant, impossible world. He's imagined walking beside her on this beach. Just the two of them, and the grey waves and the dull sky of some abandoned winter morning. But not like this.

Kimberley blinks and blinks and rubs her eyes and blames it on the rough wind. They are halfway home now. Behind them the waves draw in over the shipwreck. Ahead he sees his mother on the front verandah, watching him.

And this is progress, reaching the wreck, so this is a good day. But even then, even leaning on the bow with breath coming back to him, he could see the long beach beyond, and the progress not yet made.

And Kimberley was there, and almost the Kimberley of his imagination, just when he was thinking only of the practicalities, the lecture notes, the summaries.

And every breath twists pain through his chest and every step jolts. He could cry now, he thinks, just when he was holding on.

back soon with fish

I'm in the cab on the way into the city when Frank Green calls.

'Phil,' he says, 'You're back.'

'Yeah, just now.'

'I was thinking of taking the boat out tonight. Get a few of us together and get out on the bay. The bream are running.'

'Yeah, sounds good, but I'm in Sydney.'

'I thought you were back today.'

'Yeah, in Australia. I don't get to Brisbane till tomorrow. I'm doing a film thing down here, going to a film thing. The producer I'm going to be working with? It's the premiere of her new thing. It's on now. I'm going to the after party. See who's around, you know?'

'Bummer,' he says, and uses the word like he means it. 'I reckon you could've hooked a beauty tonight.'

'Yeah, sure.'

'So when are you back at work?'

'Tonight's work.'

'Yeah, right. When are you back at the healing-the-sick work rather than the schmoozing-the-starlets work?'

'Monday.'

And with that he goes to catch fish, and for me Monday seems too close and impossibly far away, like a nearby day in a different life.

Tonight's my first after party. My first serious film event and my body feels so far from sensible. Four meals, three movies, a disrupted sitting-up sleep and however many time zones there are between Toronto and Sydney. That's how far from sensible. And I wanted to be better prepared than that. Mainly, I wanted it not to look like my first after party. These film people, they know how to have fun. Do I? Sometimes I'm still not sure.

But jet lag brings out my melancholy side. I should get all this out of my head. And some time before the age of twenty I should have worked out that extensive self-analysis isn't worth the trouble. I could, had I chosen to, have learned that from Frank Green long ago.

For Frank, all of life makes sense and Monday is probably just where it should be. Tonight he'll fish. He'll go out on the bay with a few uni friends, drink too much, use language he's never allowed to in front of his baby, piss recklessly over the side the way he likes to (thunderously autographing his name into the quiet night sea), catch something or nothing, sleep a few hours, cruise back home, continue cruising through the rest of his mid-thirties and beyond. There's something straightforward about his life that I quite admire.

And on Monday he'll be an orthopaedic surgeon again, I'll be a part-time GP again, with my film dreams eating away at me, yet to become as much as I'd like them to.

'Now this is why I went to all that bloody trouble to pass those exams,' he told me two months ago when he bought his boat and named it after the Medicare item number for an operative knee arthroscopy, since he'd figured that was what was going to pay for it.

And he dragged me round the Boat Show an entire weekend, as though I had nothing better to do with my time, and got himself so caught up in it all that he'd not only bought a four-berther by the time we left, he'd also gone up to Ron 'Thommo' Thomson, the host of 'Stoked About Boats', and got him to autograph an Evinrude engine catalogue.

And I can remember Ron 'Thommo' Thomson, demonstrating more sensitivity than I'd expected, giving us the once over and asking if he should make it out to both of us (as though we had some permanent catalogue-sharing thing going). And Frank saying, 'Nah, just to me, he doesn't know shit about boats.'

So Frank is living the life he'd always planned to, back in our poverty-stricken uni days in the early eighties. 'I'm not afraid of debt, mate,' he said even then, as he ticked off the boat and the car and the house on his fingers. 'The second I've got any kind of earning capacity I'm going to live it to the max.'

I always thought he was kidding, right up until he leased the BMW a year ago. 'Five series,' he said breathily, as though it was sexual. And I think he used the word *plush*. I've never had those kinds of plans. I wandered into part-time general practice, wandered into film-making, almost turned thirty before I'd done anything that I liked. And now I've made six shorts and had a couple of turns as assistant director on something bigger. Which is how I met Jacqui Lynnot at the time when she was looking for a new project, and how I come to have spent a week with her in LA before the short-film festival in Toronto.

And even though we didn't achieve too much in LA and my film played in Toronto to a mostly empty room, Jacqui says this is too good a project not to get up, and that I'll be directing my first feature by mid-next year. And though I've never been much given to optimism, she's a good enough producer that I almost believe her.

So we decided I'd overnight in Sydney for the after party before going home. Check out the talent, get a feel for things. Even though I'd like nothing more than to be in my own bed right now.

Of course, that's not my alternative. My alternative is a night on the bay, catching no fish, drinking too much and falling asleep to the noise of Frank driving his urine stream into the sea like a drill bit while singing the classic hits of the eighties.

I check in at the hotel, dump my bag in my room, shower and try to convince myself that changing into my bottle-green shirt – my last clean garment – will make me feel more up to this. I go to the rooftop. And I can hear the party from two floors down in the stairwell. Music, plenty of people well settled in to a good time. I wish I'd got here earlier. I wish we'd all started the good time at the same time. I wish, as I have had cause to wish more than once or twice, that my comfort zone wasn't quite this slender. The thickness of the bottle-green shirt and not far beyond it.

I pick up a glass of wine from the bar and decide I'll leave the getting a feel for things, and any schmoozing of starlets, for a little later. No hurry. I walk towards the edge and away from the crowd, tuck myself next to a dense, manicured shrub.

I gaze out at the skyline, in case I can look as though I'm genuinely interested in it and am, for a moment only, painlessly between conversations. I wonder if I could go to my room now, tell Jacqui in the morning that I had a great time, and where was she all night, and that I talked to plenty of people before the jet lag got the better of me.

I'd even rather be on Frank's boat than this. Hating the predictable, reasonable things to hate about boating and fishing. Slumped on one of the four berths wishing I was somewhere else as Frank spouts rod 'n' reel jargon and spins some bullshit about his bait preferences and tells joke number one thousand that begins, 'The Pope, Bill Gates and Monica Lewinsky go fishing and . . .' Frank is someone who should never have been given Internet access.

But my night's not working out to be that good. For the next half hour the only conversation I have is with an actor who lurches up to me and says, 'Eric. Eric. Hey, you're not Eric,' and then goes.

I'm floundering here. I'm aware I'm not Eric. I don't need it pointed out to me. I'm pretty much nobody. I shouldn't be here. Why didn't I pick some socially less intense career, like lighthouse keeping? Damn them for automating lighthouses. I can't face conversation tonight. I can't even remember how any of those Pope/Bill Gates/Monica Lewinsky jokes end, and Frank never stops telling them. I concentrate on my next sip of wine, the horizon, and flounder with as much quiet dignity as I can manage.

My mother calls. So no quiet dignity now, either.

'Did they like your film in Toronto then, Philby?' she says.

'Yeah, it seemed to go down all right.'

'Nice people, Canadians. What's all that noise?'

'I'm at a party, remember? The film party in Sydney, the one I told you about.'

'The one Christopher Reeve might be going to?'

'Keanu Reeves, yes.'

'So have you signed anyone up yet? For your film?'

'It's not quite like that.'

'Oh come on, Philby. I know the way these things work. All the big deals are done in someone's jacuzzi. Everything starts at parties. These people, film people, they swing, Philby.'

'Yes. Um, I've got to go. And I suspect I'm interrupting you in the middle of something very Jackie Collins anyway.'

'Now Philby, that's not nice. I just wanted to make sure you're being sensible.'

'I'm always sensible. I've sent a sample of the jacuzzi

water off for analysis and I won't be getting in till they can confirm there's no Legionella. Now, I've got to go. I've got Nicole Kidman here to talk through a couple of contract clauses with me. And she'll catch her death of cold if she's not back in the water soon.'

'Nicole Kidman? Can I say hello to her?'

'No, you can't.'

'Oh. Well, will you tell her I liked her in *To Die For*?'

'I'll tell her you liked her in everything since *BMX Bandits*. Now, I've got to go. She's a very busy person.'

'Yes, of course. Don't spend the whole night bothering her, though. She might be very nice but make sure you work the room.'

I thank her and hang up, and it's just me and the shrub again. A situation I'm beginning to quite like, and I'm wondering how long I can spin out this glass of wine. Before Nicole hassles me about a contract clause, or something.

'Phil,' someone says behind me. And, surprisingly, it's not Nicole Kidman. 'Laura, from Jacqui's office,' she says, just as I'm working out she's Laura from Jacqui's office. 'We should introduce you to a few people.'

'No, it's fine, really. I'm a bit tired.'

'No, come on,' she says, probably figuring she's outnumbered me by referring to herself in the plural. 'I'm sure there are plenty of people here who'd like to meet you.'

'I don't know that I'm really up to sensible conversation. I just got back in.'

And, of course, I don't mention it, but these people swing. I'm way better off out of it.

'I was only thinking, like, soap star, you know? We're not talking brain surgeon.'

'Brain surgeon would be fine.'

'Here, come and meet Chloe.'

Chloe is at the bar getting herself a mineral water. I know who she is, and Laura doesn't need to point. Chloe in her burgundy dress, the kind of girl I used to stand near at Med Balls, just in case she'd decide to talk to me. The kind of girl I practised conversation for, but never got to meet. But several degrees worse, of course, since Chloe's also on TV.

And why is it that people think brain surgeons make problematic partners in conversation? I've met several who are pretty personable, and happy to talk about anything. It's the Chloes I'm not so sure about.

But it's not that I'd lack material. I've never seen her show, but I know her well from *TV Week* covers and endless promos and my reading of crappy waiting-room mags (which is, to say the least, extensive). I know she loves horses and everyone she's worked with says she's really nice. I know she's got the traditional soap-star soft spot for Ethiopian kiddies. I know the battles she used to have doing her homework on set. But, shit, I also know Gwyneth Paltrow better than Blythe Danner does by now, and it doesn't make me ready to talk to her.

Laura calls out to Chloe to pin her down before she escapes, hands me a glass, does the intro and leaves, casting a kind of blind-date aura behind her in a well-meaning way that makes us both uncomfortable.

So I tell Chloe I like her work, in case that helps. Fifty

things I could have said, and what I actually tell her is, 'I like what you do,' with a bit of a nod, and I downplay it just enough that I think she believes me.

And I always thought she looked attractive in the ads, Chloe with her famous big eyes and her wide mouth, and she still does in person, but much younger. Well, not much. I seem to be drawing some line between nineteen and seventeen, as though it's reasonable to find her attractive if she's slightly more than half my age, rather than slightly less. Chloe, I realise now as she sucks at her mineral water, is a child. And that, I tell myself, is the reason I lied to her about liking what she does.

'So what do you do?' she says, in a way that seems like trained politeness. (Now I've decided she's a child it's as though she can't have a thought of her own.)

'I'm a director. I'm going to be working with Jacqui on a project. So far I've made a few shorts. A couple of them were on SBS.'

'SBS,' she repeats, and somewhere behind her eyes a portcullis slides quietly down, a drawbridge lifts. 'I like what they do,' she says, in a way that doesn't begin to hide the fact that she never watches SBS, but that does suggest she knows I lied about watching her soap.

Then we both adopt a fairly adolescent kind of silence which I, as the non-adolescent, decide it's up to me to end, but as soon as I'm saying, 'Me too,' and then going on to say, 'That's why I've done a couple of things with them,' I realise that SBS is a dead issue and Chloe is already rationalising this whole conversation as just part of the price of fame, and willing it to stop.

'I'm sorry, I'm a bit jet-lagged,' I decide to tell her, hating the thought that I'm boring a teenager. 'I just got in from Toronto.'

And she says, 'Right,' as though I'm a liar or a wanker or even more boring than she'd thought, and it doesn't particularly matter which.

'You've got horses, haven't you?' I sicken myself by saying, suspecting I'm about to begin some horse-owning lie of my own just to keep the talk happening. And where has all that well-rehearsed Med Ball patter gone? I'm sure it was fool-proof.

'Chloe,' someone's voice says next to us, saving us, probably, from the Ethiopian kiddies or her next-door neighbour's fight with MS. (Who knows where I was going to take it, but it wasn't going to be good). 'Dan, from *Who Weekly*. Let's get a shot of you,' he says, lifting up his big camera in case she wouldn't otherwise know what he meant, 'you and, um . . . Sorry, I . . .'

'Phil Harris.'

'You and, um, Phil Harris,' he says, as though someone just stuck a pin in his great idea and let all the air out. 'Actually, how about we get you over to these guys? You don't mind if I grab Chloe for a sec, do you Phil?'

'No, go ahead.'

And Chloe smiles as she's led away by the elbow, and I think she wishes me luck with SBS, but since she doesn't continue the sentence all the way to the end I'll never be sure. And she looks so seventeen as she goes, and I notice the pale rectangle of a Band-Aid detaching itself from her right heel, just above the top of her not-quite-fitting shoe.

I wander. I explore an introverted side I thought I'd put behind me in the mid-eighties. I try to side-step the feeling that Chloe gave me the boring-grown-up treatment. I resolve to learn that no conversation can be saved by a horse question, and few by mentioning SBS. I try to forget that the last thing anyone at work said to me before I left for LA was 'see you in *Who Weekly*'. I make a specific effort to avoid Laura, just in case she'd think my night might be saved by another intro.

I adopt a great air of pseudo-purpose. I'm supposed to be scouting anyway, so it's not so bad. Even if there's no chance to negotiate finer contractual points with Nicole.

And just as I'm laughing at my mother for going with my stupid Nicole Kidman remark, Keanu Reeves makes an appearance. Keanu Reeves, with a minder on either side, a grey beanie, his left elbow poking through the sleeve of an old black jumper. Perhaps I should phone my mother back and see if she'd like to say hello.

He picks up a glass of wine at the bar and stands between his minders drinking it, aware, I'm sure, of being very watched. For a while I think we're the only two people in the room no-one's talking to. Probably for different reasons. Then one of us is approached by Dan from *Who Weekly*.

I hang around near my shrub, grazing from the passing trays of nibblies, and using each one as a chance for transient conversation in case it makes me look slightly busy.

I seem to be totally invisible here, and I should be doing better. I'm next to a circle of people, close to Ben Mendelsohn's back, and they all seem to know each other. The room is working, but I'm not working it. I'm beginning to wish that that guy would come up to see if I'm Eric again. I'd do my best to be Eric, rather than being a total loser with a row of nibblies lined up along his forearm. And even if I couldn't pass for Eric, I certainly wouldn't let the guy go in a hurry.

I notice that Ron 'Thommo' Thomson, the host of 'Stoked About Boats', is here, and I even come close to saying hello to him, just because he autographed Frank's Evinrude catalogue. And the only thing that stops me is I know I'll tell him I like what he does, then end up excusing myself and boring him about Toronto. Because I hate what he does, and any praise would be completely unsustainable.

He stands close by with a bunch of other guys in their forties, and he's belly laughing loudly, tossing down beers and dribbling Thousand Island dressing onto his *Dark Side of the Moon* T-shirt. Ron 'Thommo' Thomson obviously dresses himself after hours, and the deck shoes and pressed shorts of 'Stoked About Boats' are nowhere to be seen. White canvas shoes, peach jeans. And plenty of people talking to him as he stands there affecting a life-of-the-party ambience.

The tray people keep circling, now with little plastic cups of green jelly.

'I suppose you could call them a palate cleanser,' one of them says to me as he urges me to take one.

Which I do, as a fitting-in thing, assuming that palate-cleansing little plastic cups of green jelly are all very after-party. I take it as though I really know what I'm doing, and to back it up I take another.

The problem is, no-one else in the room has taken one and it's not a fitting-in decision at all. The other problem is, I've got no idea what I'm supposed to do with them. Each one has a toothpick in the middle of it, which I start by removing, since I know I'll only get hurt otherwise. Did they have olives? Did the olives fall off? I don't get these drinks. I'm faking it here, and not well.

I try to sip, but nothing moves. I smell mint, but that's as far as I get. I hate these after-party people for knowing that you don't take these things. For nibbling only occa-sionally, for avoiding behaving like complete tray pirates, and for knowing that the little green cups just do a few laps of the room and meet with disdain.

I slide my tongue down into the cup and I can just touch the jelly, lift it at one edge. I tip my head back, tap the bottom, flick the jelly with my tongue. No luck. I put my mouth around the top of the cup, shake my head. Nothing moves. I try suction. I try suction until the cup cracks, and then some of the jelly slurps into my mouth and I feel like a minor-league winner.

And that's when I realise I'm not invisible here after all. And the entire group of people next to me, previously noisy, has stopped talking, and they're all now watching me, seeing how far I can take this.

'There's usually a toothpick in it,' one of them says.

'So you can break it up a bit, make it easier to shift.'

'I kind of like it this way,' I tell him. 'Bit of a challenge.'

And he says, 'Good for you,' and they stand there waiting to see where I can take it. I crack the second cup open in one move, eat the jelly like a schucked oyster, walk away. Fuck them all.

That's it for me, I reckon. Time for a lie down.

'Christ, mate, that first one put up a fight,' Ron 'Thommo' Thomson says, a fistful of tiny cups of green in his left hand and one in his right. He slurps it in one go and says, 'Not your fault. Tongue like a camel, see.' And he slides it out to give me a better look. 'Biological advantage, hey? Goes down a treat with the ladies. Here, have another.'

'No, I've . . .'

'Come on. It's a party.'

So he talks me into another one or two and tongues his own way through another six.

'Mint,' he says. 'Don't mind this.' And he draws a big noisy breath in through his nose. 'Hey, don't think I've breathed in through that side since I broke it playing footy.' And he looks into the cup and says, 'Where have you been all my life?'

He commandeers a passing tray loaded with more green jelly cups (easy, since no-one else in the room wants one), and he says, 'Go you halves.'

And again my protest is weak and pointless, so we're soon over next to the shrub, slurping away. Thommo with his huge, advantageous tongue, me piling up my cracked empties like pistachio shells. And once or twice I talk about leaving and he says, 'Come on, the fun's just starting when they bring out these babies. And it doesn't really get going till I start to sing.'

And I hope he's kidding, but of course he isn't.

'You know, I thought these'd be Midori when they came out,' he says, as though it matters. 'I think it's much better that they're cream de menth.'

And we set there in our sludgy minty smell, and the jet lag creeps over me again, pulls up onto me like a doona this time, and I know I won't last.

And I find myself starting to tell Thommo about Frank, behaving like the bloke equivalent of a clingy new friend, saying something like, 'I reckon I know your biggest fan,' in a voice that sounds as though I'm trying to copy him. Except my version sounds like it's had more to drink.

'Robyn?' he says. 'You know Robyn? Oh, she'd root anything, don't listen to her. I'm not sure it makes her my biggest fan.'

'Yeah, and I know Frank Green too. You signed an Evinrude catalogue for him a while back.'

'Oh, righto.'

'He actually wanted me to go out with him on his boat tonight. Catch a few bream.'

'Bream. Mate I could show you fucking bream,' he says, even though, as far as I can recall, it's beside the point.

'Yeah, I bet you could,' I tell him, since I bet he could. 'Hey, you know what? I've got a phone and he's got a phone. He'd get a big buzz out of it if you gave him a call. Just to say hi. Pretty big fan, you know.'

Frank's somewhere out on the bay when we call. I ease myself down into the plant pot once I handed the phone over, and, take this as an opportunity to regroup. And Thommo says the hi we talked about and then plenty more. They talk bream, and boats, and they try to work out which Evinrude catalogue it was that Thommo signed, but they've both had too much to drink by now. And Thommo's saying, 'Yeah, but was it one with norks?' and Frank can't quite remember.

And I'm sitting there realising that they watered the shrub today and feeling the cool water seep up into my pants, but not exactly able to move and I'm thinking, with an unnecessary and ungenerous discontent, how the fuck did this get to be about boats? When do I get my turn to talk about something? Wasn't this just bloody hi, just hi to a fan, not all this yacking about tackle and lies about big fish? Mate, mate, you should've seen . . .

I've had hardly anything to do with Frank's boat, quite deliberately. I'd be happy never to talk about it again. I've actually been totally off boats for ages. Years. I was just thinking hi. Totally off boats since it was always my job to hose ours down every time we went out in it when we were younger. And, no, technically it wasn't too much to ask, but I was thirteen, so it certainly seemed like it was. And I liked fishing less.

Thommo presses the stop button, hands me the phone, says, 'Sounds like a good bloke. Reckons he's pulled in a couple of small whiting already. Now, how about another tray?'

'Never caught a fish big enough to eat,' I hear myself

saying, before I realise it's probably quite an admission of failure to Thommo. 'Never, but that's okay.'

And he gives me a look that could only be pity. 'Sure it is,' he says. 'Sure it's okay.'

'No. Really. It's okay.'

And he puts his arm around my shoulder and says something quiet about having a problem with premature ejaculation, probably to make me feel better, probably in a nobody's-perfect kind of way. And then he quickly follows it up with a few jokes focused on the brevity of Australian male foreplay, so that we can both relax again.

'Yeah,' I say, 'and there's this thing. This thing with a boat. And Monica Lewinsky . . .'

But that's where it ends.

He nods and says, 'Yeah. Don't know about that. Reckon we could get you a fish, though.'

'Yeah? Could we?' I say, since anything else would seem ungrateful.

Sometimes fish matter so much to people that you just have to go with it.

He helps me to my feet before I work out that I need it, before I work out that he might have meant right now with the fish, rather than saying it just as a gesture of affirmation. And I think it's the jet lag that's closing in as we weave through the crowd. Well, mainly the jet lag.

And Thommo's murmuring and then singing something about plenty more fish in the sea, and I want to pull him up now and remind him that it's only a metaphor in its common usage, generally something about relationship possibilities (offered to someone who, at the time, doesn't have any). And, besides, no-one just makes up songs and sings them to someone the first proper time they meet. It looks foolishly disinhibited.

And that's what's in my mind, none of it getting out, as we stagger down the stairs like a creature that's slightly too wide for the architecture and has an odd number of legs (probably seven). Only one of mine's touching the ground most of the time though, and I can't for the life of me see where the other one's gone.

And then we're outside just as I'm thinking of screaming, 'Where's my fucking leg?' and I can't make much sense of the dark. Thommo yanks open the door of a limo and everyone talks at once, as though there's a problem, but it's soon fixed.

'It's cool, it's cool,' an American voice is saying and Thommo's saying, 'Mate, I've got a proposition to put to you.'

And he climbs in and lowers me in after him, does my seat belt up carefully, says, 'Comfy?'

I nod, feel my knees with both hands. Then both knees with one hand at the same time, just to check that I'm not fooling myself. All is well. I'm a biped still. Jet lag, though, is murder.

And Thommo's talking on to the guy with the American voice, telling him we're out for bream, and once the American realises what he's on about he's saying 'bream' in quite a reflective way, and deciding he's part of it. And he tells his driver, 'This guy'll show you where to go,' and his driver says, 'Righto, Mister Reeves,' and I think I say, 'Fuck,

Superman,' before I can stop myself, but so much into my left shoulder that I taste bottle-green shirt and none of the sound gets to the outside.

I resolve not to talk. I find the switch for the window and buzz it down a little so that the cold air comes in and hits my face. The lights of Sydney, the late uncluttered streets of the CBD, pass by. Thommo, who by now has introduced himself as Thommo, is explaining that I've never caught a fish before, as though this is some kind of virginity.

'Never? Like never?' Keanu is saying, and I nearly tell him at least I don't ejaculate prematurely, but Thommo means well so I keep it to myself.

The car sways around corners the untroubled way limos do, and my head feels cold and my stomach starts to sway like a hammock with a fat green man in it, and I smell far too much mint seeping from my skin.

I wake when we stop at a pier. Someone opens the door and Thommo lifts me out.

'Just a nap,' I tell him as my feet meet the concrete and my knees go bendy.

'No worries,' he says. 'Maybe you'll have sea legs.' And he laughs.

'Back soon,' I hear Keanu say to the driver as the door shuts behind us. And then he stops and I'm sure he's about to say dude but he says, 'With fish.'

'You walk in the middle,' Thommo tells me. 'That way there's always someone between you and the water.'

And I know good advice when I hear it, and the planks of the pier give me some kind of lines to follow too, even though they're also kind of mesmerising, so I handle it better than I thought I might.

'Fucking jet lag,' I hear myself say. 'I just got back from Toronto, you know.'

Thommo takes us to a boat that seems so big I can't see the end of it in the dark and for a second the idea of hosing it down afterwards makes me pretty glum. They sit me in a soft squishy seat and within minutes we're out on the water, and that's when I remember the other thing I didn't like about boating. Motion isn't good for me. Boat motion worse than limo motion. Far worse.

And now even the cold air on my face isn't enough and the sloppy green waves from inside are clashing with the dark green waves from outside in a way that's very bad physics.

'I'm going to be lying down now,' I tell them, wondering a little about the formality of it, and the tense.

Thommo starts baiting hooks and singing a sea shanty and he gives Keanu the wheel and tells him, 'Just point her for the heads, mate.'

Keanu cranks up the revs, adjusts his beanie to a nautical angle and says, 'Man, look at those lights.'

And I'm lying at his feet in a place that might, if I recall correctly, be called the bilges. Lying there listening to the engine buzz its way up through the hull and into my head. Lying there, thinking that it's seventeen years since my first green-drink experience, and I'm getting that nasty bitter kind of green rising at the back of my throat again.

My phone rings and Keanu says, 'Here, let me get that for you,' as polite as a bus boy, and he unclips it from my belt and answers it. 'It's a guy called Frank,' he shouts down to me, 'he's just caught another fish, or something.'

And Thommo sings random bits of The Cars' 'Candy Oh', begins a thundering piss over the side and down into the waters of Sydney Harbour, and I feel my face sweat, the reverse peristalsis about to begin.

And, yes, there is vomiting. In the boat, over the side of it, Thommo gripping my collar, Keanu doing his best to negotiate the swell delicately. Vomiting and more vomiting. And lying down and sitting up and a cup or two of plasticky tasting water and more waves, and a struggle, a struggle with something. Cheering.

I wake in early daylight, still in the bilges, a loose pile of green jelly not far from my head. A rod I've never seen before fixed in my hand, gripped as though if I let go I could fall off something. Next to me, a fish of fascinating proportions. Maybe a mullet. As if I'd know.

'Hey tiger,' Thommo says as I lift myself to my knees and wipe the green dribbly slick from my chin. 'You did good. Wait till you get back home with that bugger.'

And Keanu says, 'Man. You and that fish. It was like . . . Hemingway, or something.'

ACKNOWLEDGEMENTS

First, I'd like to thank my publisher, Clare Forster, for raising the idea of this book with me, and then for her enthusiasm for its early parts and the encouragement to write more. Together we steered it away from the 'collected works' idea that we started with, and came up with the plan that 'head games' would dictate the composition of the book, and that, under this umbrella, I'd play whatever head games I liked.

Among others at Penguin, I'd like to thank Rachel Scully, my editor, for offering her usual wisdom, intuitiveness and attention to detail; also for indulging me in my unreasoned dislike of semicolons and my various other idiosyncrasies. And Imogen Cook, for making me work hard, but never too hard, helping me stay close to sane while I'm doing it, and providing a dog to walk and good stretch of riverbank when I'm in Melbourne.

My agent, Fiona Inglis, steered me into a few anthologies I wouldn't otherwise have been in, particularly early on, and is always there for me to whinge to, when necessary. And Sarah, Al and Doug generously tolerated all that extra keyboard time, the mood swings and the days when personal hygiene came a poor second to fiction.

I'm also grateful to the anthology editors who commissioned some of these stories in the first place, particularly Matt Condon for calling me about *Smashed – Australian Drinking Stories* after he'd called everyone else and commissioned stories on so many drinks that the only choice left to me was Creme de Menthe and the story 'Green'.

I'd like to thank the University of Queensland medical graduates of 1998 for asking me to talk at their graduation dinner, and leading me to think of trying something new with the 'Green' formula, just as Clare was about to suggest the same. Also Don Jefferys, for the *Medical Observer* article on trichotillomania that put Rapunzel Syndrome back in my mind for the first time in years.

Now, how clear can I be that I made this lot up? Some of it I want to seem very real, other stories obviously aren't, but none of them should be taken as fact in any way. So if you think you notice pants you once wore, someone who cut your hair and worked your scalp tenderly, unicorns you've flatted with, Bunsen burner hoses that once lashed your personal areas, dogs you've once been, hair you've sucked, races you didn't win, ice creams you've coiled (whether in a northern or southern hemisphere way), names you once tried on for size, that bastard who taught you PE, monkeys with whom you might have contemplated a family, blunders in chat rooms, exams that made you spin out, travelators that have held you for interminable periods, grass you once rolled in (while getting nowhere with a person of your preferred gender), escapes aided by plastic surgery, survival aided by cardiac surgery or movie stars with whom you once fished, please put it down to coincidence. That's all it is.

Lastly, I'd like everyone to know that no goldfish were harmed in the making of this book.

Some of the stories in this collection first appeared in slightly different forms as follows:

'Green' in *Smashed – Australian Drinking Stories*, edited by Matthew Condon and Richard Lawson (Random House, 1996)
'The Goatflap Brothers and the House of Names' in *Picador New Writing 3*, edited by Drusilla Modjeska and Beth Yahp (Picador, 1996)
'Headgames' in *Blur*, edited by James Bradley (Vintage, 1996)
'The Haircut of a More Successful Man' in *A Sea Change – Australian Writing and Photography*, edited by Adam Shoemaker (SOCOG, 1998)
'Dog 1, Dog 2' in *Queensland – Words and All* (Phoenix, 1993) and *Review Independent Monthly* (1996)
'There Must Be Lions' in *Medical Observer* (1995), *There Must Be Lions* (Ginninderra Press, 1998), *The Bulletin* (1998)
'Moving' in *Queensland –Words and All* (Outrider Phoenix Publications, 1993)
'Box Shaped Heart' in *Original Sin*, edited by Robyn Sheahan (University of Queensland Press, 1996)
'PE' in *A Sporting Declaration*, edited by Manfred Jurgensen (Phoenix, 1996)
'Plaza' in *Passion*, by Nick Earls (University of Queensland Press, 1992) and *The Gift of Story*, edited by Marion Halligan and Rosanne Fitzgibbon (University of Queensland Press, 1998)
'Sausage Sizzle' in *Penguin Australian Summer Stories* (Penguin, 1999)

BACHELOR KISSES

Nick Earls

Jon, Rick and Jen share takeaway food rituals, sporadic cocktail nights and the quest for love. Rick seems destined to long, lonely nights beneath his Porky Pig doona. Jen consumes men like chocolate bars. And Jon gets lucky in a way he's never expected – more women than he knows how to handle. A young doctor with grand plans for the hormone of darkness, he finds his life is spiralling way out of control.

Bachelor Kisses is the mess Jon Marshall makes of his life when it stops making sense. It's the story of one man's hilarious search for meaning: a chaotic comedy of misjudgements, misinformation and misguided intimacy.

'Cute, funny, sexy.'
   - *Cleo*

'A fast-paced comedy written with verve and intelligence.'
   - *The Bulletin*

'A chaotic comedy with hidden depths, it's a rollicking read.'
   - *The Australian*

'Buy a Nick Earls novel and you need never be sad again.'
   - *Who Weekly*

BACHELOR KISS

Nick Laird

48 SHADES OF BROWN

Nick Earls

A few months ago, Dan had to make a choice. Go to Geneva with his parents for a year, board at school or move into a share house with his 22-year-old bass-playing aunt, Jacq, and her friend, Naomi. He picked Jacq's place.

Now he's doing his last year at school and trying not to spin out. Trying to master calculus and work out the meaning of the fish-tank scene in Baz Luhrmann's *Romeo+Juliet*. Trying to pick up a few skills for surviving in the adult world. Problem is, he falls for Naomi, and things become much, much more confusing.

A brilliantly observed and very funny novel about being not quite seventeen – a time when everyone is offering you advice, and nobody is taking your seriously.

Hg2 Tallinn

A Hedonist's guide to
Tallinn

BY Laurence Shorter
PHOTOGRAPHY Laurence Shorter

A Hedonist's guide to Tallinn

Managing director – Tremayne Carew Pole
Series editor – Catherine Blake
Production – Rupert Wheeler
Design – P&M Design
Typesetting – Dorchester Typesetting
Repro – PDQ Digital Media Solutions Ltd
Printers – Printed in Italy by Printer Trento srl
PR – Ann Scott Associates
Publisher – Filmer Ltd

Email – info@ahedonistsguideto.com
Website – www.ahedonistsguideto.com

First Published in the United Kingdom in 2004 by
Filmer Ltd
47 Filmer Road,
London SW6 7JJ

ISBN - 0-9547878-4-6

Hg2 Tallinn

CONTENTS

How to…

A Hedonist's guide to… is broken down into easy to use sections:
Sleep, Eat, Drink, Snack, Party, Culture, Shop, Play and Info. In each of
these sections you will find detailed reviews and photographs.

At the front of the book you will find an introduction to the city and
an overview map, followed by introductions to the four main areas and
more detailed maps. On each of these maps you will see the places
that we have reviewed, laid out by section, highlighted on the map with
a symbol and a number. To find out about a particular place, simply
turn to the relevant section where all entries are listed alphabetically.

Alternatively, browse through a specific section (i.e. Eat) until you find
a restaurant that you like the look of. Next to your choice will be a
small coloured dot – each colour refers to a particular area of the city
– then simply turn to the relevant map to discover the location.

Updates

Due to the lengthy publishing process and shelf lives of books it is
very difficult to keep travel guides up to date – new restaurants, bars
and hotels open up all the time, while others simply fade away or just
go out of style. What we can offer you are free updates– simply log
onto our website www.ahedonistsguideto.com or www.hg2.net and
enter your details, answer a relevant question to provide proof of pur-
chase and you will be entitled to free updates for a year from the date
that you sign up. This will enable you to have all the relevant information at your fingertips whenever you go away.

In order to help us with this any comments that you might have, or
recommendations that you would like to see in the guide in future
please feel free to email us at info@ahedonistsguideto.com.

The concept

A Hedonist's guide to… is designed to appeal to a more urbane and stylish traveller. The kind of traveller who is interested in gourmet food, elegant hotels and seriously chic bars – the traveller who feels the need to explore, shop and pamper themselves away from the madding crowd.

Our aim is to give you the inside knowledge of the city, to make you feel like a well-heeled, sophisticated local and to take you to the most fashionable places in town to rub shoulders with the local glitterati.

In today's world work rules our life, weekends away are few and far between, and when we do go away we want to have the most fun and relaxation possible with the minimum of stress. This guide is all about maximizing time. Everywhere is photographed, so before you go you know exactly what you are getting into; choose a restaurant or bar that suits you and your demands.

We pride ourselves on our independence and our integrity. We eat in all the restaurants, drink in all the bars and go wild in the nightclubs – all totally incognito. We charge no one for the privilege for appearing in the guide, every place is reviewed and included at our discretion.

We feel cities are best enjoyed by soaking up the atmosphere and the vibrancy; wander the streets, indulge in some retail relaxation therapy, re-energize yourself with a massage and then get ready to eat like a king and party hard in the stylish local scene.

We feel that it is important for you to explore a city on your own terms, while the places reviewed provide definitive coverage in our eyes; one's individuality can never be wholly accounted for. Whatever you do we can assure you that you will have an unforgettable weekend.

Tallinn

When you first walk into Tallinn you'll notice something unmistakeably Disney about the town – its medieval spires glinting in the sun, the charming narrow streets and the perfectly preserved merchant's houses – all of them overlooked by the stern towers of an ancient fortified hill. The impression is reinforced by the throngs of tourists walking the streets, the handicraft shops, and the polite young students kitted up in medieval clothing who will accost you with inducements to join a Hanseatic feast in one of Tallinn's many themed restaurants.

But Tallinn is never as it first appears. While there is a thriving tourist industry in the centre, where foreign visitors are drawn like bees to honey by the bizarrely picturesque atmosphere, the city also hides many other worlds. Outside the Old Town there is a small modern metropolis – the Soviet and post-Soviet sprawl where most Estonians live and work (although many commute into tourist-land for their day jobs, along with shoppers and diners). But far from being a frozen museum-piece, the Old Town is host to some of the city's best nightlife and restaurants, shops and galleries. And there is also plenty going on outside the ancient walls, from the modern city centre – more active and vibrant with every year as business grows and new shops and services open – to the trendy port area. This was once an industrial wasteland, but today is home to some of Tallinn's choicest

nightspots. More leafy and serene, Kadriorg Park lies a few minutes' drive outside the bustle of Tallinn's centre and hides some of summertime's best jewels: a beautiful park, gorgeous museums and a forest right next to the ocean. Further along the coast and you're in Pirita, Tallinn's marina and beach.

Like its Baltic neighbour, Riga, Tallinn has garnered a reputation for legendary nightlife, full of racy clubs and beautiful, willing women. The truth is a little different, although not always far off. Rather than cater uniquely to the fantasies of drunken sex tourists, Tallinn has the beginnings of a truly sophisticated night-time scene, from its excellent restaurants and cafés to bars and nightclubs that would hold their own in London or Paris. There is a wonderfully disorganized element to the development of the city's entertainment, with themed restaurants ranging from Italian and Georgian to Russian, Indian and Thai, and inventive bars and cafés which will strike any pose to stand out from the crowd. The vast majority of these 'ethnic' businesses are owned and staffed by Estonians, proving that Tallinn has gladly embraced the role of themed town – except that no one seems sure what that theme should be. Expect waitresses costumed in medieval dress rubbing shoulders with Sikh-style doormen, and sushi bars next to Irish pubs.

Finally, it is worth remembering that this small city of 400,000 people crammed next to the Baltic Sea is long used to visitors: from the foreign armies that crossed its borders for 2,000 years to the legions of Finns that flood over every weekend from Helsinki, less than two hours away on the ferry. As a result Estonians are open-minded, curious and welcoming to guests – and tolerant of their excesses – and it's worth getting to know a few as you pass through.

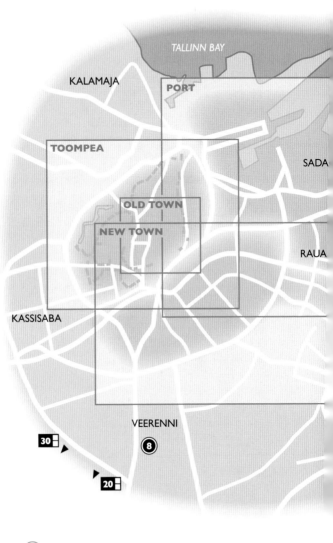

KALAMAJA

TALLINN BAY

PORT

TOOMPEA

SADA

OLD TOWN

NEW TOWN

RAUA

KASSISABA

VEERENNI

30

20

(8)

PARTY

8. Nightman

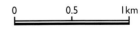

0   0.5   1 km

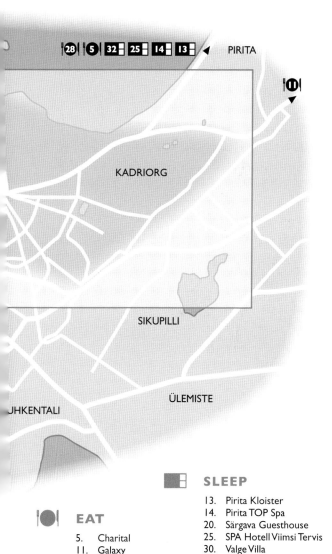

PIRITA

KADRIORG

SIKUPILLI

ÜLEMISTE

JHKENTALI

SLEEP

13. Pirita Kloister
14. Pirita TOP Spa
20. Särgava Guesthouse
25. SPA Hotell Viimsi Tervis
30. Valge Villa
32. Villa Mary

EAT

5. Charital
11. Galaxy
28. Paat

Old Town

For many visitors, Tallinn *is* the Old Town – and tourists coming for the history and the culture have little reason to wander beyond the city walls. With its perfectly preserved Hanseatic buildings and medieval Town Hall Square, old Tallinn looks almost too convincing to be true – as if it's really a theme park. With thousands of Finns and Swedes flooding through each week, tourists wander the streets at all times of day and night. In addition, every year the town attracts ever greater volumes of visitors from further afield, and although at the moment it remains largely unspoilt, this may not last. Despite the restaurants, shops, cafés and bars, and thriving modern service industry, the medieval architecture of old Tallinn is still perfectly preserved. There's something for everyone here – whether you are a romantic couple or a carousing stag group. And some excellent museums provide all the culture you could possibly want.

One of the great advantages of Old Tallinn is that it is small enough to walk around in a single day – and a lot can be fitted into one afternoon. Take in a gallery, spend an hour sipping hot chocolate in a cosy cellar, visit an artisan's workshop and walk around the living museum of the ancient buildings before you settle in for a cocktail and then dinner. Dancing is never that hard to come by in the Old Town, either, with its selection of up-market and cheesier bars, disco pubs and popular nightclubs.

Old Tallinn has not been ruined by tourism. Although much of what goes on is geared towards tourists there are real Estonians making their lives here, and this is reflected in the range of excellent establishments – from faux medieval to trendy and cutting-edge. Hotels in the Old Town tend to make the most of their medieval setting – the best and most expensive are to be found in renovated merchant's houses, with one or two slicker, more modern exceptions. Prices can be steep in high season as available accommodation gets quickly booked up and good-quality, cheaper rooms in the Old Town can be hard to come by. However, if you have the budget, this is the place to come.

The range of restaurants in the centre is superb, with everything from medieval tourist-orientated places (some of them excellent) to smart Italian and Japanese restaurants playing club-style lounge music and staffed by Prada model lookalikes. Avoid the tourist cellar restaurants on Viru; these are targeted at day-trippers from Helsinki.

Cafés come into their own in both seasons. In winter there is no lack of warm bolt-holes where you can escape the weather and enjoy well-prepared coffee and delicious hot chocolates, as well as fresh herbal teas. In summer the terrace culture emerges – and the Town Hall Square is the place to be, sitting in the sun with a cappuccino. The quality of the hot drinks is generally very good; we also recommend you try an afternoon liqueur.

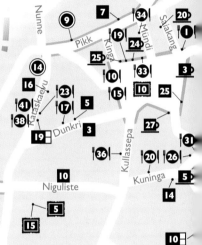

Old Town   local map

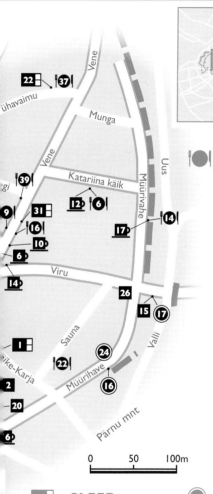

Toompea/Old Town

Looming over old Tallinn and the surrounding modern city, Toompea Hill became a feudal stronghold in the 13th century when crusading German knights arrived on a Baltic campaign. As the capital developed over time the hill became home to Tallinn's warrior classes and their servants – while the citizens of the land lived and worked underneath in what is known today as the Old Town. When medieval Tallinn began to flourish as a merchant centre the people started bargaining for greater rights: as members of the Hanseatic League (an alliance of merchant cities across Northern Europe) the citizens of the Old Town were subject after 1248 to their own set of laws and rights (the 'Lübeck Laws') freeing them from feudal obligations (and taxes). The folk on the hill were less lucky, although a slave could win his freedom by escaping Toompea and living in the town for a year and a day.

Today the ancient hill and its tiny quaint town remains, still fortified and medieval, very much as it might have looked in the 17th or 18th century – with the exception of the Alexander Nevsky Orthodox Cathedral, a controversial, onion-domed fantasy which is still considered heavily symbolic of Russian power. The parliament building stands next to it, cresting the eastern edge of the hill, and is today the modern seat of Estonia's political life.

Toompea in the 21st century, however, is largely a tourist haven – the winding walk up to the fairy-tale alleys and streets are the high point of any historical tour. And the views from the look-out points are spectacular, with the rooftops of the ancient city spread out below, the modern buildings of the town centre behind them and the Baltic port full of ferry boats beyond. Unsurprisingly, there is a reasonable concentration of little restaurants, museums and cafés – some of them excellent – although you will be surprised by how empty these streets really are. Here, real life seems to have been put on hold.

Toompea is Estonia at its most Walt Disney. Other than those who work for the parliament– which exists in its own private world – the only locals you will encounter on the hill are there to serve you (although a few Talliners may wander up at sunset to catch the view). However, it is not an area you can afford to miss – not only is the medieval settlement dramatic and beautiful but it also lies at the very centre of Estonian history – so it is worth kicking back and enjoying a picturesque meal or a cup of coffee along with the tour groups.

SLEEP

4. L'Ermitage
6. Imperial Hotel
7. Meriton Grand Hotel
8. Meriton Old Town
11. Olematu Rüütel
12. Olevi Residents
23. Skåne Hotel
26. Taanilinna
28. Three Sisters Hotel
29. Uniquestay

SHOP

Pikk, Vene and Lai Streets
Viru

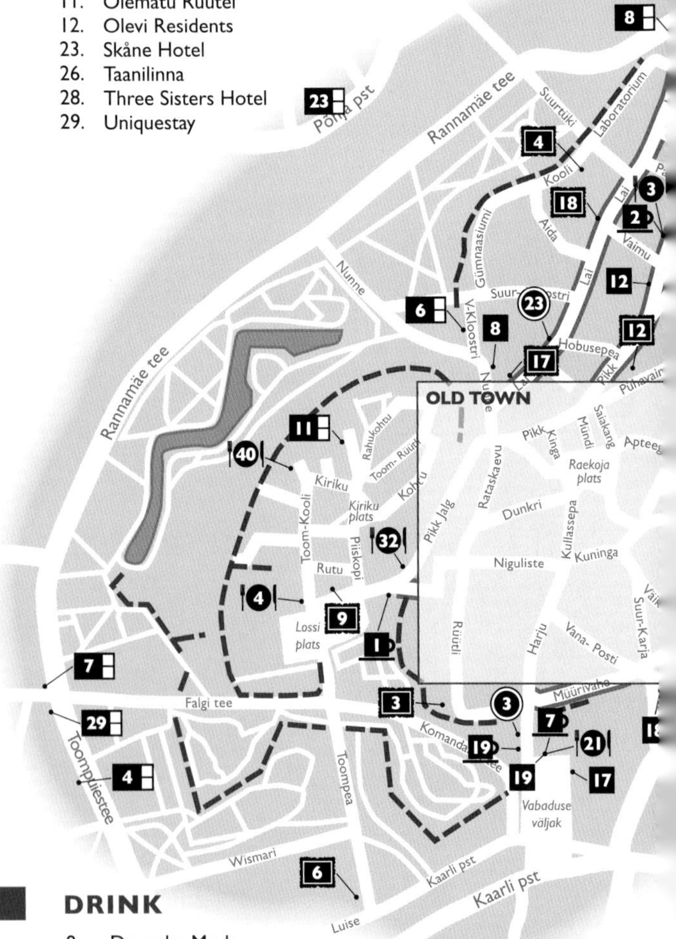

OLD TOWN

DRINK

8. Depeche Mode
12. Hell Hut
17. Kuku Klubi
18. McCools
19. Moskva
23. Popular Café

0   125   250m

🍴 EAT

2.   Bocca
3.   Le Bonaparte
4.   Cathedral
8.   Egoist
21. Moskva
32. Pika Jala
40. Toomkooli

◼ CULTURE

1.   Estonian Maritime Museum
3.   Kiek in de Kök
4.   Laboratorium, Kooli and
     Gümnaasiumi
6.   Occupation Museum
7.   St. Olav's Church
8.   Tallinn City Museum
9.   Toompea Hill
12. House of the Brotherhood
     of the Blackheads
17. Estonian Puppet Theatre
18. Town Theatre
20. Kinomaja

🍴 SNACK

1.   Boga Pott
2.   Le Bonaparte
7.   Café Moskva
18. International Press Café
19. Karoliina

⬤ PARTY

3.   Club Privé
7.   Mr Robinson
13. Venus
22. Atlantida
23. Börsi Bar

City Centre

For the tourist, the Old Town offers everything you really need from a visit to Estonia: history, nightlife, pretty buildings, men in tights. But for dedicated shoppers, business travellers or anyone looking for a bit of real-life action, you will need to stray a few hundred yards outside the city walls to the modern City Centre to understand what it is really all about. Just follow the (small) skyscrapers south-east of the Old Town to find yourself in the heart of bustling modern Tallinn, full of offices, hotels and shops. Within a square kilometre you will come across Tallinn's two largest department stores (Kaubamaja and Stockmann), the massive SAS Radisson hotel, and the rather more Soviet-looking (but equally monolithic) Reval Olümpia. Around them you can sample the growing handful of cafés and bars crammed with office workers, students and real Estonians going about their business.

Great nightlife is here in abundance, if you can be bothered to go the extra mile – although it's less compressed than in the Old Town. Try the touristy, lively bars and nightclubs of the big hotels or check out the Hotel Olümpia's funky all-night café, a pick-up joint in its own right. Closer to town on Parnu mnt near the evocatively named Vabaduse Square ('Freedom Square', now a car park), VS Café draws in locals and trendy ex-pats with its combination of Indian food and

dance music. For a real local favourite navigate your way to Hiireloks ('the mousetrap'), a seedy but warm (and hilarious) Russian karaoke bar hidden in the backstreets.

If you've had enough of drinking, Deli 24 provides all-night hot food and drink, excellent coffee and a perfect spot for people-watching. For afternoon snacks, newly opened City Gourmet heralds great things to come in the City Centre, with its luxury deli-café atmosphere, imported Italian food and stylish interior. Or go to Energia café opposite Kaubamaja for the buzz of shoppers and workers, and a slightly kitschy, Soviet-era flavour.

There is little choice in the restaurant department, although what there is, is excellent: from trendy Moskva with its air-hostess waitresses in Vabaduse Square, and Rusthaveli, a top-notch Georgian restaurant on the second floor of a block opposite the Radisson, to Eesti Maja, a characterful Estonian restaurant Tardis-like and hidden away below street level, there is little danger of starvation here.

If you want to meet real Estonians at work and play, this is the place to be.

0   250   500m

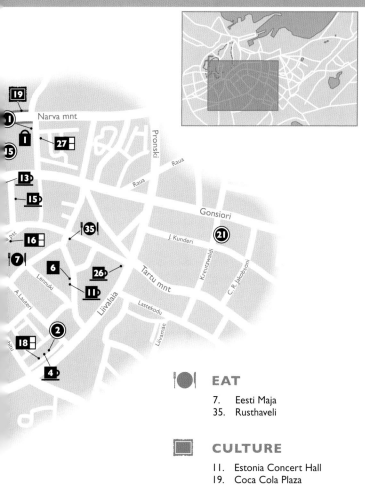

EAT
7. Eesti Maja
35. Rusthaveli

CULTURE
11. Estonia Concert Hall
19. Coca Cola Plaza

SNACK
4. Café Boulevard
8. Café Palace
11. CityGourmet
13. Deli 24
15. Energia Khovik
26. Stockmann Café

PARTY
2. Bonnie and Clyde
5. Hiirelõks
11. RIFF
15. Café Amigo
20. Casino Metropol
21. Olympic Casino

Portside, Kadriorg and Pirita

Tallinn is built right next to the Baltic Sea, so unsurprisingly the coast plays a vital role in the city's life – with a huge range of maritime history and activities compressed into the few miles near the Old Town. Just outside the city walls, the ancient seaport still operates, today as a conduit for the millions of Scandinavians (mainly Finns) who arrive here every year. Take a walk past the regenerated industrial wasteland just off Mere pst, and you will find yourself face to face with the giant white ferries that make this crossing every day – spitting day-trippers out for weekend breaks and the cheap Estonian booze.

The port brings paradoxical flavours to Tallinn: formerly an area packed with factories, it is now home to some of the city's trendiest restaurants and nightclubs, the Metropol Hotel, the London Casino and a string of popular bars. Right next to them sit a couple of dodgy hotels, a strip club and a line of shops selling cheap alcohol and catering mainly to the Finns. Estonians come to the port area for the good nightclubs (flavour of the month BonBon and student favourite, mega-club Terrarium), as well as the modish restaurants (such as the enig-matically named 'Ö') and live music (in bar Scotland Yard).

A mile or so along the shoreline you find yourself in altogether different surroundings – the summery district of Kadriorg, a residential suburb built by the Russians around an attractive, rolling park and an
Italianate palace that has now become the celebrated Foreign Art
Museum. Wood-boarded 19th-century houses give the district its special character, and on one side of the park you can watch the Baltic
waves through the trees. This is a perfect daytime get-away if the
weather is fine – and increasingly the choice of habitat for Tallinn's
more affluent young professionals. If you're staying here be aware that

there's not much in the
way of nightlife, but you
can start here at the
chichi, minimalist
Restaurant Ö and then
progress to the bar (or
restaurant) of Bally's
Casino if you really can't
be bothered to make
the 5-minute drive into

town. For those wanting accommodation in this *rus in urbis*, there are a
few boutique hotels – including Bally's Casino itself and the Villa Stahl.

If you keep driving along the coast you will eventually find yourself in
the seaside complex of Pirita: a string of spas, shops and restaurants
that caters mainly to the summer and water-sports market, but is
active all year around. You can stay at the unique, pristine Pirita
Klooster guesthouse – run by an order of nuns – or at one of the gargantuan spa-hotels that cater mainly to Scandinavians visiting for residential beauty treatments, and offer large swimming pools, massage,
saunas and excellent sports facilities. There is a marina in Pirita, a
trendy beauty/health salon (Finissage), public tennis courts and also a
couple of top restaurants to round off a day of virtue, including smart
Charital and (further on the road out to Viimsi) the Noah's Ark-shaped
Paat. All worth a try.

SLEEP

3. Domina Ilmarine
9. Metropol Hotel
15. Poska Villa
33. Villa Stahl

EAT

24. Novell
25. Ö
29. Palermo

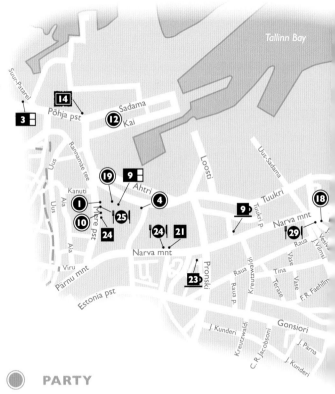

PARTY

1. BonBon
4. Decolté
10. Panoraam
12. Terrarium
18. Bally's Casino
19. Casino London

DRINK

21. Novell Bar
24. Scotland Yard

Portside, Kadriorg and Pirita   local map

SNACK

9.   Café Peterson
23.   Narva Kohvik

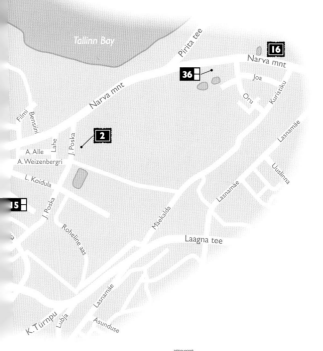

Tallinn Bay

Pirita tee

16

Narva mnt

36

Joa

Oru

Kuristiku

Narva mnt

Filmi

Bensiini

Lahe

2

Lasnamäe

A. Alle
A. Weizenbergri

J. Poska

L. Koidula

Uuslinna

15

J. Poska

Roheline aas

Maekalda

Lasnamäe

Laagna tee

K. Türnpu

Lubja

Asunduse

Lasnamäe

CULTURE

2.   Kadriorg Palace
14.   Linnahall
16.   Song Festival Grounds

sleep...

The last decade has seen explosive growth in Tallinn's hotel sector – gone are the days when only a few grand old institutions or monolithic Intourist hotels dominated the market. Today there are nearly five thousand rooms available in the city – a thousand of them created during 2004 in response to the heavy increase in demand from tourists. There is already a broad range of hotels serving visitors of every type, with new sites appearing every spring. In winter many of these businesses lie empty, but in summer it can be impossible to find a room.

At the top of the spectrum, Estonia's hoteliers have taken advantage of Tallinn's unparalleled medieval setting to create a handful of beautiful boutique hotels, which compete at the top end of the international market and do not come cheap; these include the city's only five-star hotel and a historic renovated merchant's house. The other way to enjoy the ancient city is to rent an apartment in the Old Town, available for either short or long stays from a range of providers. We mention a couple here. You will find that good quality hotels in the old part of Tallinn are more expensive than you might imagine, although prices remain reasonable – a decade of tourism from Helsinki has done its bit to level the market.

The gap in the middle market has been filled by a whole run of modern, high-quality developments just outside the Old Town – many of them opening in the last year or two. Because old Tallinn is small, nothing is very far on foot – and most of these new hotels are situated less than 5 or 10 minutes' walk from the action. Estonia's hotel decorators tend to favour the Scandinavian style, fashioning interiors in pine and neutral colours to create a simple, restrained elegance. Generally speaking, the cheaper you go, the more kitsch they come.

Estonia's wealthier Finnish visitors and business people tend to favour Tallinn's mega hotels, such as the SAS and Reval Olümpia – a little further from the Old Town. The gargantuan VIRU hotel, a Soviet rectangle that looms over the gates of the Old Town, is still a famous and popular destination for many Scandinavian tourists. For better deals you may need to look further afield in suburbs – try the pretty Kadriorg district, or dramatic Pirita on the coastal road. Most low-budget hotels have not been included in this guide.

The hotels have been rated according to their style, location and atmosphere. Style ratings take into account the furnishings and the appearance of the hotel from inside and out. Location ratings are based on how central and convenient they are for shops, restaurants and tourist attractions. Atmosphere ratings are based on the feel of the place: it might be fantastically furnished and stylish but feel like a morgue, or it might be done up like a 1970s service station motel but still manage to create a great ambience.

Prices quoted here are per room per night, and range from a double room in low season to a suite in high season. High season runs effectively from the beginning of May through to the end of September, and includes New Year, which is regarded as the top season.

Our top ten hotels in Tallinn are:

1. Three Sisters Hotel
2. St Petersbourg
3. Villa Mary
4. Taanilinna Hotel
5. SPA Hotell Viimsi Tervis
6. Schlössle
7. Baron's
8. Gloria Guesthouse
9. Old Town Maestro
10. Domina Ilmarine

Our top five hotels for style are:

1. Three Sisters Hotel
2. St Petersbourg
3. Taanilinna Hotel
4. Villa Mary
5. SPA Hotell Viimsi Tervis

Our top five hotels for atmosphere are:

1. Villa Mary
2. St Petersbourg
3. SPA Hotell Viimsi Tervis
4. Schlössle
5. Gloria Guesthouse

Our top five hotels for location are:

1. St Petersbourg
2. Three Sisters Hotel
3. Baron's
4. Meriton Old Town
5. Schlössle

Barons, Suur-Karja 7/Väike-Karja 2.
Tel: 699 97 00 www.baronshotel.ee
Rates: 2,200–4,200kr

Formerly a commercial bank, Barons joined the growing list of
luxury Tallinn hotels in 2003. It was redeveloped by an Egyptian
and English partnership to address the lack of quality boutique
hotels in the middle of the Old Town. And indeed, you could not
find a hotel closer to the centre than this one, which looks
directly onto the cobbled streets that run into Town Hall Square.
With 34 rooms decorated in elegant browns and greens,
art-deco lighting, masculine leather chairs and original pre-war
plasterwork, there is a statesman-like, period feel to this hotel
that is unique. Look out for the giant safes and vaults that function today as safe deposit boxes and a plutocratic cigar/wine cellar. There is an impressive sauna/steam room available at 450kr
per hour, and a slightly stuffy restaurant as well as a downstairs
bar. Every room has free high-speed internet access, but bring
your own computer. 'Just take a walk in the Old Town,' says the
marketing literature. 'And with every step you'll feel more and
more like a baron.'

Style 8, Atmosphere 7, Location 9/10

Domina City, Vana-Posti 11–13.
Tel: 681 39 00 www.dominahotels.com
Rates: 1,800–3,500kr

Italian chain Domina has established an elegant presence in central Tallinn with its City branch, opposite the mock-classical columns of the Hollywood nightclub and the Sõprus cinema. Housed in a handsome municipal building, this smart hotel has a young, bright feel to it, which suits its location in this most bustling corner of the Old Town – an intersection thick with shoppers, workers and partiers, where real Estonians mingle with the tourists. Behind its colonnaded façade, renovated after bomb damage sustained in the war, the entrance leads through to a large, white, split-level lobby that feels a little like a modern art gallery – full of striking paintings by contemporary Italian artists. Look over the balcony to locate the downstairs bar and restaurant, complete with baby grand for live music. There are 68 rooms decorated in simple but professional style – and each room has its own computer terminal with internet access, a real innovation in Tallinn hotels. The Domina City also offers special package deals for honeymooners, culture enthusiasts and families.

Style 8, Atmosphere 7, Location 9

Domina Ilmarine, Põhja pst. 23.
Tel: 614 09 00 www.dominahotels.com
Rates: 1,700–2,800kr

Set in a trendy location in converted industrial buildings less than 10 minutes' walk from the old town walls, this Italian venture exudes novelty and style. Resisting the temptation to play to medieval nostalgia, the minds behind the Ilmarine have created a spectacular split-level hotel. Creative, unique and a little surreal, this hotel is a lot of fun. While the warehouse-sized atrium and dining area are full of experimental shapes and striking modern art, the bedrooms feel rustic and comfortable in tasteful blues and pines. Many of the rooms are built on two levels joined by a staircase, giving them the feel of a miniature house with its own sitting room, kitchen and upstairs bedroom, joined by one enormous Alice in Wonderland window. The Deluxe Suite offers an extra bed for families with children. A tunnel is planned between the main hotel and the extension building, which is more restrained but just as comfortable. Ilmarine also rents out apartments, which can work out to be good value for larger groups.

Style 9, Atmosphere 8, Location 7

L'Ermitage, Toompuiestee 19.
Tel: 699 64 00 www.nordichotels.ee
Rates: 1,400–2,400kr

With 91 rooms on six floors, Hotel L'Ermitage joined the mid-sized, 'three-star plus' hotel market in May 2004, adding its handsome presence to the traffic-laden ring-road that circles the Old Town. With a view of historic Toompea Hill, the hotel is only 5 minutes' walk from most of Tallinn's tourist fun and a stone's throw from former Intourist hotel, the Meriton Grand. Targeted at tourists and business travellers, the hotel has a restaurant, conference room and sauna. Each room comes with its own internet access. L'Ermitage belongs to the same group as the low-price, high-quality Skåne (next to the train station). Parking is included in the price of the room, which is a bonus in crowded Tallinn.

Style 7, Atmosphere 7, Location 7/8

Gloria Guesthouse, Müürivahe 2.
Tel: 644 69 50 www.gloria.ee
Rates: 1,250–2,500kr

This imperial little guesthouse does not advertise, but instead depends on word of mouth to introduce customers to its tiny, beautifully located rooms, discreetly tucked away on the first

floor of an old building constructed in the city wall. Gloria is part of the same up-market business as the famous Gloria restaurant downstairs, together with wine cellar and *tabacaleria* – a tiny luxury complex favoured by wealthy ex-pats, racy Russians and Estonian bankers. The six bedrooms have only been available since 2000 – although you wouldn't guess it from their old-fashioned appearance, which ranges from chic to chintzy, with a slight hodge-podge of styles. Despite the exclusive feeling, prices are not too outrageous, but the rooms are small. Guests share a reception with the restaurant, which can be fun, but come and go via their own private stairway.

Style 7, Atmosphere 8, Location 8/9

Imperial Hotel, Nunne 14.
Tel: 627 48 00 www.imperial.ee
Rates: 2,400–5,000kr

Located in one of the most charismatic corners of old Tallinn underneath vertiginous Toompea Hill, the Imperial comes from the same stable that brings you up-market sisters Schlössle and St Petersbourg. The old city wall runs right through this small hotel, opened in May 2003, and the designers have done their best to incorporate it into a modern four-star service – although the mix of old stone and new brick may leave you with a slightly sterile impression. With large rooms at a reasonable price and a luxurious basement sauna (complete with leather chairs and

minibar) this is a great location for visitors who want to be in the centre of the action without breaking the bank. The hotel also grants guests use of its elegant and atmospheric pub and a café offering tempting cakes and pastries.

Style 7, Atmosphere 6, Location 9

Meriton Grand Hotel Tallinn, Toompuistee 27.
Tel: 667 70 00 www.meriton.ee
Rates: 2,400–6,150kr

Despite its unglamorous location at the crossroads of a busy traffic junction, this venerable, former Soviet Intourist hotel is in fact right next to the Old Town – just a 5-minute walk from Toompea Hill and the Nevsky cathedral. For a building of this size (370 rooms), you couldn't get much closer to the action than this. Renovated and re-launched in 1998 by Swiss–Estonian entrepreneur Alexander Kofkin, the Meriton is a staple choice for business visitors and large tourist groups. The foyer and rooms are decorated to a mid-range smartness that falls just short of elegant but is perfectly adequate unless you are seeking a more romantic environment. There are some charming features, too – art deco lighting in the lobby, glass elevators that run up and down the outside of the building, and good views of the Old Town from the fifth-storey 'Eiffel bar': a popular choice for cocktails or private parties. Facilities are good – there is an

ATM in the lobby, a celebrated café/bakery and even a 24-hour slot machine casino with an all-night bar. The hotel's lobby is a favourite meeting-place for lawyers, professionals and army officers, as well as MPs from the nearby parliament building.

Style 6, Atmosphere 4, Location 7/8

Meriton Old Town, 49 Lai Street.
Tel: 667 70 07 www.meriton.ee
Rates: 900kr

A brand new hotel built on the site of one of Tallinn's historic towers and an ancient horse mill, facing the Baltic from the northern ramparts of the Old Town. This canary-yellow building looks like the façade of a super-rich merchant's house. Inside, however, the entrepreneur behind Tallinn's Meriton Grand, Alexander Kofkin, has gone for an affordable offering – two- to three-star quality at decent prices in an excellent location.

Rooms are simple but neat, with exposed stone in some creating a lived-in feel. With one floor for non-smokers, three rooms for guests suffering from allergies and one for the disabled, the Meriton is going for a demanding, cost-conscious market.

Style 6, Atmosphere 8, Location 8

Mihkli, Endla 23.

Tel: 666 48 00 www.mihkli.ee
Rates: 700–1,600kr

An attractive, mint-green, neo-classical building on a busy road about 10 minutes from the Old Town, the Mihkli has recently graduated to three-star status, in recognition of 11 years of reasonably priced, good-quality service. The hotel has made a virtue of its less convenient location, drawing a more cost-conscious clientele still sensitive to quality. Rooms are elegant and simple, decorated in basic colours with wood-tiled floors. Guests enjoy 24-hour free internet access downstairs and can treat themselves to a morning sauna which is included in the price of the room (unusual in Tallinn hotels). Owned by two Estonians and three Russians, Mihkli attracts mainly tourists. The restaurant offers live music events to keep things buzzing. Look out for the funky warped-glass windows at the end of each corridor.

Style 7, Atmosphere 7, Location 6

Old Town Maestro, Suur-Karja 10.

Tel: 626 20 00 www.maestrohotel.ee
Rates: 1,600–3,500kr

Named the Maestro for the artistic clientele it aims to attract, this gem of a hotel is hidden between two bars on Suur Karja,

Tallinn's most popular drinking street – a strip that rings with merry-making until the early hours. The noise does not affect the Maestro, however, six floors high and facing into an inner court-yard. Opened in 2002 by a Russian entrepreneur, it has 23 rooms

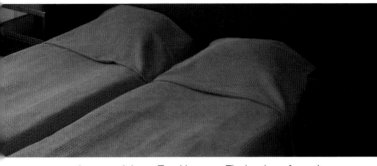

that are stylish to a T and large too. The hotel was formerly an old town residence, which gives the modern conversion a bit of grandeur. However, unlike many conversions, the place is equipped with a lift and has a thoroughly modern feel. The sixth floor houses the sauna/jacuzzi room, offering an unparalleled view of parliament and the onion domes of Nevsky church. It's the only sauna in Tallinn with an internal window.

Style 8, Atmosphere 7, Location 8/9

Olematu Rüütel, Kiriku Põik 4a.
Tel: 631 38 27 www.hot.ee/olematuryytel
Rates: 550–800kr

A rather grungy but well-located guesthouse in the very heart of historic Tallinn, Olematu Rüütel ('the Non-existent Knight') dou-bles as a restaurant and conference centre as well as a tiny hotel in a backstreet of atmospheric Toompea Hill – the preserve of the knightly classes who held sway over the city for hundreds of years. With only three rooms, this miniature boarding-house is unlikely to attract the large tourist gangs that roam through old Tallinn, leaving it free for couples or small groups looking to stay close to the centre. Bedrooms are clean and simple but definitely aimed at the budget market (two of the rooms have a common shower and lavatory off the hall). Despite this, it can quickly fill up, so be sure to reserve in advance.

Style 5, Atmosphere 7, Location 9

● **Olevi Residents, Olevimägi 4.**
Tel: 627 76 50 www.olevi.ee
Rates: 1,600–3,500kr

Almost hidden in a corner of the street, this bijou little hotel sits plumb in the middle of the Old Town. In the 18th century it was a women's prison, and the rooms still retain a slightly claustrophobic feel – one of them even boasts a set of original window bars set into the plasterwork. But the gloomy spirit is dispelled once you reach the higher rooms, which enjoy an unparalleled

view of town and sea. Mid-level rooms offer bright, mid-range luxury, while downstairs you can take the dungeon room with its own sauna. Eat breakfast or dinner in the charismatic restaurant under a gurning boar's head. The slightly chintzy feel (said to be typical of Russian establishments) is made up for by the peace and quiet of the corner setting and the thick walls. Extremely friendly staff will make your stay a pleasure, regardless of what you may think of the décor.

Style 6, Atmosphere 7, Location 9

Pirita Klooster, Merivälja tee 18.
Tel: 605 50 00 www.osss.ee
Rates: 900–1,100kr

Luckily for them, non-Christians are allowed to stay in this stylish guesthouse run by the Order of St Bridget – although card-carrying hedonists might be rather unnerved by the spotless white interiors, the crucifixes in every room and the giant chapel next to the foyer, which holds a service every morning at 7.30am. Pirita Klooster (literally, 'cloisters') is located next to the ancient ruined monastery of St Bridget, razed to the ground by Ivan the Terrible in 1577. Striking out on its own, the modern convent is shamelessly state-of-the-art, with cool spot lighting, slick elevators and minimalist Scandinavian décor. Run by nine nuns of the Order who come from all over the world (India, Mexico, Italy and Estonia at last count), it has a very special atmosphere for

those seeking real peace and quiet – but luckily there are no restrictive house rules, and guests can come and go as they please. In the summer it tends to be full, since it is walking-distance from Pirita beach, but it's pretty quiet in winter.

> **Style 8, Atmosphere 8, Location 6/7**

Pirita TOP Spa, Regati pst. 1.
Tel: 639 88 22 www.topspa.ee
Rates: 1,090–2,490kr

Inside a monstrous concrete structure that might have been built in the 1970s to welcome an alien landing, the Pirita TOP Spa is really a summer place – situated next to Pirita beach, Tallinn's summer hang-out 15 minutes' drive from the centre of town. Once inside the flaking, gargantuan exterior the foyer is reassur-ingly clean and warm, with the look (and smell) of a vast sports centre, complete with gym and swimming pool. The Top SPA is essentially a residential health and fitness centre, frequented by sports teams and ageing Finns alike, who come here for the amazing range of health treatments, therapies and massage as well as the great facilities and summery location. Sauna and pool are included in the price of the room, while use of the gym comes at a 50% discount for guests. Rooms are simple, modern and fresh, with fantastic views of the sea – although you are still 1km walk from the action at the beach. And it has possibly the

longest corridors of any building you will ever see.

Style 6, Atmosphere 6, Location 6

Poska Villa, Poska 15.
Tel: 601 36 01 www.hot.ee/poskavilla
Rates: 760–980kr

Located in the pretty 19th-century Kadriorg district 10 minutes'
drive from the Old Town, Poska Villa is an intimate hotel guesthouse with nine rooms, built next to a social club for the elderly
(which owns the hotel, giving it a pleasant family feel). Like its
surrounding buildings, Poska is a lovely century-old clapperboard
house renovated in the 1990s to provide clean and modern
accommodation. With the air of a budget ski lodge, Poska's
rooms are small and simple, with pine furniture and pleasant
views, although the décor is slightly tacky. It has regular guests
from all over the planet, tending to attract visiting academics and
professionals who come for longer periods than most tourists
and therefore seek a cheaper, more homely option. It is also perfectly located for the beautiful Kadriorg Park and museums.
Guests share a fridge (stocked with water and beer) on the
landing.

Style 6, Atmosphere 8, Location 6/7

Radisson SAS, Rävala pst. 3.
Tel: 682 30 00 www.radissonsas.com
Rates: 2,112–15,992kr

While the Radisson's skyscraper exterior might call to mind a
soulless business mecca, don't let appearances fool you. The
moment you step inside this international chain hotel, you feel
the scope of its 21st-century luxury. The service, the lobby and
the rooms manage to be intimate on a grand scale – at 24
storeys this custom-made building is still the highest in Tallinn
(although new developments are rising all around in this central
shopping and office district just 10 minutes' walk from the Old
Town). Still fresh from their design in 2001, there are 280 rooms
decorated in four different styles: Italian, Oriental, Maritime and
Nordic, and each comes equipped with its own 'power tower'
(complete with TV, radio, trouser press, kettle, etc.). Find Lounge
24 for the best views in Estonia – this conference room is available for hire most of the year but becomes a summer café
between June and August.

Style 9, Atmosphere 7, Location 7

RED Group, Valli 4.
Tel: 620 78 77 www.redgroup.ee
Rates: 700–1,920kr

RED Group provides apartments for long stay or short rent – so they can be used as an alternative to hotels for those who are travelling in larger groups or simply want a little more privacy. Most of RED's flats are converted spaces in old town houses in central locations and atmospheric surroundings, with slick

Scandinavian interiors and plenty of light (although some of their attic properties are a little darker). All include the necessary amenities, such as televisions and basic cooking facilities. Prices are of course better if you stay longer, but single night visits are possible depending on availability. Call to meet a guide who will show you a selection of places and will be happy to help you with car rental, bookings and other activities.

Style 8, Atmosphere 7, Location 8/9

Reval Hotel Olümpia, Liivalaia 33.
Tel: 630 53 33 www.revalhotels.com
Rates: 1,950–3,800kr

This vast four-star flagship of the Reval group, which started life in 1997 before expanding to become the Baltic's major hotel chain, feels something like an airport terminal on first arrival. Not surprising when you consider the range of services on offer: the hotel has its own florist and all-night café as well as health club, medical centre, swimming pool and bar – downstairs you can even find an English pub and a nightclub. With a lobby redesigned in 2003 in fashionable black and browns, the reception feels modern and luxurious. Upstairs many of the 390 rooms are older and more basic, with simple, functional décor. With fewer business customers than most, the Olümpia has become a tourist haven, although it is a walk to old Tallinn. Compensate for your location with a spectacular group jacuzzi and sauna on the 26th floor offering an incredible view of the city – it's available for group hire and ideal for small parties.

Style 7, Atmosphere 6, Location 6

St Petersbourg, Rataskaevu 7.
Tel: 628 65 00 www.schlossle-hotels.com
Rates: 1,950–7,450kr

Unlike many of its competitors in the Tallinn luxury hotel business the St Petersbourg can lay claim to real pedigree – it has been a hotel for 150 years, making it the oldest in the city. It wears its Russian roots with pride – it was built in the 15th century by a Russian merchant, and was home to the first Bolshevik ambassador in 1921. Today it is owned by American real-estate developer Paul Oberschneider, who four years ago added the Schlössle to his portfolio. After the comfortable luxury of the lobby (small enough to feel intimate, unlike many of the larger hotels), the quality of the rooms is outstanding and the interiors well designed. There are also some unique touches – every bathroom has its own rubber duck and telephone – and there are

rooms equipped for guests with disabilities or suffering from allergies. All the rooms are equipped with fast internet access.

Style 9, Atmosphere 9, Location 9/10

Särgava Guest House, Säragava allee 4.
Tel: 605 61 05 residents01@hot.ee
Rates: 950–1,950kr

This grand residence in the middle of stately grounds was originally built as a summer home but has been used as a guesthouse by the Tallinn city government since 1961. Today the mayor still uses it to house official guests, from top-ranking NATO officers to the Dalai Lama – and companies hire it out for weekend seminars – but Särgava is still (sometimes) available for private hire.

Although they prefer not to advertise (and are even trying to cut down visitor numbers) it is possible to stay in one of the house's six grand rooms or its suite – provided you book far enough in advance. Särgava guesthouse is located in the middle of a suburb some way out of the city centre, accessible by bus or taxi, but greets you with an imposing, municipal splendour protected by electric gates, guard dog and the stately blue and white flag of the Tallinn city government. Inside the rooms are large, simple and old-fashioned, decorated in classic, Soviet-mansion style.

Style 7, Atmosphere 7, Location 6

Scandic Hotel Palace, Vabaduse väljak 3.
Tel: 640 72 62 www.scandic-hotels.com
Rates: 2,400–3,900kr

The Palace Hotel has been a fixture of Estonian hospitality since 1936, when it was the first hotel in Tallinn with warm water and lifts, but only the wooden staircase and the façade remain from the original building. Reconstructed in the 1990s and owned today by the Hilton-Scandic group, it still commands one of the most impressive and accessible corners of Tallinn, overlooking the southernmost tip of the Old Town from its vast rooms and its plate-glass foyer. Although it is modern, the Palace still retains some of its Soviet era, 1970s allure – the huge lobby buzzes with customers at the front desk and the low-seated bar, and the

doors and elevators are made of dark, solid wood. With 91 rooms, the hotel is large enough for social or business gatherings. An entire wall has been dedicated to photos of eminent guests – mainly East European premiers. But, when we visited, Deep Purple were checking out.

Style 7, Atmosphere 8, Location 8

Schlössle, Pühavaimu 13–15.
Tel: 628 65 00 www.schlossle-hotels.com
Rates: 2,500–6,450kr

The current reigning aristocrat of the Tallinn hotel world, Schlössle was until this year the only five-star hotel in town. For lack of competition this well-run hotel has picked up the cream of the visiting public – from touring rock stars such as Duran Duran and Deep Purple, to royalty, statesmen and VIPs, including Prince Charles, Gerard Schroder and George Soros. Despite opening as recently as 1998, Schlössle is relatively venerable in Estonian terms – and is therefore a safe bet for anyone looking for certified quality and service in a great location. Now competing with newer, slicker operations aiming for the same quality market, its traditional charms can seem a little stodgy. But with its emphasis on standards Schlössle can always be sure of a loyal customer base. Behind the main building there is a separate lodge housing some medieval rooms particularly popular with Americans. Note the green-faced oil painting in reception.

Skåne Hotell, Kopli 2c.
Tel: 667 83 00 www.nordichotels.ee
Rates: 800–1,000kr

Open since summer 2003, Skåne is located in the bustling and
characterful environs of the train station – offering plenty of 'real
Tallinn' charm but also a princely view of the Parliament building
on Toompea Hill. Named after the nearby Skåne bastion (an
ancient Swedish fortification that has long since disappeared),
this new two-star enterprise has set up its quality, low-cost
operation in an area previously ignored by developers – although
less than 10 minutes' walk from the Old Town's best sights.
Formerly a Soviet railway hotel, Skåne traces its origins back to
the 1920s, evident still in the carved wood panelling on the stair
rails. Elsewhere the hotel's interior has been completely renovated – with tasteful, wood-floored rooms in a simple, Scandinavian
style – making it better value than many more expensive places.
In return for the low price there is a no-frills approach – no elevators, internet, or sauna. All 38 rooms differ in size and shape –
go for one of the attic rooms if they're available, with their
charming low ceilings and skylights.

Sokos Hotel Viru, Viru Väljak 4.
Tel: 630 13 90 www.viru.ee
Rates: 1,757–4,381kr

Once a legendary Intourist business, this landmark hotel is now part of a Finnish chain, which is appropriate, given that the majority of its customers have traditionally been Finns. Housed inside a giant 1970s block, the Viru was once a famous symbol of contact between the USSR and the West – with many a shady deal said to have been done in the hotel lobby. Today it remains the largest hotel in the Baltics – with more than 500 rooms, 93 of them added in 2004 – and a huge new shopping centre. It's

still considered the classy place of choice by Finnish visitors, who arrive in their droves for the sightseeing and the cheap booze, although you may feel as if you are lost in a creaking retro space station. This impression is fast changing, however, as the owners gradually redevelop the hotel and bring it up to date. The rooms are a surprise – comfortable and tastefully decorated, with parquet floors and framed prints. Take a tour upstairs for some of the best views of Tallinn and a peek inside the former KGB surveillance room – not always open to the public!

Style 8, Atmosphere 8, Location 7

SPA Hotell Viimsi Tervis, Randvere tee 11.
Tel: 606 10 00 www.viimsitervis.ee
Rates: 990–2,290kr

Opened in 2002, the spanking new Tervis spa in Viimsi is a 20-minute drive out of Tallinn but continues the tradition of mega-health centres built along the coast. With fewer rooms and more health and beauty facilities than its main competitor, TOP Spa in Pirita, the Viimsi spa is aimed at the same basic market – visiting Finns crossing the Baltic for the excellent value world-class therapies, massage and even plastic surgery. Guests usually book into the spa for week or half-week treatment holidays – but the hotel is open to anyone wishing to take advantage of the low tariffs and the great facilities. Like the super-modern, modish lobby rooms are decorated in fail-safe Scandinavian style. Guests have free use of the 25-metre swimming pool and gym, as well as sauna and steam room. Downstairs in the lobby you can find most things you need this far from town – including a restaurant and pharmacy – giving Spa Viimsi the air of a health and beauty cruise ship. Packages include full board, medical consultations and treatments, and start from as little as 480kr (excluding the cost of a room). Make sure to book in advance during peak season (March–April, Oct–Nov – the bleakest months).

Style 9, Atmosphere 9/10, Location 6/7

● **Taanilinna Hotel, Uus 6.**
Tel: 640 67 00 www.taanilinna.ee
Rates: 1,500–2,400kr

This tasteful little hotel spent two years as a three-star until its unusual quality was recognized in January 2004 and its accreditation was raised. Housed inside a modest building tucked just inside the old town walls, the Taanilinna has 20 perfectly decorated rooms with dark wood floors and gorgeous beds. Owned by a Russian couple who defy traditional Estonian prejudices about

Russian 'taste', the hotel was built inside a renovated army building bought in 2002. It is inviting from the moment you arrive in the lobby, where designer Evar Riitsaar has painted the wooden beams of the ceiling and the floor of the pretty restaurant with simple Renaissance arabesques. With its warm yellow windows, aquamarine bathrooms and fast internet access the Taanilinna strikes the perfect balance between old-fashioned comfort and modernity… not too trendy, not too slow. You'll have a comfortable and stylish stay.

Style 9, Atmosphere 8, Location 8

Tallinn K, Laikmaa 5.
Tel: 630 08 00 www.tallinnk.com
Rates: 2,050–3,900kr

A brand new four-star just 5 minutes' walk from the Old Town, the Tallinn K looks set to carve itself an easy place among the city's other mega-hotels. With its striking metal facade the Tallinn K stands directly opposite the new Viru shopping centre, both of them part of the new generation of Tallinn services opened in

2004. The foyerr and the rooms are beautifully designed in the expensive, minimalist style so loved by modern Estonians. And while this look might seem bland to some, considerable attention has gone into the materials and the aesthetics, lending intimacy and style to a hotel that, with its 10 storeys, 298 rooms and endless corridors, could otherwise feel sterile. Services are good – with an hourly sauna, nightclub, travel agency, restaurants and classy lobby bar as well as the obligatory business centre.

Style 8, Atmosphere 6, Location 7

Three Sisters Hotel, Pikk 71/Tolli 2.
Tel: 630 63 00 www.threesistershotel.com
Rates: 3,880–9,234kr

Built inside a picturesque Old Town merchant residence, the Three Sisters are in fact three medieval houses built in a row, standing side by side next to St Olaf's church – in the 16th century the tallest man-made structure in Europe. Dating back to 1362, the Sisters are some of the most striking and well-preserved buildings of the Old Town, although their current incarnation is very new – this luxury hotel only opened late in 2003. Already counted among Tallinn's top boutique hotels, it has a stunning interior that combines historic elements (18th-century stencilling) with minimalist standards – note the hyper-chic black-themed library. For unashamed plutocrats the Piano Suite, com-

plete with grand piano and vast reception room, would be suitable for entertaining heads of state, rock stars – or possibly you. Owner Tarmo Sumberg knows all about grandees: in a previous career he worked for the Estonian prime minister as well as hotel group Reval. Breakfast runs all the way through to 6pm.

Style 9/10, Atmosphere 9, Location 9/10

Uniquestay, Paldiski mnt. 3.
Tel: 660 07 00 www.uniquestay.com
Rates: 1,300–1,400kr

Open since 2003, the Uniquestay hotel has come to the Tallinn market with an ambitious vision – to provide four-star quality at three-star prices, a target it achieves by offering friendly service and atmosphere with slick, clean design. From the same school of branding as easyJet (good standardized quality, lower-case logos, bright colours), it has a distinctly youthful, dot-com feel. Each room in this 58-room hotel is alike and interchangeable – and priced on a flat fee for single or double – although bathroom tiles come in different colours from room to room. The most striking thing about the hotel, other than the sparse, Nordic décor and the IKEA atmosphere, is the space-age, floor-lit corridors, which add some real atmosphere. Perhaps the biggest selling-point for most young travellers is the fact that each room has its own computer terminal with free unlimited internet access – a feature we found in only one other Tallinn hotel. The British-owned Uniquestay is located right next to the Meriton Grand Hotel, and since 2004 is based in two buildings across the road from each other, one a former sauna, the other a German nobleman's residence. Five minutes from the Old Town.

Style 7, Atmosphere 8, Location 7

Valge Villa, Kännu 26.
Tel: 651 74 50 www.white-villa.com
Rates: 700–1,400kr

Valge Villa ('The White Villa') is a large family house converted into a hotel 10 years ago by an enterprising couple in the Kristiine suburb, 3km from central Tallinn. Despite the distance, guests continue to be attracted by Valge Villa's homely atmosphere, cheap prices and friendly service. Enter the guesthouse through a large living/dining room next to the kitchen and you feel as if you are visiting old family friends – although the neon strip lighting in the dining room is reminiscent of a youth hostel. Ten double rooms (including four suites) are decorated in rural style, complete with sofa and desk in each to add to the homestay feel. Room price includes fast internet access as well as breakfast, while the nicest suites look like luxury, ski-lodge apartments. The hotel's finest feature is a set of beautiful ceramic fireplaces hand-made in Pärnu. Ask for the room with the view of the Old Town.

> Style 7, Atmosphere 8, Location 5

Villa Hortensia, Vene 6.
Tel: 504 61 13 www.jpgoldart.ee/masterseng.htm
Rates: 800–1,200kr

Jewellery designer Jaan Pärn runs the Villa Hortensia as a non-profit-making guesthouse in the Master's Courtyard, a ram-shackle 13th-century courtyard only 50 metres from Town Hall Square. Famous past residents of the yard's dwellings include *burgermeisters* and mayors, goldsmiths, barons and fellows of the Blackhead guild. Today it stands in need of renovation and is being redeveloped as a home for artisan workshops – as well as a much-loved café, and now Villa Hortensia, a guesthouse with four rooms. These basic but comfortable lodgings are offered

first to visiting craftsmen as well as elderly or handicapped visitors but are otherwise available to tourists. The rooms are simple and built on two levels, with a bathroom and kitchen downstairs and beds upstairs underneath attic windows.

Style 7, Atmosphere 7, Location 9

Villa Mary, Viimsi, Rohuneeme tee 103.
Tel: 667 70 00 www.grandhotel.ee/villa
Rates: 4,500–9,000kr

Built by the owner of the Meriton Grand Hotel as his private seaside retreat, Villa Mary looks and feels like the home of a millionaire Dr No. The hotelier Alexander Kofkin spends part of the year here next to the windy ocean in Viimsi, but also makes the house available for hire by private groups – accommodating up to 12 people in five rooms and one apartment. With a spectacular view of the sea – less than 20 metres away at the foot of the garden – Villa Mary combines rugged, windswept charm with unimpeachable luxury. A large salon and balcony look out over prospects of distant Tallinn through a vast window, while dining room and upstairs club room (complete with giant television) make this the perfect setting for a group event or high-budget stag –although the drive from town takes 20–30 minutes. Mr K's private art collection is housed inside the villa, giving it the feel of a slightly madcap gallery, with paintings and sculpture of all varieties. Each room has a different theme – there's even a

special 'white' room for bridal couples, with a four-poster bed. There is a sauna and Japanese grill in the garden, although most catering is done in the Meriton hotel and driven over.

Style 9, Atmosphere 9/10, Location 7

Villa Stahl, Narva mnt. 112.
Tel: 603 17 30
Rates: 990–1,290kr

'The setting sun can cast strange shadows', say the staff at Villa Stahl, built as a private house in the 1930s but later used by the Red Army and the Wermacht as a headquarters. With its view of the Baltic Sea and Tallinn's Kadriorg Park on either side of the house, this romantic claim may well be true. A 10-minute drive from town on a busy coastal road, the reconverted Villa sits right between the two, although suburban-looking houses and heavy traffic also play their part in the vista. Eight large, elegantly decorated rooms are named after different cities of Europe, and there's a beautiful attic apartment with windows on three sides, a private sauna and a central fireplace. This small hotel is a good spot for summer visits – close to the lovely park with its museum and walks, and the beach in Pirita.

Style 8, Atmosphere 7, Location 7

59

eat...

The Tallinn restaurant scene as we know it today – with its wide variety of ethnic and local cuisines – has existed only for a few years. There have always been fine restaurants in Tallinn, from hotel dining rooms to smart old establishments dating back to the First Republic, but they were available only to the few. Since the end of the Soviet period there has been a flowering of business as Estonians have shown themselves to be uniquely skilled at one special art: mimicking the food and presentation of foreign cuisines in order to create successful enterprises. To prove this point, spend some time sampling the non-Estonian food in the city: you will find almost everything, from Greek, Russian and Caucasian to Japanese, Thai and Italian. You can even feast on Birmingham-standard Indian curries, not to mention French classics, and 'international' food is also much in evidence.

If you are looking for good Estonian food you can find it, although not on every street corner. Like much Eastern European cuisine, local food is rural, heavy and rather meat-oriented, although fish from the Baltic features strongly as well. Traditional dishes include eel, boiled pork, tongue (popularly known as 'gossip's fate') and black pudding. The national pudding is called 'kama' – a tasty dessert/drink made from sour milk, blended grains and peas. There are several up-market restaurants turning out this cuisine for locals and visitors alike, and some are excellent – Maiasmokk, Kuldse Notsu Kõrts, Vanaema Juures and Eesti Maja among them. In fact the really touristy businesses tend to play more to Tallinn's medieval history, exploiting its status as one of Europe's best-preserved Hanseatic cities to create an 'olde' fantasy. The best of these, including Olde Hansa and Peppersack, are well worth a visit, providing hearty and interesting food in an enjoyable environment.

The rest of the tourist fare is more grungy. A market has evolved that targets weekenders and day-trippers over from Scandinavia on the ferry, providing grill-houses, cellar-diners and cheap local restaurants, as well as the usual Tex-Mex offerings. Most of these are concentrated around Viru Street and the fringes of

Town Hall Square. Avoid them if you can.

But for the best dining experience you will be looking to international cuisine – this is where the most innovative food entrepreneurs have focused their attention. Restaurants fall into one of two categories: trendy, minimalist places that would look perfectly at home in New York or Berlin, with high standards of cuisine and lounge club music; and formal, French-influenced dining rooms. Of the former variety, the hippest restaurants in town currently include Italian (Bocca, Controvento), Japanese (Sushi House) and international cuisine (Ö), attracting the local smart set, fashion-conscious ex-pats and business people. With a similar but perhaps older market in mind, Tallinn's more formal restaurants continue to hold considerable sway, far above the sights (although not the budgets) of most tourists. Some of the most famous include Gloria, Egoist, Charital, Stenhaus and Karl Friedrich, as well as classic Russian restaurant Nevskij.

There are a couple of things you should know in advance about Estonian restaurants: they all play music, often rather loudly – and the quality of this music can vary greatly, with even the best restaurants sometimes spoiled by cheesy *musak*. A few restaurants (including Klafira) play live, ethnic music – which can be a pleasant experience. Also, restaurants will not usually offer specials or *plats du jour* – so don't be surprised if you see the same items appearing day in, day out, even in the best places.

The restaurants are all rated according to food, service and atmosphere, and prices given are for three courses for one and half a bottle of wine.

Our top ten restaurants in Tallinn are:
1. Controvento
2. Egoist
3. Stenhus
4. Nevskij
5. Pegasus
6. Gloria
7. Olde Hansa
8. Ö
9. Bocca
10. Vanaema Juures

Our top five restaurants for food are:
1. Ö
2. Charital
3. Maikrahv
4. Stenhus
5. Maiasmokk

Our top five restaurants for service are:
1. Egoist
2. Controvento
3. Pegasus
4. Tanduur
5. Must Lammas

Our top five restaurants for atmosphere are:
1. Controvento
2. Egoist
3. Olde Hansa
4. Nevskij
5. Stenhus

Balthasar, Raekoja plats 11.
Tel: 627 64 00 www.restaurant.ee
Open: noon–midnight daily   700kr

An imperious doorman stands to attention in the lobby of this famous garlic restaurant to welcome you and lead you upstairs – although you may get the feeling that perhaps you are being checked for suitability. This fine-looking venue is built inside a Hanseatic grandee's house above Europe's oldest pharmacy, open for business since 1422. Established five years ago by Estonian partners who also run classy Karl Friedrich across the square as well as a range of up-market restaurants, Balthasar creates an atmosphere all of its own, with soft classical music, oil paintings and attentive service, as well as healthy prices and plenty of businessmen on expense accounts. The garlic element is not traditional but rather an inspired novelty to attract customers. Dishes are drenched in the stuff, with marinated meats making up a large part of the menu – beautifully presented but not always as flavoursome as you might expect. Garlic beer and garlic desserts are also available.

Food 6, Service 7, Atmosphere 9

Bocca, Olevimägi 9.
Tel: 641 26 10 www.bocca.ee
Open: noon–midnight daily   665kr

Two planet-sized light shades made of brown crêpe chiffon signature the whitewashed vaulting of this post-modern cathedral to Italian food. One of the mellowest places in town for a relaxed lunch or a schmoozy dinner, Bocca was started in fact not by Italians but by a couple of Tallinn locals, who also own trendy restaurant Ö and hip nightclub BonBon. Don't come here if you are looking for the traditional Italian experience – instead Bocca is the sort of fashionable yet stylish eatery you might find in downtown Milan, or London, or any modern capital. When it comes to tips for top joints, Bocca is the word on everyone's lips – and deservedly so – for its good looks, polite service and classic Italian fare with a dash of international colour. There is definitely a yuppie element to the clientele, with elegant and successful 30- and 40-somethings at tables alongside corporate groups. Bocca plays piped music of the ambient nightclub variety – the staple requirement for a 'modern' atmosphere in Estonia. Even the loos are stylish, with impressive granite flat-sinks.

Food 8, Service 8, Atmosphere 8

● **Le Bonaparte, Pikk 45.**
Tel: 646 44 44 bonaparte@bonaparte.ee
Open: noon–3pm, 7pm–midnight. Closed Sunday.   930kr

Housed inside a 13th-century building refurbished to its 17th-century incarnation as a merchant's residence, Le Bonaparte is one of the most convincing of the Estonian-owned French restaurants. Unlike most foreign-inspired establishments in Tallinn, Le Bonaparte originally had a real French chef, although the kitchen is now run by an Estonian, head chef Artur Ovchinnikov. Enter the restaurant via a large, medieval gallery which has been put to use as a cosy, luxurious café hidden from the tourist-ridden streets outside and a favourite haunt of locals. The restaurant itself sits in a spacious, wood-beamed nobleman's dining room, decorated in rustic, Renaissance style – resplendent with pewter tableware and crisp linen. Le Bonaparte's menu promises 'an entire culinary philosophy' – and like the French, Ovchinnikov takes his food very seriously, offering gorgeous feasts of classical French cuisine combined with some trendy, high-end experimentation ('Prawns flamed with Pernod', 'Cranberry coulis with Vodka'). Owner-manager Kadri Kroon is a trained sommelier, so the wine list is well placed to complement the food. Characterful, atmospheric and, unsurprisingly, rather expensive.

Food 8, Service 7, Atmosphere 8

Cathedral, Lossiplats 2/Toom-Kooli 1.
Tel: 644 35 48 www.cathedral.ee
Open: noon–11pm (6pm Sunday) daily   530kr

As the name suggests, Cathedral restaurant stands right next to the mind-boggling, politically sensitive Alexander Nevsky

65

cathedral – seat of Russian Orthodoxy in Estonia since 1900 and symbol of their mighty neighbour's domination for over a hundred years. On its other side sits the parliament building, home to modern Estonian politics, cresting the top of Toompea Hill. All things considered, you couldn't choose a better place to get a sense of history happening in front of your eyes – and the convergence of old and new Tallinn in a setting of medieval grandeur. Perhaps in homage to its location in the shadows of the cathedral, the restaurant offers a variety of splendid-sounding Russian as well as French dishes. Frog's legs and *magret de canard* alongside caviar blinis and Siberian dumplings make Cathedral an adventurous spot for a bit of cuisine-hopping. Decked out in plush harlequin colours, the interior has a slightly kitschy feel that keeps the restaurant just the Walt Disney side of classy, an impression enhanced by hotel-lobby style *musak*. But for a fun and expensive night out on the grand medieval hill – without the hordes – you could do a lot worse. You'll leave wishing you could have tried everything on the menu.

Food 7, Service 7, Atmosphere 6

Charital, Kloostri tee 6.
Tel: 623 73 79 www.charital.ee
Open: noon–midnight daily   745kr

Charital is Pirita's answer to uptown Tallinn – a 'classy' formal restaurant characterized by pristine table linen, sparkling glasses and pastel curtains – as well as uniformed, old-fashioned waiters. A little neon-blue lighting adds some spice to the dance-floor and the black grand piano around which the tables are arranged. Music, dancing and live acts are not regular fixtures here but can

be organized. Charital may be on the *frou-frou* side for younger hedonists, but you couldn't ask for a better approach to food – with complimentary snacks to kick off your meal, delicious flavoured breads baked on the premises and classic old-world service. The cuisine is French with a Russian slant: everything from frog's legs, snails and langoustine to caviar, elk and hare. There is also a good vegan menu – and generally something for everyone. Quality is excellent. Charital's delicious, hearty food and beautiful presentation make up for its slightly fuddy-duddy image. Come here also for beautiful views of the Pirita river (or the less attractive coast road depending on where you sit). A safe choice, 15 minutes' drive from town.

Food 9, Service 8, Atmosphere 6

Controvento, Vene 12/Katariina käik.
Tel: 644 04 70
Open: noon–11pm daily   600kr

Located in a tiny alley bordered on one side by the crumbling wall of a medieval church and crammed with hidden ateliers and tiny boutiques, this famous Italian restaurant complements its setting. Be warned, however, that you can walk past this celebrated alleyway a hundred times if you didn't know it was there. It would be hard to find a more romantic spot for dinner, inside an ancient building decorated in a rustic, Renaissance style opposite a wall covered with 14th-century marble tombstones. A heavy wooden door opens into the warm glow of the Italian bar, where staff will direct you upstairs to the restaurant or seat you in the cosy café downstairs. Upstairs there are two rooms: a smart, stylish area more suited to formal or corporate dinners, and a second cosier, wood-beamed room with pretty stencil murals. Controvento is famous for its excellent food, its atmosphere and its international staff and clientele. It's owned by real Italians, a rarity in the Tallinn restaurant business, but the kitchen today is run by three chefs – from Italy, Peru and Ecuador. The menu is versatile enough for all budgets, from simple pasta dishes to four-course feasts with truffles. Make sure you book in advance.

Food 8, Service 9, Atmosphere 9/10

Eesti Maja, Lauteri 1.
Tel: 645 52 52 www.eestimaja.ee
Open: 11am–11pm daily   345kr

An unpromising entrance opens out downstairs to one of the quirkiest Tardises in town. Unlike some 'Estonian'-themed restaurants, Eesti Maja takes its traditional role very much in earnest: the restaurant is a temple to Baltic patriotism – from the *Global*

Estonian magazine on sale to arty photos of famous Estonians and a room devoted to the Estonian army. The most striking

aspects of the restaurant's sprawling interior (four or five large rooms stretched along a basement floor) are the stuffed folk dolls and huge cartoon-like mural of fairy-tale monsters. Food is similarly folksy: from 'cold piggy' and mustard to 'gossip's fate' (tongue) and spiced Baltic sprats. You can even eat a 'fellow Estonian', a dish inspired by the expression that 'an Estonian's favourite dish is another Estonian' (in fact, veal). Owned by an Estonian expat raised in the US, Eesti Maja feels like a cultural centre but with the atmosphere and warmth of a family business.

Food 6, Service 7, Atmosphere 7

Egoist, Vene 33.
Tel: 646 40 52 www.egoist.ee
Open: noon–midnight daily   980kr

Ascend the steps of this quietly glamorous restaurant and you will find yourself treated like an honoured guest at a private château – from the butler who answers the doorbell to the antique silverware and linen. Egoist springs from the creative mind of chef and entrepreneur Dmitri Damianov, owner of equally grand Gloria and a man who is not afraid to decorate his restaurants with oil paintings of himself. With prices to scare away all but the most confident locals, you are likely to be sharing the dining room with jolly businessmen, 40-something *braggadacios* and wealthy Russians. Low-key classic jazz and golden oldies keep the atmosphere from getting too stodgy, while eccentric paintings of bearded dwarves bring good luck to diners. The food is excellent and presented beautifully. The French/English menu goes for simplicity, preferring to call a spade a spade ('The Lamb' and 'Old Fashioned Duck'). Caviar and *foie gras* are always available. There are several rooms upstairs and down – and one good-sized private table, surrounded by the splendour of the *ancien regime*.

Food 8, Service 9, Atmosphere 9

Elevant, Vene 5.
Tel: 631 31 32 www.elevant.ee
Open: noon–11pm daily   430kr

A cosy, luxurious, international restaurant with a vaguely Indian theme, Elevant targets the Estonian lounge/club scene. High-earning locals who shun the tourist traps of the city centre come to chill or entertain in sofas and comfy wicker chairs dotted around this old merchant's house, situated on the first floor above one of the central old town streets. A lovely ceramic fireplace in the corner, bare wooden floors and laid-back *bosanova* music make dining at this medium-sized, two-roomed restaurant a unique experience – although with its giant chairs and large square tables it is not ideal for groups. Brace yourself for world-

food blurb set out in an artistic menu, but enjoy the imaginative approach to Indian, 'ayurvedic' and international cuisine – although the food may disappoint if you are looking for a good, old-fashioned curry. Instead go for the 'wild boar korma' or 'moose curry'. If you don't eat meat, don't worry – there is a good selection of vegetarian foods, and the 'ecologically clean' interior, decorated with 'eggs, cottage cheese and natural pigments' will please many a modern Londoner.

Food 6, Service 7, Atmosphere 8

Fellini, Raekoja Plats (Kinga 1).
Tel: 631 47 75 www.byblos.ee
Open: noon–1am daily   400kr

Touristy Italian restaurant Fellini is not afraid to revel in Italian glitz: *Dolce Vita* photos on the black baby grand, beauty spa promotions on each table and a discreet little disco ball ready to spin on the ceiling – not to mention the emotional Italian *musak* playing constantly throughout the restaurant (and outside the front door, in Town Hall Square below). Friendly bow-tied waiters, who also staff the snazzy silver bar, can be overstretched at times. With decent-quality standard Italian fare, the menu offers helpful 'combination' menus of starter and main course at reduced prices (a pasta followed by meat or salad, Italian-style, for example). Fellini also makes pizzas, so you can eat well or quickly depending on your mood. Although its eye is firmly on the tourists milling around the square, the atmosphere inside this movie-themed restaurant is comfortable and relaxed.

Food 7, Service 7, Atmosphere 6

Galaxy, Kloostrimetsa 58a (top of the TV tower).
Tel: 623 82 50 www.teletorn.ee
Open: 10am–1am daily   442kr

Although it can be a mission in itself to get out to the giant television tower near Pirita, it is an experience you should not miss if you have enough time. Built in the 1980s (when Estonia's architectural style was the equivalent of 1970s Western European building), this icon to Soviet modernization has become a cult hang-out for retro tourists and locals alike. The circular Galaxy restaurant sits on top of the 170-metre concrete tower – rising

from an empty civic fairway in the middle of dense woodland.
Here you can sit at kitschy tables next to a window that stretches the full 360° – or just walk around and around until you are
dizzy – with a view that includes most of eastern Tallinn, the
bends and bays of the coast, and on a clear day (apparently) even
Helsinki. A broad menu includes everything from caviar and
Canadian lobster to local salads, pork dishes and steak. Galaxy is
also a popular venue for private parties – it has a dance-floor
and a disco – and when it's windy they say that you can feel the
tower moving.

Food 5, Service 7, Atmosphere 6/7

Gloria, Müürivahe 2.
Tel: 644 69 50 www.gloria.ee
Open: noon–midnight daily   900kr

An extravagant, Tsarist-style dining room. If you are looking for
Tallinn's version of sumptuous old Europe, come to Gloria,
where you will find that the Baltic is equally at home in the
grand restaurant tradition. Although the current kitchen is little
more than a decade old the establishment was first opened during the 1930s, when it was known as 'Dancing Paris' – hence the
splendid Art Deco interior and large cabaret stage, which can
still be hired for private shows. Today it is owned by Dmitri
Damianov, a high-profile entrepreneur (and chef) who also started fancy Egoist restaurant on the other side of the Old Town as

well as the guesthouse and wine cellar downstairs. Gloria offers a menu refreshingly free of French jargon and unnecessary clutter – the kitchen is confident enough to tell it straight, with dishes organized into fish, meat, game or poultry. The quality of the dishes is not as consistently high as the price range might suggest, but at its best is excellent. Vegetarian options are also available.

Food 7/8, Service 8, Atmosphere 9

Gloria Veinikelder, Müürivahe 2.
Tel: 644 69 50 www.gloria.ee
Open: 11am–11pm daily   230kr

Downstairs from the legendary restaurant of the same name, Gloria wine cellar doubles as an abundantly stocked wine merchant and a warren-like cellar restaurant. Romantic and cosy (although at times a little draughty), the cellar is not widely promoted as a restaurant – and you must enter the maze-like rooms through a pretty wine shop. Once inside you can sample up to 2,000 wines or enjoy a meal from the same kitchen as the celebrated Gloria upstairs, so your peppersteak or soup may come from the same hand that prepared the beef stroganoff for Bill Clinton or the Pope. The cellar menu is restricted to a small selection of meat and fish dishes, a pasta of the day and a couple of starters, all shoehorned onto one list. You can get away with a three-course meal, together with attentive service, for as little as

170kr (plus drinks), or you can order from the upstairs menu if you feel like *foie gras* and the works. Wine is only available by the glass. Call in advance to reserve a romantic niche or the table for two by the open fire.

Food 7, Service 8, Atmosphere 9

Illusioon, Müürivahe 50/Uus 3.
Tel: 641 98 33
Open: 9am–10pm daily   420kr

Situated in a secret passage inside the ancient city wall, you come across Illusioon down the narrow alley Müürivahe (literally 'between the wall') or through the Kinomaja art cinema. Illusioon is both a restaurant and a café, which sit next to each other in modernized rooms that span the surprisingly spacious ground floor of the old wall. Smooth pastel surfaces are offset by a touch of exposed stone – but Illusioon's designers have resisted the temptation to squeeze 'medieval atmosphere' out of the place, instead opting for arty elegance, with chairs styled after Rennie Mackintosh and a minimalist bar. Illusioon falls just short of really stylish by international standards with its easy-listening versions of golden oldies and not-quite-chic local art on the walls. But the atmosphere is warm, the service friendly and the food tasty. Above all, this is an intimate corner which remains hidden from most tourists, although it is right in the thick of the action. Upstairs via a spiral staircase you will find a beautiful little

dining room nestled in an old guard's chamber, decorated with gorgeous modern ceramics, and available for private bookings. The menu is dominated by fish and pork, with pasta, soups and salads also available.

Food 6, Service 8, Atmosphere 5

Karl Friedrich, Raekoja plats 5.
Tel: 627 24 14 www.restaurant.ee
Open: 10am–midnight daily   715kr

An antidote to both medieval and minimalist design, Karl Friedrich is a formal French-style restaurant, which manages to be homely as well as polished, avoiding the stuffy character of similar restaurants in its class. The restaurant is enormous – as it needs to be, given its amazing location on the old town square, where it caters to tourists, businesses and locals alike. Professionals tend to congregate upstairs in the large, formal dining room overlooking the square or in a series of beautiful private rooms. Sit downstairs for a more relaxed, seafood-restaurant feel or in the fun back room next to the kitchen. Built inside a grand old house, the restaurant still has the same, light, spacious, 18th-century layout – with kitchens visible through thin bamboo curtains at the back. Their speciality is fish – salmon in particular – but there's also a good range of meat dishes for the carnivorous, including classic steaks and pork chops. On the other hand there is next to nothing for vegetarians, except green

salad and some creamy soups. Karl Friedrich is owned by the same group that manages Balthasar (near the square) and a clutch of establishments out of town.

> **Food 7, Service 8, Atmosphere 8**

Klafira, Vene 4.
Tel: 667 51 44 klafira@hot.ee
Open: noon–midnight daily   605kr

For hundreds of years the Russians ruled Estonia, first as emperors, later in the guise of the USSR. And while Soviet nostalgia still remains out of bounds, the Tsarist past has become rich territo-

ry for the tourist industry. Klafira is one of a handful of Russian restaurants that celebrate this splendid, extravagant tradition – and it looks and feels the part. Customers are welcomed inside by costumed waitresses and seated at gorgeous, old-fashioned tables, with live traditional songs performed throughout the evening by a small band. With four rooms, including a private table upstairs and a basement dining room, the restaurant is large enough to absorb tourist groups without losing its intimacy. All the Russian standards are available, from stroganoffs and blinis to pastries and borschts, although, strangely, there is no real caviar to be had (only salmon and trout roe), and prices can be high considering the quality of some of the dishes. Experiment with nine types of vodka and eight flavoured teas.

Kuldse Notsu Kõrts, Dunkri 8.
Tel: 628 65 67 www.schlossle-hotels.com
Open: noon–midnight daily   480kr

A cosy Estonian restaurant, the 'Golden Pig tavern' feels like a
sort of rustic nursery school, in stark contrast to its owner and
patron, the glamorous Russian-styled hotel St Petersbourg
upstairs. Despite its size and brightly lit rooms, Kuldse manages
to feel both cottagey and intimate, with its blonde wood floors
and tables, cheerfully painted ceilings and series of amusing
proverbs painted on the walls. Items of country furniture and
handicrafts complete the picture. With traditional music playing
in the background (or cheesy Estonian pop, depending on your
luck), you can try a range of hearty local foods served in huge
portions. It's all about meat – especially pork (or black pudding,
liver and boar) – although there is also a reasonable vegetarian
menu. Waiters in traditional dress can be sleepy, but they are
polite to a fault. Ask for a taste of *kama*, a timeless local dessert
made from sour milk and ground grains that may or may not
appeal, but must be tried!

Food 8, Service 6, Atmosphere 6

Maiasmokk, Pikk 16.
Tel: 646 40 70 www.maiasmokk.ee
Open: noon–11pm daily   445kr

Not to be missed. Wedged between two ancient churches just
behind Town Hall Square, the oldest Estonian restaurant in Tallinn
calls to mind an age when the nobility lived in style – and a time
when anything French was still the epitome of good taste. Sitting

like a stately island at the confluence of two cobbled, Old Town
streets, Maiasmokk was founded in 1864 and does not appear to
have changed much since. Antique chairs and silverware, grand
white walls and high ceilings give it the feel of a 19th-century
ambassador's residence. Classical music and some of the cutest
views of the old streets complete the picture. The kitchen serves
excellent Estonian food without the rough, hearty presentation
common to local cuisine, but cooked in a French style. You could
spend a whole afternoon in one of the restaurant's romantic
niches overlooking the street, or entertain friends in the faded
splendour of a private dining room. Walk upstairs through a tiny
café to find the restaurant. It's best to book in advance.

Food 8/9, Service 6, Atmosphere 9

Maikrahv, Raekoja plats 8.
Tel: 631 42 27 www.maikrahv.ee
Open: noon–11pm daily   700kr

Named after the 'Count of May' – figurehead of the famous spring festivals that mobbed Old Town Square in medieval Tallinn – Maikrahv is a smart, business-friendly restaurant in a cavernous downstairs hall on the main square. Going for a medieval theme with a modern twist, the restaurant offers beautifully presented international food as well as a full Estonian menu. 'Banquet'-type menus are also available with Disney-esque names such as 'The Feast of the Merchant Guild' and 'Blackheads Brotherhood Workaday Supper' – a common strategy in Tallinn's themed kitchens, but one that is managed without compromising quality. With costumed waiters, murals and a pageantry motif, the décor is interesting but doesn't try very hard to look authentic. The restaurant is going for a less touristy, more formal crowd who care more about elegance than gimmicks. Service and food are excellent, with a wine list selected by Maikrahv's award-winning sommelier, but it's nevertheless on the expensive side.

Food 9, Service 8, Atmosphere 6

Mõõkkala, Kuninga 4.
Tel: 641 82 88 www.mookala.com
Open: noon–midnight daily   625kr

Mõõkkala is Estonian for 'swordfish', which is the speciality of the house in this newly renovated fish restaurant – along with a wide selection of aquatic fare from pike and perch to shark, cod or eel (fried with apple or boiled in white wine). Relocated in

2003 to new quarters in Rüütli street, right next to the main square, this old-time fish favourite is now guaranteed vigorous business from the tourist crowd who can't fail to spot the modish, nightclub interior as they pass the medieval-styled eateries

next door. Shamelessly extravagant but toned down by dark greens and blues, this is a medieval building put to interesting modern use. Food is served with artistic flair, decorated with exotic fruits and other baubles (although the hearty portions and creative touches may hide less than wonderful flavours). Along with salads, soups and hot and cold starters, you'll only find a couple of meat dishes in this shrine to the sea. This is the only restaurant in Tallinn that includes service in the bill, fixed at 50kr.

Food 6, Service 7, Atmosphere 8

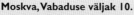

Moskva, Vabaduse väljak 10.
Tel: 640 46 94 www.moskva.ee
Open: 8:30am–midnight Monday–Friday;
11am–midnight Saturday–Sunday   325kr

People come to Moskva as much for the trendy ambience in the adjoining bar and café as for the food, which is both affordable and inventive. Its interior is stylish and typical of the modern restaurant scene. Packed with Tallinn's 20-something beautiful people, and staffed by frosty waitresses in red air-hostess uniforms, Moskva serves a range of classic dishes with imaginative seasonings, such as cowberry, ginger and lemongrass. Food is served in characterful tilted plates and bowls, to the accompaniment of loungey dance music which can suddenly accelerate mid-bite into hardcore club stuff. The upstairs café/bar occupies the same table area, so expect to share the waitress's time with cocktail drinkers and coffee-heads working on their laptops. The interior looks like a pull-out from *Wallpaper** magazine: easy on the eyes and a bit too cool for school. Enjoy the lavatories.

Food 6, Service 6, Atmosphere 8/9

Must Lammas, Sauna 2.
Tel: 644 20 34 www.mustlammas.ee
Open: noon–11pm (6pm Sunday) daily   460kr

Another Estonian-run 'ethnic' restaurant: Tallinn entrepreneurs are so talented at mimicking the cuisine and culture of other countries that you often cannot tell that there is not a foreigner in sight. In this case, Caucasian cooking and ambience are done with conviction and perfectionism. Even the waiters seem a little imperial: older and more polished than the average, with little Georgian moustaches. Soft jazz and low lighting add to the charm – imagine yourself as a laid-back Russian official on the Empire's southern coast and you're almost there – and although the interior is absolutely modern, a few choice decorations do

the trick. The food is good – Must Lammas (literally 'Black
Sheep') specializes in grilled meats but also offers the stuffed
peppers and olive leaves, onion salads and meatballs typical of
the region. It's not *haute cuisine*, but the dishes manage to be
both hearty and delicate at the same time – perhaps a legacy of
the (real) Georgian chef who trained the kitchen staff at the
beginning, seven years ago. All meals start with a free shot of
vodka. Ask for a table on the mezzanine.

Food 7, Service 9, Atmosphere 8

Nevskij, St Petersbourg Hotel, Rataskaevu 7.
Tel: 628 65 60 www.schlossle-hotels.com
Open: 6pm–11pm daily   935kr

For a taste of Tsarist splendour come to this classical Russian
restaurant in the St Petersbourg Hotel just behind Town Hall
Square, set in a gorgeous room overlooking the cobbles of an
Old Town street. The building has long been used by Russian
ex-pats for top-notch entertaining – this was formerly the
Embassy – and today this historical tradition continues with a
menu ranging from pickled vegetables, bear stew and *pelmeni* to
stewed salmon and beef stroganoff. Vodka is of course *de rigueur*.
Part of Nevskij's charm comes from its intimate dining-room
atmosphere, and the whiff of oriental luxury in the cushioned
seats and romantic mezzanine tables hidden near the window.

Come on Thursday evenings and at the weekend to catch live Russian *balalaika* music. Waiters wear splendid, old-fashioned costumes.

Food 8, Service 7/8, Atmosphere 9

Novell, Narva mnt. 7c.
Tel: 633 98 91 www.revalhotels.com
Open: noon–11pm (1am Friday–Saturday) daily   530kr

This slick new restaurant came into being when Reval Hotel Central decided to improve its mediocre restaurant and compete at the top end with the trendy Tallinn establishments, although it has yet to make an impression on the real opinion-makers of Estonian nightlife. Attached to the Norwegian-owned Reval, the restaurant has been keen from the start to establish its own separate identity and to escape from the mid-market reputation of the hotel. Thus you will most probably enter and experience the restaurant without realizing that it is part of the same business – there is no connecting door, and it has a very different ambience. Novell faces the world through huge plate glass windows, looking out onto one of Tallinn's busiest (and least glamorous) commercial streets. Signatured by a stunning yellow light-mural that spans the length of the restaurant, Novell would look at home in any major capital of the world, and ranks confidently among the most stylish interiors in Tallinn. Estonian chef Andrus Laanister, an American-trained Spanish television personality, offers an international menu, combining elements of French, Estonian, Russian and Japanese cuisine. Novell will probably soon establish itself as a favourite of corporate diners.

Food 7, Service 7, Atmosphere 5

Ö, Mere pst. 6e.
Tel: 661 61 50 www.restoran-o.ee
Open: noon–midnight daily   625kr

A funky name for a funky place. Ö comes from the same stable as fancy, achingly minimalist Bocca – it's owned by the same *Wallpaper**-magazine obsessed entrepreneurs who made the mod-ish Italian restaurant such a success with fashion-conscious corpo-rate entertainers as well as the fast crowd in Tallinn. Named after a Swedish island, Ö is based in the ultra-trendy post-industrial strip on Mere, formerly the site of the Rotermaani factory complex and only a few minutes' walk from the old town. The interior looks for a softer-edged, more decadent modernism than its sister – steel girders and stone are offset by low lighting and 20-foot drapes that hang, harem-style, across the doorway and the middle of the restaurant. The walls are enlivened by Old Master nudes printed on transparent glass, while the waitresses dress in Prada black. Ö offers two menus: a full sushi list and a more regular, 'world food' menu – although most dishes lean towards French classics with a Japanese twist. Your food arrives in delicately arranged portions – small, though filling, and extremely tasty. Delicious olive and walnut breads are served with oil in little pewter jugs. A *menu dégustation* allows you to sample several of Ö's more inventive dishes, should you be unable to choose just one.

Food 9, Service 8, Atmosphere 7

Olde Hansa, Vanaturg 1.
Tel: 627 90 20 www.oldehansa.com
Open: 11am–midnight daily   600kr

Not so much Estonian as Hanseatic, Olde Hansa harks back to the days when Teutonic merchants ruled the cities of the Baltic with a passion for trade that made Tallinn a great medieval capital. Built in an imposing merchant's house next to Town Hall Square, this enormous restaurant is a fixture of the Tallinn scene and should not be missed. Much more than just a tourist venue

(although it does cater to thousands of visitors every week), Olde Hansa is built upon the vivid imagination of the owners – two medievalists who believe in bringing Estonia's history to life. Sit at one of the rough-hewn tables in the huge, candlelit galleries downstairs or go up for the full medieval experience (which the costumed waiters take as seriously as method actors). The food is convincingly hearty, seasoned with sweet garnishes and served with honey beer, the house speciality. Try boar 'marinated in rare spices and cooked over a fire in honour of Waldemar II, the brave king of Denmark'. For the very hungry, there is a range of extravagant multi-course banquets. Choose upstairs to enjoy live medieval music, performed on a raised platform on genuine period instruments.

Food 7, Service 8/9, Atmosphere 9

Paat, Rohuneeme tee 53, Viimsi.
Tel: 609 08 40 www.paat.ee
Open: 11am–midnight (10pm Sunday) daily   505kr

Opened in 2000, this upturned Noah's Ark of a restaurant still looks incredibly spick and span. An interior decorated (literally) like the inside of a boat contains a café bar on the lower deck and a smart restaurant on the upper. Both floors offer incredible views of Tallinn across the bay, and the windswept, ragged shoreline in between. Built right next to the sea in remote but glamorous Viimsi 20 minutes outside Tallinn, Paat is a great summer

location – with a huge terrace right next to the water when the sun is out. Marred slightly by its choice of *musak*, the atmosphere is nevertheless inviting and smart. Attractive blue-stained pine and rounded, sloping walls and windows create a nautical atmosphere that has a genuine feel. Tables are lit with genuine paraffin lamps. Seafood and fish unsurprisingly top the menu, but there are also tasty-looking meat and vegetarian dishes cooked in British and French styles. The café bar offers a separate menu with all the same dishes plus a selection of light snacks – including soups, salads, omelettes, pastas and sandwiches.

Food 7, Service 7, Atmosphere 8

Palermo, Köleri/Vesivärava.
Tel: 606 19 66 palermopub@hot.ee
Open: 8am–11.30pm Monday–Friday;
11am–11.30pm Saturday–Sunday   310kr

Palermo is an excellent new Italian restaurant located in the Kadriorg distict of Tallinn, a summery residential area full of characterful wooden houses built in the 19th century, and about 10 minutes' drive from the centre. If you're visiting Kadriorg for a walk around the park or a visit to the famous Foreign Art Gallery, Palermo is another good reason to linger. The first thing that strikes you when you enter this basement restaurant is the pungent smell of fragrant wood from the ceiling beams and exposed floor. Originally intended to cater to high-rolling cus-

tomers of the casino, which shares the same building, Palermo is now a popular neighbourhood restaurant in its own right, packed with local office workers and business lunchers. With its real Italian chef (unusual in Estonia), the kitchen offers a range of classic dishes with a Baltic twist: you can order caviar, herring or dumplings, standard fish and grill dishes, or Italian favourites such as *bruschetta*. There are three rooms decorated to a hunting-lodge theme, and a more formal, business-friendly room at the back.

Food 8, Service 8, Atmosphere 6/7

Pegasus, Harju 1.
Tel: 631 40 40 www.restoranpegasus.ee
Open: 8am–1am (2am Friday) Monday–Friday;
10am–2am Saturday. Closed Sunday.   620kr

Pegasus has been wowing customers with its London-style interna-tional cuisine since the mid-1990s, while its bar has fast become the meeting-place of choice for Tallinn's trendier, more grown-up set. With its space-age chandeliers, porthole windows and spiral metal staircase, Pegasus might have walked fully grown from the pages of *Wallpaper** magazine, with a touch of Tate Modern thrown in for good measure. The kitchen prepares a beautifully presented fusion of French and Italian cuisine given a strong Asian slant (such as the *foie gras* terrine with Thai soup). The delicious selection of fish, fowl and meats – and a few desserts – are all served by

friendly staff. Pegasus also provides the best hot breakfasts in town.

Food 8, Service 9, Atmosphere 7/8

Peppersack, Viru 2.
Tel: 646 68 00 www.peppersack.ee
Open: noon–midnight daily   475kr

Peppersack is more straightforward than its arch-rival Olde
Hansa across the street; the waitresses in this huge medieval-
themed restaurant dress in similar costumes but don't necessarily
believe they live in the Middle Ages. It is, nevertheless, a splendid
medieval space, with an evocative, candlelit atmosphere, and
caters to the hundreds of tourist groups that pass through this
central location every week. These it manages to absorb without
unduly compromising the authentic atmosphere, although the
edges of modern Estonia are visible in the simple, laminated
menus. Peppersack is housed in an enormous merchant's quarters, which the owners have used to build a complex of con-
sumer businesses – a café upstairs, a grill downstairs and a small
bakery in the foyer. Yet it does enough to let you pretend you
are munching on genuine Hanseatic fare. With playfully named,
well-cooked dishes ('Against Plague', 'Lady Margareta's weakness'), Peppersack also brews its own medieval-style house beer
and vodka, made with honey and spices. Food is presented in
hearty portions with a big basket of bread (although the bread
can be rock hard at times from reheating). The décor adds to

the Hanseatic fantasy, with glass cases full of alchemist's retorts and stills, impressive tapestries on the walls and splendid coats of arms.

Food 7, Service 6, Atmosphere 8

Pika Jala, Pikk Jalg 16.
Tel: 644 13 44 www.pikajala.ee
Open: 10am–11pm (10pm Sunday) daily   460kr

Despite its evocative Estonian name (literally 'long leg') borrowed from the ancient walkway up to Toompea Hill, Pika Jala is a thoroughly French-inspired restaurant. Enter this cosy, single room eatery to find yourself in a strange and charming universe combining Gallic and Estonian elements, both old and new – from the Tricolor bunting on the windows and Parisian-style music to contemporary Estonian art and impressive modern handicrafts. Wicker chairs and white tablecloths weave a charming rustic fantasy – preparing you for rustic 'French kitchen' cuisine with favourites such as frog's legs, snails and onion soup – while twisted metal chandeliers offset a stylishly modern decorative scheme. Perfectly situated for sightseers touring Tallinn's medieval scenery, but with prices that would probably deter the bus and ferry crowd, this is a pleasant stop-over for a quality lunch or more leisurely dinner. With its good range of traditional French food, the kitchen avoids the 'world food' option so prevalent in Tallinn's restaurants. A small terrace is open in summer.

Revalia, Raekoja plats 8.
Tel: 631 47 75 www.byblos.ee
Open: 9am–midnight Sunday–Thursday;
8am–1am Friday–Saturday   585kr

Sitting right in the middle of the action on Town Hall Square,
Revalia grill comes from the same stable as neighbouring restaurants Old Estonia and Fellini – all of them capitalizing on their
great location to catch the busy tourist trade that centres on
the square throughout the year. You may get the impression that
Revalia is not completely sure of its identity, with its inconsistent
mixture of kitsch and elegant styling – but that does not stop
the restaurant being a decent place for a bite, given its convenient location and great view of the square. There are some genuinely tasteful touches: pleasant lighting, diaphanous partitions
and well-placed pot plants help to give the restaurant a relaxed
atmosphere. Go for the grill items rather than crêpes or vegetables, which can be on the tired side. The restaurant's name
comes from the old Germanic tag for Tallinn that dates from the
city's heyday as a Teutonic merchant colony.

Food 6, Service 6, Atmosphere 5/6

Royal Siam, Mündi 3.
Tel: 641 24 56 www.siam.ee
Open: noon–11pm daily   700kr

Tucked away in a tiny alley off the main square, in the basement
of a medieval building and opposite an Irish pub, a top quality Thai
restaurant might be the last thing you'd expect to find. But nip
downstairs from Mündi and you enter another world – an atmospheric and beautifully appointed cellar with an oriental feel and a

reputation for great food. Wooden lanterns are suspended from
the ceiling, and slowly rotating fans and wicker partition screens
add to the intimacy. A long and detailed menu includes most Thai
classics, from *pad Thai* to coconut and green-chilli soups and curries. Various sub-menus cover stir-fried fish and meat dishes, rice
and noodles or 'hot pots'. Reasonably expensive, Royal Siam is
nevertheless a laid-back and enjoyable place to dine.

Food 8/9, Service 7, Atmosphere 8

Rusthaveli, Maakri 19/21.
Tel: 610 85 15 www.rusthaveli.ee
Open: noon–11pm daily   562kr

Named after a 16th-century Georgian poet, this smart Caucasian
restaurant reflects Estonia's history as part of the sprawling
Soviet empire that stretched from the Baltic to the Black Sea.

Today it's the Estonians who are in charge, although everything else is Georgian – from the music and the décor to the chefs themselves. This is a high-quality offering that goes for business customers as well as the affluent guests of the Radisson hotel just across the road. Located outside the Old Town in the main shopping area, Rusthaveli has been decorated in simple brick and plaster, with silk drapes and evocative Georgian paintings. The menu ranges from eggplant and local cheese dishes to 'tender fried chick' and *gotsi*, an oven-roasted piglet (to be ordered in advance). An entire section is devoted to 'meals on spits', but there are also plenty of good vegetarian options – with tomatoes, garlic and mushrooms in abundance.

Food 7, Service 8, Atmosphere 8

Silk, Kullassepa 4.
Tel: 648 46 25 www.silk.ee
Open: noon–midnight daily   490kr

Not cheap by local standards, this new, platinum-cool sushi restaurant just off Town Hall Square seems to target a chic international clientele. Yet after a year of business the place is full of Estonians and ex-pats alike – dropping in for a glass of wine while they take in the Prada-esque ash-black interiors. With its ultra-hip approach Silk could hold its own in New York, London or any world capital. Fresh orchids hang, individually, in metal vases across each wall, strung along diagonal wires. Despite the

lack of Japanese staff in the kitchen or on the floor, service is orientally polite and the sushi decent, although the rice can be a little dry. Helpful combination tips and platters at the back of the menu will assist those easily confused by the range of sushi available, while cooked dishes are available for the ambivalent.

Food 7, Service 6, Atmosphere 7

Stenhus, Pühavaimu 13–15.
Tel: 699 77 80 www.schlossle-hotels.com
Open: 7am–10.30pm daily   1,300kr

Stenhus is a distinguished, luxury restaurant set in a series of cloister-like tunnels decorated to a pinnacle of good taste – as Henry VIII might have liked it – but without the medieval pretence so prevalent in Tallinn cellars. This deservedly famous restaurant in the basement of Tallinn's only five-star hotel definitely ranks as one of the best bets in town for a romantic dinner or a special occasion. The French-influenced kitchen is directed by Estonian chef Tõnis Siigur, who has been with the restaurant since it opened five years ago. Dine on classic dishes of game, meat, fish or fowl complemented by excellent wines – including Château Petrus, if you feel up to it. With its huge open fireplace and tapestried rooms, and its outside courtyard seating, Stenhus is a solid (and reliably expensive) choice for any season. It also offers a wine cellar/cigar room for plutocratic loungers.

Food 8/9, Service 8, Atmosphere 9

● **Sushi House, Rataskaevu 16.**
Tel: 641 19 00 www.sushihouse.ee
Open: noon–midnight daily   400kr

Flawlessly chic – from its hyper-cool, coloured-glass sliding doors
to the *bosanova* lounge music and sexy bead curtains – Sushi
House is a slick and inventive take on the minimalist fantasy of
21st-century Tallinn, a neat combination of medieval and ultra
modern. Goblet-sized wine glasses, five-star service and classy
booze put this new restaurant squarely in the affluent yuppie
market covered by Bocca and a handful of other Tallinn joints.
The kitchen offers several menus (decorated with grinning
manga-style samurai): a classic sushi selection, wok menu and

grill dishes. The sushi is good, although expensive, with two combination choices: a six-piece or a *dégustation* of 14. Nice touches
and attentive service make this restaurant more than just a style
parade – they bring honey with your oriental tea and a hot flan-
nel for your hands and face before the meal begins. The Estonian
waitresses wear stunning black outfits trimmed with striking red,
speak perfect English and take an obvious pride in their restaurant. If you're coming as a couple, ask for the cosy alcove, while
the upstairs mezzanine room is good for private parties. Very
laid-back and very relaxing.

Food 8, Service 9, Atmosphere 7

Tanduur, Vene 7/Apteegi 6.
Tel: 631 30 84
Open: noon–midnight daily   585kr

If you are nonplussed to find an Indian restaurant in the middle of
medieval Tallinn, be bold and go in – you'll be surprised by the
delightful atmosphere and great food in this decade-old favourite.
Descend a staircase through a bamboo ceiling and you'll find in
front of you a low archway giving onto a horseshoe of Mogul-
style banquettes arranged around a serene water fountain. By
British standards Tanduur would be a good Indian, serving
excellent regional food in a pleasure-dome environment – so well
presented that you almost don't notice the tough curry house
carpet underneath the tables. Sharing premises with an Indian

craft shop, the restaurant is decorated with items imported by the owner from his bi-annual expeditions to the country, silver hookahs and marble vases included. There seems to be plenty of space, upstairs and down – but this is often filled to capacity, so make sure to book in advance. Not cheap by local standards.

Food 8, Service 9, Atmosphere 7

Toomkooli, Toom-Kooli 13.
Tel: 644 66 13
Open: noon–midnight daily   655kr

Built inside the former stable yard of a feudal lordship (the family Stackelberg) on the edge of the fortified Toompea Hill above the old town, Toomkooli is a beautiful, rather pricey international restaurant that sits in the middle of the tourist circuit yet manages to stay aloof from the budget crowds. The restaurant's current owners have aimed for a 'modern medieval' look, a pageantry theme under high, beamed ceilings and draped with knightly motifs. In the winter there is a cosy fire, which makes the enormous space feel intimate. In summer you can sit on the terrace or enjoy dramatic clifftop views of the lowlands. A broad menu covers all bases – fish, meat, poultry and vegetarian options, as well as a special 'granny's kitchen' offering a range of hearty cottage dishes. Look for intriguingly named specialities such as 'Total Kill' and 'Hiphopkins'. The dessert menu offers a *dégustation* of five pudding specials if you are unable to decide on one.

Food 6, Service 6, Atmosphere 8

Vanaema Juures, Rataskaevu 10.
Tel: 626 90 80 vanaema.juures@mail.ee
Open: noon–10 pm (6pm Sunday) daily   270kr

Full of Estonian charm as you would like to imagine it, Vanaema Juures ('grandmother's place') is hidden behind a heavy wooden door, its presence signified only by a heavy frying pan and a single, picturebook egg. Descend a little stairway to a tiny, homely dining room. Although it is less than a decade old – and there is no grandmother involved – this little whitewashed den is busy all year around with regulars as well as more discerning tourists. The small, tunnel-like room is decorated in a classic, folksy style, which draws its inspiration from the period of the first Estonian republic (the 1920s), and is full of black and white photos and period bric-à-brac. A good selection of Estonian food covers meat, fish and vegetarian dishes as well as traditional favourites such as salted or pickled fish and hearty soups. Vanaema Juures manages to be smart without being expensive.

Food 8, Service 7, Atmosphere 9

drink...

Very few public drinking spots existed in Tallinn before the 1990s. There were hotel bars and a couple of folk music venues or art clubs, but otherwise locals had to content themselves with home consumption. Today, however, a full-time party culture has burgeoned forth, reflecting not only the explosion of tourist interest in the country but also the increasing affluence of the Estonians themselves. Because the scene is so new, virtually anything goes, and the broad variety of venues concentrated in tiny central Tallinn reflects almost every taste – from trendy minimalist cocktail bars to dingy drinking dens. Estonians seem to take naturally to self-invention, whether it's boasting tenuous medieval pedigrees or importing entire 100-year old pubs from Amsterdam. All this means one thing: a rich and lively nightlife.

Most pubs and bars are concentrated in the Old Town, and have opened in the last five to eight years to serve the booming tourist market. However, there is an increasing amount of activity outside the city walls that's aimed at a more discerning local clientele who prefer to steer clear of tourists. As far as tourists are concerned, Tallinn's streets are dominated by Finnish visitors coming over to take advantage of the cheap prices: Helsinki is less than 2 hours away by boat (or 18 minutes by helicopter), resulting in an estimated five million journeys each year (and the Brits are running fast to catch up). This has brought a flood of money (and drunken men) to Tallinn's streets.

Tallinn's only real 'strip' is concentrated in and around Suur-Karja at the edge of the Old Town. Here a string of British-style pubs caters to mainly English-speaking as well as Scandinavian visitors. These are relatively grungy places which get extremely lively on weekends when they effectively become late-night discos, with DJs keeping the party going until the early hours – a budget nightclub scene for more price-conscious locals and an excellent meeting-place for foreigners and Estonians. At the other end of the spectrum, the area also plays host to a couple of Tallinn's trendiest, least tourist-orientated bars: these include Kaheksa and Pegasus, tucked around the corner behind the Hollywood nightclub. McCools is also a recent entrant onto the scene.

Go closer to Town Hall Square and Viru Street if you feel like drinking with the visiting Finns, in dingy cellar bars and beer halls. Here you will also come across some lovely, up-market wine bars and cigar lounges, although these are a little harder to find. This central area also includes a couple of the city's artiest haunts, frequented by students, theatre-lovers and film-makers (one of them a private bar).

Take a look as well outside the Old Town, at the small industrial port area that's now revamped and home to a growing number of trendy bars. Here you'll also find drinking dives aimed at the Finnish day trippers, who disembark a few hundred metres away in the ferry port. And there are a couple of great bars in the area around Parnu mnt, popular with locals and ex-pats but less well known to tourists.

Finally it is worth remembering that few Estonians go out every night: while prices appear cheap to visitors from Western Europe, most locals simply can't afford to go out frequently. Many will keep their powder dry until the weekends and splurge it all on one big night out. One club owner has estimated that there's a limited pool of roughly 4,000 Tallinites willing or able to go out regularly – so you will tend to see the same faces again and again. And, inevitably, over half of your fellow drinkers will be foreigners.

Door policy is generally relaxed, unless you find yourself among a gang of paralytic lads. Licensing laws are very liberal, so bars will often stay open as long as there are customers, although some of the classier places close early on weekday nights – which can often be empty. Don't be disappointed if the bar of your choice is quiet. Wait until the weekend and the nightlife really takes off.

Amsterdam Pub, Pärnu mnt 16.

Tel: 631 32 15.
Open: 11am–10pm (midnight Thursday–Saturday) daily

Open since 1992, Amsterdam was one of the first and most popular pubs in Tallinn, and justly so. The entire 100-year-old, dark wooden interior was shipped over whole from Holland, preserving intact a gorgeous, perfectly symmetrical bar and two other rooms, each as packed with character as the last, and including a low-ceilinged lounge at the back. Today Amsterdam faces more competition from bars inside the Old Town walls (it sits 5 minutes' walk from the Old Town, just outside Vabaduse Square), although management does everything it can to keep its regulars happy and attract the party crowd, from employing friendly and welcoming staff to staging music events (there is a piano in the bar). Come here for a quiet pint and a chat or just to enjoy the pretty stained-glass windows, the carved wooden bar and the characterful, 'olde' pub atmosphere.

Avenüü, Suur-Karja 10.

Tel: 644 10 19 www.clubavenue.ee
Open: 24 hours daily

Tallinn's only 24-hour bar, Avenüü sits right in the middle of the action on Suur-Karja Street, a strip of pubs and cellar bars that stay open until the early hours, and is a favourite watering-hole for tourists and ex-pats. Unlike its neighbours, Avenüü is full of character, and has a unique selling-point: the kitchen is open at all times, making it the only place in old Tallinn where you can find chicken and chips at 4.30am. It is also a mixed bag – there are times when you may be the only paying customer in the joint, watched over by off-duty bouncers and their tough-looking girlfriends. During the weekend, however, Avenüü becomes an atmospheric chill-out spot, the calm eye in the drunken storm, where partiers come for a break from the action and a bite to eat before they head back – or go home. Arrive at 3am on a Saturday and there is something distinctly *fin-de-siècle* about the place – middle-aged couples sipping a coffee; young sharps in suits; beautiful clubbers catching their breath between raves – the flotsam of the night in all its glory.

Beer House, Dunkri 5.
Tel: 627 65 20 www.beerhouse.ee
Open: 10am–midnight Sunday–Tuesday; 10am–2am
Wednesday–Thursday; 10am–4am Friday–Saturday

A huge, hearty, German-style beer house full of warm lights, thick wooden tables, oompah music and a vast copper micro brewery, which sits in the middle of the room like a Dr Seuss contraption. A large flat-screen TV showing cable and sports may look out of place with the 'Olde Teutonic' atmosphere but reflects the type of clientele of this mega bar/restaurant opened in 2002 – merry coach-class Finns on day trips from Helsinki. It's a fun place to eat, drink and be drunk without inhibitions, so you may suddenly feel yourself in cheerful, stein-wielding mood as you sit in Munich beer-fest rows, or drink from your own private 15-foot mug. The brewery makes its own, reasonably priced, micro-beers: choose from Pilsner (light, 5%) Märzen (medium, 5.5%) or Dunkles (dark, 6%). The choice of food is overwhelmingly large – with separate menus for grill dishes, pizza, bar snacks, or 'gourmet'. You can even buy a cappuccino.

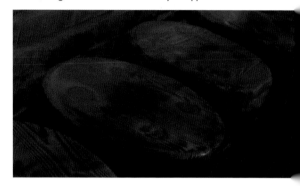

Café VS, Pärnu mnt. 28.
Tel: 627 26 27 www.cafevs.ee
Open: 10am–1am (3am Friday) Monday–Friday; noon–3am Saturday; 1pm–1am Sunday

Outside the radar of most tourists, Café VS is nevertheless a favourite hang-out for ex-pats and trendy young Estonians. Located on busy Pärnu mnt. just 5 minutes outside the Old Town, Café VS is run by a dedicated English raver with a passion for Indian food and good club music. VS triples as an edgy, hot pink nightspot, a daytime café and an Indian restaurant. In the evenings, diners mingle with drinkers in the space-age bar lounge at metal tables on metal floors – while upstairs there is a darker, atmospheric back room decorated with spinning, green wall-fans. The ambience is fuelled by 'internet DJs' downstairs who play everything from pop to hard house. Café VS is rightly popular for

its cheerful, friendly staff and its laid-back atmosphere. Dozens of cocktails are available as well as inventive non-alcoholic drinks, and ice-cream shakes make it a great place to start a long night.

Casa Del Habano, Dunkri 2.
Tel: 644 56 47 www.havanas.ee
Open: 10am–midnight Monday–Saturday; noon–6pm Sunday

Regulars come to the Casa Del Habano's famous cigar lounge for a variety of reasons: some to cherish the exclusive feel of this little-advertised hideaway, others for the unfailingly warm atmosphere or simply for the interesting guests – the Casa, despite its unpretentious approach, draws the big wheels of Estonian society at all times of day. Above all, however, this little business is home to Tallinn's best collection of cigars, watched

over by a management with a fine eye for keeping its customers happy – whether this means tutoring them on the subtler points of handling a Gran Corona or advising them on the best whisky to accompany a Robusto. On arriving, you find youself in a quiet, relaxed bar where you can sit back, enjoy your smoke and have a chat in the company of other cigar lovers. Downstairs in the cellar is the well-stocked *humidor* – ask for a tour from the expert bar staff or the owner himself if he is at large. The Casa owes its charm mainly to its owners – real cigar enthusiasts who have secured the official rights to market Cuban Habanos around the world. Visit their excellent website for an education in cigar lore.

CityGourmet, Maakri 36.
Tel: 056 498 839 www.citygourmet.ee
Open: 8am–11pm (1am Friday) Monday–Friday;
10am–1am Saturday; 11am–11pm Sunday

Located in the modern city centre near the giant Radisson hotel, CityGourmet is a boutique deli-café that also functions as a wine merchant and bar, getting lively in the evenings with affluent Tallinners dropping by to enjoy the fine imported wines and snacks (*foie gras*, sandwiches, delicious olives and *antipasto*). With a stunning plate-glass window and a wonky, artistic slant to the room – as well as excellent music – this wine bar is a charismatic option far away from the tourist hordes and the medieval theme pubs. A soothing atmosphere, perfect for lounging with a date or for chatting with the locals.

Club Havana, Pikk 11.
Tel: 640 66 30 www.jjj-bars.com
Open: 10am–2am (4am Friday–Saturday) daily

Standing apart from the main boozing action on Suur Karja, the Latin-themed Havana club is a popular and unique nightspot just the other side of the Old Town Square. From the palm tree on the window to the salsa music at the back, Havana's atmosphere

is more about cocktails and dancing than beer and shouting. Consequently it seems to attract a slightly higher class of Estonian as well as plenty of tourists and ex-pats. Above all a cocktail bar, Havana offers 42 drinks organized in the (laminated) menu under categories such as 'Ladies', 'Classic' and 'Sexy' cocktails – although these can be less than perfectly made. It has a pink-lit, attractive interior, a large dance-floor at the back, and some seductive corners tucked away from the bar, giving Havana its reputation as a good spot for encounters as well as partying. Once a month there is a proper salsa dance party, where Tallinn's dance fanatics gather for some real action.

Depeche Mode (DM bar), Nunne 4.
Tel: 641 16 08 www.edmfk.cafe.ee
Open: noon–1am (4am Friday) Monday–Friday;
4pm–4am Saturday; 4pm–1am Sunday

A bizarre tribute bar started by a sincere Depeche Mode fanatic, this is a downstairs grotto dedicated to the band from Basildon, who naturally have visited their namesake and autographed the UV-lit, whitewashed walls. More like a shrine or art installation than a drinking den, this is a fun place to visit for a quick dose of Estonia's real culture – just as pop-obsessed and media-conscious as anywhere – although perhaps DM Bar would look more at home in edgy, weird Berlin than in straight Tallinn. Needless to say, the majority of jukebox airtime is devoted to Depeche Mode, played over a powerful sound system. You can also buy special Depeche Mode cocktails – 'Never Let me Down Again', 'Blue Dress' or 'Rush' – as well as all the standard sticky cellar beers and liquors. Bar snacks are limited to Pringles and chewing gum, which somehow get a listing on the menu.

Dr Mauruse Pub, Estonia pst 8.
Tel: 646 60 47
Open: 11am–11pm Monday–Friday; noon–11pm Saturday;
1–10pm Sunday

Hidden underneath a large pink library next to the opera build-ing, Dr Mauruse Pub is a favourite with locals – both as daytime café and after-work drinking spot. Since it is less than 2 or 3 minutes' walk from the Old Town, you should try this place out. With its low green desk lamps, brown walls and library full of paperbacks and board games, Dr Mauruse Pub almost defines cosiness, Estonian-style. A variety of chairs and tables, some of them antique, make this a comfortable place to grab a light lunch

or dinner, a coffee or a glass of wine. With a menu ranging from salads and soups to grills and *kievs*, Dr Mauruse is crowded with local lunchers and office workers, old and young. And, indeed, it's a good place to whittle away a few hours – wireless internet access is free for those with laptops. Meal prices range from 30 to 75kr, which is excellent value, although be aware that the menu comes in English, and waiting times can get long at lunchtime. The place is named after a famous Estonian writer and educator.

Excelsior Vinoteek, Niguliste 6.
Tel: 631 38 91
Open: 3pm–midnight daily

Judging by the number of corks in the window, Excelsior is having little trouble cracking open the bottles – and justly so, given

this little wine bar's cosy, luxurious atmosphere. Located directly opposite beautiful Niguliste Church, below the looming fortifications of Toompea, the two-room lounge opened in 1999 and has been building a loyal clientele ever since. Run by the friendly and attentive proprietor and a small staff (in Möet et Chandon uniforms), this is the place to come for a quiet drink or a proper wine-lover's tour. The intimate back room can be reserved for private parties, while relaxed jazz music creates an excellent atmosphere for a date.

Gloria Tabacalera, Müürivahe 2.
Tel: 644 03 77
Open: noon–10pm. Closed Sunday.

Managed separately from Gloria upstairs, this tiny little cigar shop and lounge is tucked underneath the stairway to the world-renowned restaurant – hang-out of presidents and touring rock stars. Built inside part of the old town wall, the *tabacalera* also shares space with a wine cellar and a tiny little guesthouse – all of them part of the same luxury complex. The *tabacalera* is owned by a Russian who travels personally to the Dominican Republic to source his cigars. Barely large enough to seat 10 people, Gloria cigar lounge comprises two tables in their own niche, fitted to the summit of Bond villain/country hotel style, with thick leather armchairs, dark wood and discreet lighting. Here you can enjoy the largest selection of Dominican cigars in Tallinn, with a coffee or a cognac. We advise booking in advance; cigar tastings and lectures can also be arranged.

Hell Hunt, Pikk 39.
Tel: 681 83 33 www.hellhunt.ee
Open: noon–late daily

Reputedly the first ever pub in Estonia (built in 1993), Hell Hunt reopened this year under new management, with the aim of targeting visitors and locals looking for more reasonable prices than currently found in the main bars of the old town. With a logo designed to entice the lads (naked lady on running wolf), Hell Hunt also has plenty of charm – with a large, tastefully designed interior situated in one of Tallinn's quiet, historic streets. Only

time will tell how Hell Hunt's clientele will develop, but with the management focused on making this place a top party venue and Tallinnites' natural interest in new venues, you can expect plenty of action in its opening year.

Kaheksa, Vana-Posti 8 (door on Müürivahe).
Tel: 627 47 70 kaheksa@bdg.ee
Open: noon–midnight (2am Wednesday–Thursday,
4am Friday–Saturday) daily

Kaheksa is still the uncontested meeting-place for Tallinn's richer and more discerning patrons – a mix of media types, party animals and affluent professionals. The bar is located right next to famous Hollywood club (owned by the same company) but is aimed at an older, more choosy market. The room is laid out as a simple square, decorated according to a tropical theme with plants and bamboos surrounding an amphitheatric lounge area in the middle – full of comfy sofas and excellent for people-watching. Come on a Friday night for the real buzz, when practically everyone in Tallinn seems to pass through Kaheksa at least once on their way to parties or clubs. The drinks menu is dominated by good cocktails and non-alcoholic fruit drinks. If you want to get into Hollywood ask the bar staff and they will lead you through a side door to shortcut the queue. '*Kaheksa*' means 'eight', a shorthand often used by regulars.

Kolme Näoga Mees, Kuninga 1.
Tel: 648 42 61
Open: noon–11pm (midnight Friday–Saturday) daily

This intimate, beautifully decorated wine bar is hard to classify – with its thick sofas and lounging niches, it looks the sort of ultra-cosy café where you could sit all day with a hot chocolate and a good paper. KNM is less than two years old, but it exudes a Renaissance charm – housed in an ancient cellar adorned with a gorgeous antique fireplace and thick covered sofas. And although it feels laid-back, this comfortable cave is almost always buzzing with activity – popular with locals as well as tourists (who often land up here accidentally, as it neighbours a strip of tourist pubs). Owned and managed by an Estonian mother-and-daughter team, KNM classifies itself as a wine bar rather than the more formal *vinoteek* since it offers not only 200-odd wines from the cellar at the back but also a large selection of cakes, sandwiches, *tortillas* and hot drinks – and a proper Italian coffee machine.

Kompressor Bar, Rataskaevu 3.
Tel: 646 42 10
Open: 11am–1am (3am Friday–Saturday) daily

Kompressor is a favourite haunt of younger Estonians, playing the more grungy varieties of pop and enticing a student clientele with its budget prices and almost-trendy interior. Set right next to the Old Town Square on a gorgeous medieval street, the bar nevertheless manages to avoid attracting the day-trippers and package tourists that dominate the neighbourhood. Kompressor is a huge, loft-like space with exposed ceilings and vast windows looking right onto the street. A good place to view the younger

contingent of Tallinn society, get drunk, eat a light meal or watch cable TV projected onto the back wall. Alongside standard bar fare you can also enjoy Newcastle brown, Hoogvein and a *smorgasbord* of sweet and savoury pancakes, apparently the best and largest in Tallinn. The kitchen usually stays open until 10pm.

Kristostomus Kolumbus , Viru 24.
Tel: 627 74 64 kristostomus.kolumbus@mail.ee
Open: noon–midnight (1am Friday–Saturday) daily

A cheery, playful pub located right next to Tallinn's historic Viru gate, but not yet completely swamped by tourists. Climb the stairs to reach this sprawling establishment, decorated with rabbits and ducks painted white on sangria-coloured walls across two main rooms and a dog-leg full of quieter spots around the corner. The animal theme extends to the long wooden tables in the middle of the room, where fanciful animal hides – zebras, cows and even racoons – sprawl across the varnished surfaces. A stage dominates the main room, where karaoke on Tuesdays draws a teenage to 20-something crowd, offering unusual festivity on a slow weekday night. On other nights there are live acts (call to check). Drop by once if only for the décor, which resembles a charming, cheerful, adult's nursery, complemented by waitresses costumed in 17th-century maid outfits.

Kuku klubi, Vabaduse väljak 8.
Tel: 644 10 98 kuku@hot.ee
Open: noon–midnight (2am Thursday–Saturday, 8pm Sunday)

A destination for the more earnest, less yuppie arty set. Kuku was one of the first private member clubs in Tallinn – and it still has the air of an exclusive nightspot, with its black bay tables,

low lights, a string of subterranean rooms organized around the main bar, and a small stage for live music. Although the really trendy set moved on a while ago, you still feel as if you're rubbing shoulders with the film-makers, writers and Gauloise smokers of the next generation. Mellow without being grungy, this low-lit club is now open to all – an unsung hideout full of regulars – although don't expect an extravagant welcome: everyone here knows each other already, and the bar menu comes in Estonian only. The bar dates back to 1935, and is connected to the artists' studios in the building above and the artists' café on the ground floor. Kuku serves hearty, good quality Estonian meals at very affordable prices, and puts on live music on weekends.

McCools, Suur Karja 20/Pärnu mnt. 12.
Tel: 640 35 48 www.jjj-bars.com
Open: 5pm–2am (4am Friday–Saturday) daily

Don't be put off by the unpromising fast-food logo of McCools – inside this huge new bar complex (which also includes restaurant

China White) there should be something for everyone. Right in the firing line of the busy Old Town drinking strip but hidden in an upstairs room, McCools is in fact two completely different bars – a vast main room with an eye-catching oval bar, and an intimate wine bar at the back that hosts mellow live music and jazz. At weekends the place is roaring with activity and atmosphere – the 20-somethings crowded around the main bar can view each other from all angles, while more laid-back types lounge in the stylish seating area or slink into the wine bar for a completely different vibe. A huge screen at the back of the room shows pop videos and 'Fashion TV' by night, but by day McCools is contending to become the venue of choice for sports fans.

Moskva, Vabaduse väljak 10.
Tel: 640 46 94 www.moskva.ee
Open: 8.30am–midnight Monday–Friday; 11am–midnight Saturday–Sunday

Moskva is a famous café, bar and restaurant set over two floors of a former Soviet establishment looking out over Vabaduse ('Freedom') Square. It's now one of Tallinn's favourite spots, popular with a young but smart crowd drawn by the affordable chic. The bar occupies the second floor alongside the restaurant – where trendy young Estonians work on laptops while they drink cappuccinos. If you bring your own computer, wireless internet access is free and fast. Later on, the bar starts to fill out, with DJs from 8pm. On Fridays Moskva turns itself into a proper

nightclub, with themed parties (R&B, or retro, for example).
These are usually packed: good music draws a happy crowd and,
if you are in the mood for lounging, there is enough space to
chill out away from the dance-floor. The design is minimalist: low
lighting, tubular chandeliers and waitresses chosen for their
looks in red air-hostess uniforms. After a while you may start to
feel as if you are spending time on someone's private jet some
time in the 1970s. The loos are unisex with glittery seats.

Nimega Baar, Suur-Karja 13.
Tel: 641 15 15 www.jjj-bars.com
Open: 11am–2am (4am Friday–Saturday) daily

A famous meeting-place for foreigners and locals, Nimega is one
of the fixtures of the Suur-Karja pub strip. Enter through a modest façade to discover one of the longest pubs in Tallinn – a small

bar in front leads through a long corridor to the main bar and a dance-floor. Roam on to find two more rooms before Nimega finally peters out into a chill-out area at the back. During the week Nimega is more relaxed, and makes a great place for a quiet drink. If you're alone, prop up the bar for an hour or so and you are almost guaranteed to meet someone in this laid-back melting pot of ex-pats and travellers. At weekends Nimega becomes a proper party venue, with a crowded disco that stays open until the early hours – for many locals it's a lower-budget alternative to the big, expensive nightclubs. Decidedly seedy, but there is no better place to meet people and get talking.

Novell Bar, Narva mnt. 7c.
Tel: 633 98 91 www.revalhotels.com
Open: noon–11pm (1am Friday–Saturday) daily

Novell Bar came into being at the same time as Reval Central's slick new restaurant to compete with the top end of Tallinn's trendy establishments. Today it doubles as a stunning urban bar, facing the world through huge plate-glass windows, which look out over one of Tallinn's busiest commercial streets. Spanned by a gorgeous yellow light-mural, Novell is one of Tallinn's most stylish establishments. Come here to watch Estonian *Sex in the City* types from the nearby office and shopping district congregate for cocktails after work. Novell is a good 5-minute walk from the

Old Town, giving its clientele a definitively local, professional flavour – although it has a way to go before it catches the real

in-crowd. On Fridays and Saturdays there is a DJ to add an extra touch of glamour to the lounging.

Pegasus, Harju 1.
Tel: 631 40 40 www.restoranpegasus.ee
Open: 10am–2am. Closed Sunday.

Definitely on the in-list, Pegasus has been the meeting-place of choice for trendy, affluent Tallinners since it opened in the 1990s.

Located on the ground floor of the celebrated Pegasus restaurant, the modish traveller will immediately feel at home in the modernist bar with its futuristic porthole windows, metal spiral staircase and weird Braille-like art fixtures. Come to enjoy the freshly squeezed orange juice at breakfast, a relaxing afternoon coffee, or an inventive cocktail (try out blueberry *mojito*, cherry margarita or pineapple daiquiri). Pegasus also serves freshly made ice-cream shakes and smoothies, a rarity in Tallinn. The bar gets busiest on Friday nights, when the party crowd arrives for pre-clubbing drinks.

Popular Café, Vana-Viru 6.
Tel: 056 951 442 www.popular.ee
Open: 9am–1am (4am Friday–Saturday) daily

Patronized by modish, well-dressed students and 20-somethings, Popular Café may not offer the warmest of welcomes – staff and customers here are generally too cool to smile. But this doesn't mean you can't have a great night out in this small designer joint. With minimalist décor, clubby music, and a strikingly designed bar, Popular stands out not only for its clientele

but also for its opium-den atmosphere. Hookah pipes are available for rent with a range of flavoured tobaccos – making this place a refreshing alternative to the British and Scandinavian drink-culture approach to nightlife. If you are unsure about coming in, then walk past the door a couple of times: you can see the entire bar and everyone in it through the plate-glass window.

Scotland Yard, Mere pst. 6e.
Tel: 653 51 90 www.scotlandyard.ee
Open: noon–midnight (3am Thursday–Saturday) daily

With its black wooden tables, deep-red leather armchairs, sprawling bookcases and wood panelled ceilings, Scotland Yard may look at first like the typical British pub export, with a dash of cigar lounge thrown in. But with clever design, a nightclub lay-out, wall-length aquarium and some good-looking clientele, this is a stylish take on the traditional pub – which manages to feel intimate despite its enormous size. Some kitschy touches include waitresses in police uniforms with handcuffs (popular with the stag weekend crowd, although we didn't see much evidence of them here). A great place for a wild night on the large dance-floor or a relaxing, comfortable hideaway for a cigar and a quiet drink (the mezzanine bar around the back). On Sundays and Mondays Scotland Yard hosts live rock bands, with live jazz and piano on Tuesdays and Wednesdays.

Sigari Maja (Davidoff), Raekoja plats 16.
Tel: 631 47 35
Open: 11am–midnight (4pm Sunday) daily

Walking into Sigari Maja is like entering a surreal world – from the bustling medieval square straight into a London gentleman's club. A cigar lounge specializing in Dominican (Davidoff) cigars, you enter through a corridor past the main shop/*humidor* and friendly reception desk into a large room done up in the

plutocratic style of a Churchillian hideaway – thick armchairs clustered in intimate groups, open fires and low lighting. Built inside a beautiful 16th-century room, there is just enough Renaissance-style eccentricity to raise this cigar lounge above stuffy and sombre – although there are usually plenty of suits and serious conversations in the thick of the room that provide great opportunities for eavesdroppers. A smaller lounge at the back houses the bar, for a range of whiskies, cognacs and other cigar-friendly tipples.

Veinipööning, 4th floor, Viru 18.
Tel: 641 86 31
Open: 4pm–midnight (2am Saturday, 10pm Sunday) daily

Set in a secluded attic space above the main old town shopping street, you will only find Veinipööning ('wine attic') if you know it's there. There is no sign outside and you will have to walk upstairs past a glitzy casino and an Estonian tourist restaurant before reaching this mecca of quiet vinophiles and romantic corners. August Alop, the amiable Estonian owner, is a veteran of the business – he started his first wine bar at the top of the famous Viru hotel, then moved to this more discreet location in the late

1990s. Aiming for a cosy, informal atmosphere, Veinipööning achieves a laid-back, living-room quality with an esoteric, clubbish feel, growing its clientele through word of mouth and actively avoiding the tourist trade that passes under its very nose.

Consequently half of the bar's customers are locals, the other half long-term ex-pats who know the city well. The attic can be open as late as 4am, bustling with wine-adoring couples, private receptions and customers popping in to buy a crate from the wine merchant business.

X-Baar, Sauna 1.
Tel: 620 92 66 www.zone.ee/xbaar
Open: 2pm–1am daily

Open since 1998, X-Baar is the oldest gay bar in Estonia and still a popular nightspot for both sexes (the business is owned by two women). Located in one of the narrow, characterful alleys that runs off touristy Viru Street, the bar is discreet but welcoming – with a pleasant, atmospheric interior and subdued, arty lighting. X-Baar attracts a good mixture of customers, local and foreign, and there are regular parties and events to lift the atmosphere – including the 2003 gay Estonian song competition (only four contestants!). With a small dance-floor and relaxed opening hours, X-Baar has no trouble keeping its loyal customers happy. It's at its busiest from 8pm to midnight.

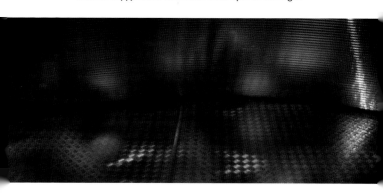

snack...

Looking at the range and quality of Tallinn's cafés and tea shops, you would never suspect that many of them were opened in the last decade. Café life, so well suited to this city, with its long, cold winters and winding alleys, was given little outlet during Soviet times – with some famous exceptions. Today cafe culture has taken off with a vengeance, reflecting the demand from tourists as well as the natives' own fondness for caffeine, reasonably priced food and good old chit-chat. Today there is something for everyone in Tallinn, from tourists looking for a hasty snack or visitors wishing to lounge in the arty atmosphere of an independent cinema. Cosy, candlelit hot chocolate specialists sit alongside slick, modern eateries. Bustling local cafés just outside the Old Town teem with real Estonian life and conversation.

In striking contrast with other European cultures, Tallinn's cafés were not traditionally the preserve of men. Politics and other weighty issues were discussed elsewhere, or in private. You will find the majority of the city's café-goers to be women, of all ages – from teenage students to venerable ladies meeting for their daily tea-cake in elegant, *belle epoque* Maiasmokk. Estonian males seem to prefer their discussions over a beer. Not that this is a problem in Tallinn's cafés – most serve basic alcoholic drinks as well as tea and coffee, including the ever popular 'Vana Tallinn', a heart-warming traditional schooner favoured in winter, and hot

glögs (mulled wine). Many cafés also offer an excellent selection of herbal and loose fresh teas – better than you will find in most UK or American cafés – reflecting the influence of Canadian entrepreneurs and a fondness for camomile.

Another likeable feature of Estonian cafés is their approach to food. While many establishments stick with the traditional cake and pastry approach (often delicious, although not usually world-class), an increasing number of cafés serve hot meals and light snacks – ranging from savoury pancakes to full pasta dishes. Others neighbour busy restaurants and share the same kitchen, offering similar quality at more accessible prices.

Finally, Tallinn cafés are a great nexus between visitors, ex-pats and the better-travelled, younger, English-speaking Estonians. It is well worth spending some time in the city's wonderful cafés getting to know the friendly locals.

Boga Pott, Pikk jalg 9.
Tel: 631 31 81
Open: 10am–6pm daily

Tucked inside a little courtyard, next to a craft shop on the main walkway up to the medieval hill, Boga Pott remains, surprisingly, an authentic and pleasant spot for a snack. Its tiny size means it's unsuitable for tour groups, although its location makes it a natural destination for foreign visitors. The café draws an endearing, art-shop atmosphere from the tourist boutique next door, which specializes in ceramics made on site – all the café's cups and saucers come from the same kiln. With a door linking the two outlets there are always staff from the shop hanging out in the café, giving it a cheerful, local feel that balances out the foreign clientele. If you don't look carefully you will miss the fantastic, almost invisible mezzanine upstairs – barely enough space for two tables, tucked into an ancient stone grotto, complete with miniature ceramic cherubim hanging off the ceiling like angelic bats. The café offers light snacks, soups and cakes as well as standard drinks. In summertime enjoy the courtyard terrace.

Le Bonaparte, Pikk 45.
Tel: 646 44 44 bonaparte@bonaparte.ee
Open: 8am–8pm Monday–Saturday; 10am–6pm Sunday

The Bonaparte café doubles as a little restaurant in its own right, serving a range of light meals, salads and soups from early morn-

ing until 10pm. Hidden from the street by a heavy medieval door this cosy, luxurious café is a favourite spot for locals and ex-pats alike. It shares the same characterful ambience and careful service as the luxury restaurant just behind it, and the food is prepared in the Bonaparte kitchen with the same degree of care, and with similarly well-chosen ingredients. With its medieval feel, heavy wooden beams, tall rustic windows and ancient-looking door, the café is a great turn on the posh French formula and a delightful spot to enjoy a quick bite, a cup of tea or a glass of wine. Enjoy the delicious spread of home-baked French pastries, from croissants and *pains aux raisins* to *millefeuilles* and gorgeous tarts – baked downstairs during the night, using butter and flour imported from abroad to meet the exacting standards of the owners. Bonaparte also serves as an art gallery, showcasing the work of individual painters whose work can be purchased from the café.

Café Anglais, Raekoja plats 14.
Tel: 644 21 60.
Open: 11am–11pm daily

Unusually for a café on Town Hall Square, the Anglais is a joint not shunned by locals, who flock to this former ambassador's house – along with the more knowing ex-pats – for the great atmosphere, soft jazz and splendid view of the square. Tucked behind large windows on the first floor you can spy the famous Town Hall Square without being seen by the flocks of tourists taking pictures and buying souvenirs all year round. In summer the Anglais has a tourist-friendly terrace in the sun – for the rest of the year it lurks upstairs like a well-kept secret, via a downstairs entrance shared with a music school and an art gallery. Serving good coffees and teas, beautifully prepared hot chocolate or wine and cocktails, this versatile meeting-place also serves light meals throughout the day. At 8pm every night a pianist joins the party to lull customers with live jazz and lounge music. We only regret that the Anglais closes so early – it's the sort of place you wish would stay open all night.

Café Boulevard, Olümpia Hotel, Liivalaia 33.
Tel: 631 58 89 www.revalhotels.com
Open: 24 hours

This slick modern bakery is a great place to sit out the early hours of the weekend watching the nightclubbers and sleepwalkers doing their thing. Café Boulevard is part of the giant Olümpia Hotel but is used as much if not more by non-residents, entered by its own front door or the imposing, redesigned lobby. A popular place for rendezvous of all kinds, the café manages to stay busy at all hours – not least with party people from the hotel's nightclub Bonnie & Clyde on the other side of the foyer, although you are just as likely to find politicians or businessmen stooped over a coffee. Good hot and cold snacks are available around the clock – from pizza and soups to cakes and desserts. With its red and white motif, the café's spacious design is a refreshing treat.

Café Elsebet, Viru 2.
Tel: 646 69 98 www.peppersack.ee
Open: 8am–10pm daily

Part of the same medieval-themed complex as the Peppersack
restaurant and the Kolme Kana grill, Café Elsebet takes up the
second floor of this beautiful old merchant's house right next to
Town Hall Square. The café has its own front door on the main
road, but you can also enter through the picturesque main
restaurant, ascending fairy-lit wooden steps over the heads of
tourist-bus diners and the heraldic emblems of Hanseatic *burgermeisters*. Strangely shaped but Tardis-like in size, Elsebet forms a
quadrangle of four rooms – the busiest being a long corridor
full of tables, which somehow manages to work. The café's
upstairs location makes it popular with locals, and when it's busy

there is a lot of atmosphere in the low-lit rooms (it's possibly the largest candlelit café you are ever likely to come across). Now more than 13 years old, the business is undergoing ambitious renovations, espousing the city restaurants' familiar medieval theme. In the meantime expect to enjoy standard café fare, or porridge, pancakes and 'hot bread and butter' dishes as well as light meals.

Café Mocha, Vene 1.
Tel: 644 64 73
Open: 8am–11pm daily

A tourist café redeemed by a charming balcony overlooking an evocative, full-size mural of Estonia's parliament hill as it might have looked in the 18th century. Downstairs a spacious and attractive room can be a little too close to the bustling crowds on Town Hall Square for comfort. Laminated menus with photographs of the different options add to the touristy feel. But sneak upstairs to the mezzanine for a slice of cake in a more secluded and romantic spot. Like most cafés in Tallinn, Mocha also serves a variety of alcoholic drinks such as 'Vana Tallinn' (literally 'Old Tallinn', the local answer to Jägermeister), or simply wine and beer, as well as coffees and teas in a range of flavours. If you're lucky, try to grab the table in the alcove by the window for a rare view of the cobbled streets in the most central part of medieval Tallinn.

Café Moskva, Vabaduse väljak 10.
Tel: 640 46 94 www.moskva.ee
Open: 8.30am–midnight Monday–Friday;
11am–midnight Saturday–Sunday

Moskva is part of a two-storey enterprise that combines café,
restaurant, bar and club in one loungey whole redolent of the
New York scene. Overlooking Vabaduse ('Freedom') Square, the
café is a great place to sit back and watch Tallinn's beautiful
people, drawn by the all-day club music, stylish décor and internet access. The café is often packed with solitary young Estonians

at work on their laptops while they drink cappuccinos – if you
bring your own computer, wireless access is free and fast. Come
here for a cream cake, a cocktail or a properly brewed pot of
tea, but don't expect an old-fashioned welcome from the cool
staff. You can sit downstairs by the window on the square –
where passers-by can spot you from the street – or head
upstairs to the restaurant/bar. Design is minimalist and fun: low
lighting, tubular chandeliers and waitresses in red air-hostess
uniforms.

Café Palace, Palace Hotel, Vabaduse väljak 3.
Tel: 640 74 00 www.scandic-hotels.com
Open: 11am–11.30pm daily

Located on the ground floor of the Scandic Hotel but with its own entrance and a distinct identity, the Café Palace is one of the busiest and most 'local' of the hotel cafés. Situated in a crowded office district just outside the Old Town, the Palace attracts an interesting mixture of business and office workers as well as personal rendezvous. Tables are arranged in a series of intimate booths by a long window overlooking busy Parnu Street, or you can sit in the mezzanine landing tucked away behind discreet partitions. Low lights and poker-faced hotel staff add to the quiet and cosy ambience, and a restaurant-quality menu (from the same kitchen as sister 'Restoran Palace' next door) offers everything from snacks to full meals. Order sandwiches, salads or interesting omelettes for a quick lunch or go for a full meal, with items ranging from 'black pudding flavoured with vodka' to 'salmon and coconut soup'. Pizzas and a children's menu are also available as well as delicious, tempting desserts. Hot drinks come served with a delicious *madeleine*.

Café Peterson, Narva mnt. 15.
Tel: 662 34 85
Open: 8am–11pm Monday–Friday; 10am–11pm Saturday–Sunday

A fairly long yomp down Narva mnt. from the Old Town, but worth the trip. Opened in late 2003, Café Peterson is among the most stylish and comfortable in Tallinn. Come before 11am for the breakfast *du jour* – a huge pot of porridge or a range of breakfast cereals and croissants, as well as freshly squeezed orange juice. Tasty flavoured pastries and other savoury snacks

are available all day. Relax on big cushions around the banquettes by the windows and walls, and enjoy laid-back lounge music and local modern art from the gallery next door – which adds a bit of eccentricity to the café's cool Nordic simplicity. Café Peterson is popular with trendy students and staff from Tallinn University, only a few hundred yards away.

Chocolaterie Café, Vene 6.
Tel: 641 80 61
Open: 10am–10pm daily

Chocolate is treated with almost religious reverence in this tiny candlelit cafeteria, which sits alongside an atelier in a hidden courtyard off Vene Street. The staff will react with humour if you ask for 'cocoa' – their speciality is real melted chocolate, piping hot, served with a stick of cinnamon and made in three flavours (as well as 'classic'): gorgonzola and grappa, rum and raisin, or chilli. Also on offer are proper sweeties – home-made (chilli) flavoured chocolate as well as delicious cakes. There is an opium-den feel to Chocolaterie: hushed female voices in an intimate, antique-shop sitting room bursting with relics (a plaster bust with a hat on, an old piano, ill-assorted chairs and wax-covered candlesticks). Music is played low – a welcome departure from most Estonian cafés. This is one of Tallinn's favourite secrets – it remains popular with locals (and especially women) despite the healthy prices. A

133

perfect place for an afternoon date, and cheerfully full by early evening.

CityGourmet, Maakri 36.
Tel: 056 498 839 www.citygourmet.ee
Open: 8am–11pm Monday–Thursday; 8am–1am Friday;
10am–1am Saturday; 11am–11pm Sunday

A stunningly decorated deli-café in the buzzing modern centre of Tallinn, near the Radisson hotel. CityGourmet is a new venture with a cool, foody ambience, aiming to fill the gap for excellent imported foods and wines. With its huge plate-glass window, dense wooden tables and fragrant deli produce, this laid-back café charms the senses in every way. It's an excellent place to drop in for a bite of *antipasto*, some great coffee or a quality glass of wine. Located near to all the serious shopping (the department stores Kaubamaja and Stockmann) and Tallinn's busi-

ness district, CityGourmet is likely to attract an up-market, professional local crowd.

Controvento Café, Vene 12/Katariina Käik.
Tel: 644 04 70
Open: noon–midnight (1am Friday–Saturday) daily

One of Estonia's most famous Italian restaurants, Controvento also offers a cosy, picturesque downstairs café located in tiny Katariina alley – framed by the crumbling wall of a medieval church and a row of indecipherable 14th-century tomb stones. Enjoy perfect coffee next to the open fireplace or sip on *spritzers* next to the cool Italian bar. Tiny Controvento café-bar shares a kitchen with the celebrated restaurant upstairs – so you

can enjoy light meals or even a full menu in the relaxed atmosphere downstairs, where staff joke behind the bar or chat with regular clients. It has a smaller selection of cakes and pastries than many Tallinn cafés, but the wide variety of light meals available from the restaurant makes it a versatile place for a quick bite – and it's one of the few places in Tallinn where you can find proper decaffeinated espresso. A glam and gorgeous hideaway from the tourist crowds.

Deli 24, Estonia pst 1 (in the Melon centre).
Tel: 630 65 45 www.deli24.ee
Open: 24 hours

An all-night café and convenience store, Deli 24 provides everything you might possibly need from a midnight shopping trip short of live ammunition. Alongside racks of beer, wine and spirits you can pick up razors, condoms, fresh fruit or washing powder – or even rent a video. Deli 24 also offers one of Tallinn's best value hot buffets, charged by the gram, or 24-hour cappuccino from the Coffee Tops concession. Loungers take a seat inside the futuristic café, which is arranged in a thin strip along the window of the Melon shopping centre, looking out over one of the busiest walkways in modern Tallinn. Sit here to watch the droves of shoppers and commuters that pass by this busy street, but be ready for an audience. Partly because of the post-industrial, electric green lighting you can see them and they can see you seeing them. It's a bit chilly compared with the over-heated store inside, but well worth the 5-minute detour outside Disneyland Old Town to Tallinn's most important shopping area. And there's free wireless internet access for laptop users.

Demini Café, Demini Shopping Centre, Viru 1/Vene 2.
Tel: 667 51 35
Open: 8am–7pm (5pm Sunday) daily

Comfy sofas, bright tiles and the clack-clack of smart ladies going shopping make this little shopping-centre café an unexpectedly pleasant place for a quick stop. You won't lounge here for hours – you're sitting at the bottom of an elegant stairway leading up to the corner of Tallinn's busiest medieval street, and around you are four floors of shopping. But it's a great spot for people-watching, both on the stairs and the floor above, which provide an almost 360° catwalk all around you. Underneath the stairs there's a little internet café – four computers tucked out of sight for privacy and available for 35kr per hour, or 5kr per 5 minutes. Lunchtime salads and snacks are also available as well as beer and spirits for the very bored. Demini café is one of the few places where good old elevator music seems completely appropriate.

Energia Khovik, Kaubamaja 4.
Tel: 660 47 06.
Open: 8am–8pm Monday–Saturday; 10am–6pm Sunday

For a cheerful, authentic Soviet shopping experience pop across the road from the famous Kaubamaja department store into this bustling, smoky café that has not changed much since 1964, when it was first opened by three Estonian sisters (who still run the place). Old ladies in fur coats rub shoulders with shop work-ers smoking roll-ups and office types from the businesses that crowd this part of the city – making Energia one of the best places to watch real Tallinn at work. It's often full to the brim, so you may have to wait for a table while you take in the chintzy wooden décor and the Estonian radio station on the overhead. This is a cosy place to try out some fattening local cakes, pas-tries and blinis (with fish, roe and ham). One of the prettiest entrances of any café, since you enter Energia through a tiny florist's. The same people also own the smaller, more modern café next door.

Gateway, Suur-Karja 17–19.
Tel: 644 67 03
Open: 9am–9pm daily

A great place for a coffee and a pastry, Gateway looks out over busy Suur-Karja street and the hectic traffic on the edge of the medieval town, where old and new Tallinn meet. Partly due to its prominent location this decade-old café is full of Estonian worker bees – you can enjoy the buzz of conversation and clinking spoons here at breakfast, lunch or tea time. With adequate (although luke-warm) lattés and cappuccinos, Gateway also serves some delicious sweet pastries bought from Papa Carlos' bakery across the square as well as a few traditional savoury

pastries made with carrot, cabbage or sausage.

Illusioon Café, Müürivahe 50/Uus 3.
Tel: 641 98 33
Open: 9am–10pm daily

There are times when this little café, tucked behind the
Kinomaja art cinema in the middle of the ancient city wall,
becomes one of the busiest places in town. During the annual
student film festival or other events organized by the cinema
Illusioon fills up with *literati* and film students earnestly drinking
flavoured tea from glass strainer pots. At other times it can be
completely empty – a nice surprise for the visitor tired of feeling
like a tourist. Literally hidden, because it has no front door of its
own, you must enter via the restaurant of the same name or
sneak through the foyer of the cinema. If you want a peaceful
drink in the company of the local media set, then this is the
place to be. The Kinomaja is Tallinn's only independent cinema,
and the café has the arty ambience to go with it. It also serves a
delicious selection of savoury pastries.

International Press Café, Viru 23.
Tel: 654 84 85
Open: 10am–8pm Monday–Friday; 10am–6pm Saturday;
11am–4pm Sunday

Once you stumble on this unexpected café upstairs from the

Apollo bookshop, you may end up spending hours flicking through newspapers or books while you sip a fresh herbal tea or a beautifully prepared hot chocolate. Brought to you by the same Canadian entrepreneur who created Le Chocolaterie and the much-loved Kehrwieder, IPC has a similar approach to music – not too intrusive and perfect for arty lounging – and an almost religious respect for the well-made hot drink. Its excellent pastries are perfect for breakfast, if you wake up too late for your hotel porridge. Internet access is available on two terminals at reasonable prices.

Karoliina, Harju 6.
Open: 11am–10pm daily

Eccentric, tiny and cosy, Karoliina may be the smallest bar/café you ever see. Built inside an old stone tunnel in the foothill of historic Toompea the place bears more than a passing resemblance to an old-fashioned bomb shelter, while lamps made from replica cannon suggest that perhaps that you might be sitting inside the chamber of a large medieval gun. Karoliina has enough room, however, for a single file of tables up against one wall, making this an intimate and fun spot for a drink. The bar tucked in at the back serves tea, cake and drinks, including *glög* (mulled wine) and everything else you might need to sit out the war. It's popular in the winter for its warm character, but summer may find it less crowded – although its location beside some of

Tallinn's top historical sites should guarantee it a steady business. Karoliina is decorated with plastic ivy, black-dyed animal skins and copies of the Jehovah's Witness magazine for good measure.

Kehrwieder, Saiakang 1.
Open: 11am–midnight daily

One of Tallinn's most characterful cafés, Kehrwieder is tucked away just below street level in an alley between Town Hall Square and the warren of the medieval city. Inside this tiny Aladdin's cave you will find candlelit tables, around which are crammed softly spoken regulars playing board games, chatting and whiling away the hours. A favourite of students and younger Tallinites, customers are drawn by the intimate atmosphere, the laid-back music and the wicked hot drinks – lovingly prepared

chocolate and Irish coffees, *glög* (mulled wine) and great cakes.
The tone is set by stone walls and a hodge-podge of tables, sofas
and chairs from old houses. If you like Kehrwieder then you will
also enjoy Tristan ja Isolde and Chocolaterie, two cafés brought
to you by the same Canadian entrepreneur, a lover of herbal
teas and rich coffees.

Maiasmokk, Pikk 16.
Tel: 646 40 70
Open: 8am–7pm Monday–Saturday; 10am–6pm Sunday

Maiasmokk has been a café for over a hundred years, so if you
want a genuinely Estonian institution – rather than something
skilfully invented in the last five years for tourists – then come
here for a bite of famous cake. Although we found the pastries
no better than in any other Tallinn café (and even a bit mar-
gariney) you cannot help but be enticed by the display of gateaux
in the window. There is a similar air of venerability here, and the
café is apparently a favourite meeting-place for older Estonian
ladies, as well as students and tourists earnestly hunched over
their cream cakes. Here you'll find old-fashioned attitudes to coffee and tea – don't expect a hundred flavours of mochaccino.
Come instead for the carved wood panels, the mirrored walls
and the ornate, marbled ceilings. This is as old Estonian as it gets.

Napsikamber, Lühike jalg 9.
Tel: 648 90 20 www.hot.ee/napsikamber
Open: 11am–10pm daily

Tucked into a corner of the beetling path up to Toompea Hill,
the entrance to Napsikamber is through a little whitewashed
hut, which forms part of the fortifications of old Tallinn. Hidden
downstairs like a cheerful little ski café, the restaurant is built
inside a cosy, stone tunnel which might have been a soldier's
bunker or a medieval chapel but, in fact, was simply the old
storehouse for the watchmaker across the road. Napsikamber
serves a mixture of standard Estonian and heart-warming
Russian dishes, in a rustic, unassuming atmosphere, which are
perfect for a sustaining lunch in the middle of a tough day of
sightseeing. This little bolt-hole has been plodding away for 20
years, making it one of the oldest restaurants in Tallinn. All food
comes with a rack of white and black bread, Tabasco and
Worcester sauce, as well as strong Estonian mustard. It doubles
as a cellar bar in the evenings and, with no more than 20 or so
seats, it can get crowded.

Narva Kohvik, Narva mnt.10.
Tel: 660 17 86
Open: 9am–8pm Monday–Friday; 10am–8pm Saturday;
10am–6pm Sunday

If you are looking for a taste of authentic Eastern-bloc charm or some real faded, post-war elegance, you will have to walk 5 or 10 minutes out of the Old Town and into the real, bustling world that is central Tallinn to find this spot, situated on busy, commercial Narva mnt. Unmistakeable, with its large, smoky windows and pink velour curtains, this old Soviet favourite is still crowded with local office workers, shoppers, and the odd trendy retro fan. Sit in dark wooden booths and drink a no-nonsense coffee or a stiff brandy – or try one of the largest selections of cakes and cookies in Tallinn from the home bakery – 29 types at last count, including the mysterious '*papaverous* roll'. There's no knowing in advance what a *Sotnik* cake or a 'Sand Bar' will look like, so you just have to be adventurous. Small meals and salads are also available, and everything at reasonable, working-people prices. Don't expect fancy coffees or big smiles from the staff – American café culture has yet to penetrate Narva café. For the time being this is a national treasure undiscovered by the tourist trade. Just pray they don't decide to 'renovate'.

Rae Kohvik, Raekoja plats 10.
Tel: 644 39 88
Open: 10am–10pm daily

Just below pavement level, Rae café is a cosy place to sit and watch the legs of the world go by. With perfect views of the Old Town Hall with its national and city flags – and the medieval roofs of Hanseatic merchant houses, the location is unbeatable.

There is a pleasant, subterranean feel to the place, which doubles as both coffee shop and wine bar. Like many Tallinn cafés, Rae serves light meals including salads and delicious local soups – and a couple of cakes, although the pastry selection is limited.

Choose from a mind-boggling range of Italian coffee styles, from 'espresso lungo' (watered down) and 'espresso corretto' (with cognac) to caffé latte flavoured with toffee, amarillo or vanilla. You can sit in a nice little alcove or stand at the window and just stare out into the world. There may be too many Scandinavian tourists for your liking but the atmosphere is good. Owned by Estonians with their hands on a good Italian coffee machine.

Rossini, Raekoja plats 8.
Tel: 641 12 20 www.rossini.ee
Open: 8.30am–midnight (2am Friday–Saturday) daily

Right next to Fellini restaurant, this smart little corner café continues the theme of famous Italians on the Old Town square. Styled in stained pine with touches of ruby red, this is a good-looking place if you like colder, minimalist décor. The best thing about this café is the fabulous location and its cool, ungimicky atmosphere: it doesn't attract the snappers and sightseers (although it can't escape them during the high season, when the terrace café spills onto the cobbles to soak up the atmosphere of the famous square). Like so many 'ethnic' establishments in Tallinn, Rossini is owned, staffed and managed by Estonians –

who simply thought 'Italian' was a great idea. Chill on hard seats
to interesting, laid-back lounge music.

Stockmann Café, Liivalaia 53.
Tel: 633 95 99
Open: 9am–9pm (8pm Saturday–Sunday) daily

Drop into this modish little café if you are shopping in Tallinn's
modern city centre and fancy a good break or need to collect
your email. Stockmann café is located on the second floor of the
Stockmann department store – one of the two largest shops in
Tallinn. Confronted by the hot pink walls and coloured spotlights
of this sizeable corner café, you might almost imagine yourself in
a nightclub, an impression reinforced by the good-looking clientele who seem willing to put their shopping aside and relax.

Delicious sweet and savoury pancakes are made on the spot, plus a range of hot and cold snacks.

Tristan ja Isolde, Raekoja Plats 1.
Tel: 644 87 59
Open: 8am–11pm daily

Probably Tallinn's smallest cafeteria, built in the ramparts of the Town Hall, Tristan and Isolde is named after the famous medieval couple celebrated in a wood carving in the state rooms. Although it is located in tourist-central (on the corner of the square) there is something enjoyable and secretive about this tiny den that attracts loyal locals as well as visitors. Sit next to old grill windows and enjoy soft jazz while you savour a delicious croissant or sample the selection of coffees and fresh herbal teas. Candlelit, intimate and dark – a great place for a date.

party...

Tallinn has fantastic nightlife, which in many ways is still developing – part of its charm is the intimacy of the scene. With few alternatives in each area and a couple of mega-clubs that everyone still goes to, you will find yourself running into the same people again and again. Above all, it is easy to go out and have a good time; venues are relatively close together, and the best nightclubs are still generally welcoming to strangers, although exclusiveness and elitism are beginning to make their appearance. This is inevitable as the city evolves, but is also partly Tallinn's reaction to boisterous foreigners rampaging through its streets.

A handful of large clubs dominates the mainstream market: Hollywood and Venus Club in the Old Town and Terrarium (further out) attract teenage to 20-something clubbers in their Sunday best, and offer chart-orientated dance music. Complete with floor shows, VIP rooms and go-go dancers, these places tend to be crowded without fail on weekends, and the atmosphere is generally excellent. Most dedicated partiers will pass through one of them at some point.

For more style-conscious and dedicated clubbers there are Club Privé and the famous BonBon (situated in the redeveloped port area), but not many other

options save for Moskva, which also offers club nights that attract the beautiful set. The crowds who frequent these clubs are more self-conscious, and tend to be frostier with those that don't seem to belong. But make a few friends, and they can be the best places on earth. Music is generally good – less mainstream, but not much. For a really interesting experience and excellent music you need to wait until 3 or 4am and then go to Nightman, Tallinn's only after-hours night-club.

In the early 1990s, when there wasn't much else on offer, hotel clubs ruled the scene, but today they have largely had their day. Nevertheless, they're still popular with the Finnish crowd and office parties, and they're not a bad place to go for an honest, 1980s nostalgia boogie. Several clubs cater to the Russian minority, reflecting the still-divided ethnic cultures that co-exist within the same country. They can be fun for the visitor, and definitely more flamboyant (see Venus, Mr Robinson and Decolté).

There are also a few nightclubs that put on live music to bring in the punters, and these can range from insane karaoke (Hiirelõks and Kristostomus Kolumbus) to rock venues (Scotland Yard, Amigo, Guitar Safari)

Londoners in particular will notice one big difference: Tallinn doormen don't care if you arrive with women or men (unless they're behaving rowdily), and the high female-to-male nightlife ratio tends to favour chaps.

BonBon, Mere pst. 6e.
Tel: 661 60 80
Open: 10pm–late Wednesday, Friday–Saturday

A Moroccan-themed member's club that opened its doors to the public while still managing to retain its exclusive feel (it is not always easy to get into). For the moment BonBon is the spot where Tallinn's trendy people go to party most Friday and Saturday nights. The club is located in the redeveloped port area between the Old Town and the Baltic in buildings that once housed industrial works – alongside a bowling alley, a restaurant and a tourist strip-club. Here you will find a seasoned, affluent party crowd, rubbing shoulders with models, local celebrities and well-dressed *mafiosi*. With a smallish dance-floor in the main room and two smaller bars across two floors, BonBon can get absolutely packed – and the atmosphere lively. Popular with ex-pats – but large groups of drunken tourists are likely to be turned away.

Bonnie & Clyde, Olümpia Hotel, Liivalaia 33.
Tel: 631 53 33 www.revalhotels.com
Open: 10pm–3am (4am Friday–Saturday); 1–4pm Sunday.
Closed Monday.

Nowadays you are unlikely to find the trendy set here, in the nightclub of the giant Reval Hotel Olümpia Hotel (see page 45);

but Bonnie & Clyde was once *the* fashionable place to come during the 1990s, when it was one of Tallinn's first nightspots. Today it caters to 30-something locals who still remember the good old days, as well as to guests of the hotel (located about 10 minutes' walk from the Old Town). The interior was redesigned in 2002, although it has kept its large circular dance-floor surrounded by tables and chairs so typical of hotel clubs, with their high proportion of spectators and wallflowers. On the other hand the dance-floor is usually full enough after midnight to create a fun-filled party atmosphere, and the customers here tend to come for a good time rather than to pose around looking perfect. Good old disco and pop are the staples here, providing the backdrop to a thousand chat-up lines – and lots of moody, low-lit corners for smooching or sulking. Combine a trip to the nightclub with a visit to the famous all-night café on the other side of reception: an excellent place to watch the citizens of the night catching their breath and grabbing a quiche.

Club Privé, Harju 6.
Tel: 631 05 45
Open: 10pm–6am. Closed Sunday–Tuesday.

A rising star of the Tallinn nightclub scene alongside fashionable fixtures BonBon and Pegasus, Privé joins the list of venues targeting the richer, trendier set. Models, media types and party kings head to this slick little club off the corner of Vabaduse

Square for an exclusive feel and good music – more London nightclub than Euro-pop – and the interesting, glamorous décor. Caged dancers at the back may keep you entertained while you wait for the (not particularly fast) bar staff to serve you. With a stage at one end of the dancehall, Club Privé is often used for private parties or fashion and cabaret shows, so you should call ahead to check the schedule. Not always easy to get into, especially if you are part of a large group.

Decolté, Ahstri 10.
Tel: 666 49 99 www.decolte.ee
Open: 10pm–4am (5am Friday–Saturday). Closed Sunday–Tuesday.

This attractive mega-club has recently been reopened with a chic new interior. With a large dance-floor and two enormous bars, the nightclub attracts a youthful crowd out for a good old dance

to mainstream music. Like a handful of other clubs and bars in Tallinn, Decolté is the preserve of Russian party animals – although just as welcoming to visitors as any of the more 'Estonian' venues. You are unlikely to encounter many non-Russians here, so best to get on and enjoy the subculture. The dance-floor can seem empty, if only because it is so huge. Situated a 10-minute walk or 2-minute drive outside the Old Town, it is within easy reach of the tourist centre.

Hiirelõks, Sakala 14.
Tel: 660 45 41
Open: midnight–6am daily

The name 'Hiirelõks' literally means 'the mousetrap' – and once you've crossed its unassuming threshold you may never escape. A cult fixture on the Tallinn nightclub circuit, this tiny Russian karaoke bar has been open for nearly seven years and has a loyal, if low-profile following. Hidden away down a small road just outside the Old Town in a grey suburban house, from the out-side Hiirelõks looks a bit like a down-market brothel. Once inside, however, you find yourself immediately enveloped in the welcoming, slightly loopy atmosphere of Russian karaoke – cen-tred on a wall-mounted monitor in the corner (there is no stage as such). Most of the songs are incomprehensible, but there is also a long list of English-language favourites to choose from. Don't expect many of your fellow customers to speak English, but this will not stop them trying to communicate. All ages are

represented, from young girls with peroxide hair to 30-
something divorcees (with peroxide hair). Since Hiirelōks opens
for business at midnight customers generally arrive fairly intoxi-
cated from other previous night-time activities.

Hollywood, Vana-Posti 8.
Tel: 627 47 70 www.club-hollywood.ee
Open: 10pm–4am (5am Friday–Saturday). Closed Sunday–Tuesday.

One of Tallinn's oldest and most famous nightclubs, Hollywood
sits in the middle of the action on the edge of the Old Town, in a
blue-lit neo-classical building that also houses the Soprus cinema.
Once you have navigated the long queue and the body searches,
you'll find yourself surrounded by a huge, good-natured party
crowd mainly comprising teenagers, dressed to the nines and
determined to have a good time. The nightclub inside reflects its
grandiose, tacky exterior – a disco with two large dance-floors
and an upstairs balcony – as well as back rooms that include a
VIP area and a sweeping staircase (a good place to watch and
chat) to the loos. Wednesday is ladies' night, when free entrance
for girls makes Hollywood the biggest midweek party in town.

Mr Robinson, Aia 10.
Tel: 627 36 00 www.mr-robinson.ee
Open: 9am–6am daily

For a surreal ethnic experience in the middle of Tallinn walk into the totally Russian world of Mr Robinson, located on the edge of the Old Town, 2 minutes' walk from the Viru gates. Here you will find a rich mix of humanity, from tsarist-chic ladies to workers in plastic jackets and teenage girls in denim skirts – drinking sweet Russian champagne and dancing all night. Be prepared for Russian pop that you've never heard before, and a dance-floor empty of men but full of women. The atmosphere is exuberant, tacky and fun, and before you know it you've spent hours in the place dancing, chatting or popping downstairs to ogle at the topless bar. Be aware, however, that the English of Russian Estonians can be noticeably worse than that of the other locals, so it can be hard to communicate. Mr Robinson also has a sauna, open from 9am until closing time, and from midday you can hang out with the lads at the billiard hall – with two 'Russian', one snooker and four pool tables. Food is served all day and night in the restaurant, 'in case you get hungry at strange times'.

Nightman, Vineeri 4.
www.nightman.ee
Open: 11pm–6am daily

Located some way out of the Old Town, Nightman is a cult favourite with Tallinn's clubbers, who descend on this (formerly gay) venue, to the south of the centre, after the other clubs are closed (or slowing down). From 3 or 4am onwards, Nightman starts to fill up with happy, relaxed clubbers who come to enjoy the excellent music and the famous atmosphere. Distinguished by its dark interior and large podium dance-floor in the centre of the main room, the club is built on two floors but is small enough to stay intimate and friendly. Most of the action happens upstairs, but a second bar next to the entrance is good for conversation. Note there is still a gay scene here, although all nights are mixed. For a unique bass experience stand underneath the DJ tower upstairs to feel the vibrations rock your bones.

Noku, Pikk 5.
Tel: 631 39 29
Open: 11.30am–12.30am daily

Favourite of the media set and art students, Noku is a late-night, private members' club that doubles as a café/restaurant until the early hours. Unlike some other private clubs, Noku is genuinely difficult to access without membership – since there is no doorman and entrance is achieved by magnetic card. However, if you are hell bent on a late drink and a look at the real art scene you should persevere: hang around outside the (unmarked) front door until you find a friendly member to take you inside. Once upstairs you will enjoy the mellow atmosphere, the comfortable, welcoming interior and a laid-back, interesting crowd – who will often stay and drink until dawn. Not much dancing happens here, although there is good music and a friendly ambience. Luckily they serve a good selection of simple but excellent hot food to keep the conversation flowing.

Panoraam Nightclub, Mere pst. 8b.
Tel: 667 45 07 www.panoraam.com
Open: 9pm–4am (5am Saturday) daily

Middle-aged Finns and their mothers watching go-go dancers and young Estonian secretaries getting down to 1990s pop hits: that's 'Playboy' night, anyway, one of Panoraam's regular Thursday-night parties, which gets hot after midnight when the live shows start. The nightclub is frequented by guests from the Metropol hotel

underneath, giving it a particular character that is reminiscent of other hotel clubs. Not a bad place to come hunting if you are single – although be aware that almost everyone will arrive in packs, then sit around in immovable groups. But there is one extraordinary feature of Panoraam that makes everything worthwhile: the fantastic, nearly 360° degree view of the Old Town and the harbour that you get from the eighth floor of this port-side hotel. Walk along the mezzanine window at dusk for a truly beautiful sunset, or come for live gigs by some of the best bands in Estonia.

RIFF, Viru Valjak 6 (in Viru Centre)
Tel: 610 14 30   www.riff.ee
Open: 10pm–late Wednesday–Saturday.

This brand new club is part of the Viru shopping centre that opened in the spring of 2004 – a shiny, white multi-storey packed with Western retail brands and modern cafes, it's Tallinn's latest idol to consumerism. RIFF opens into the Viru's forecourt a stone's throw from the old town walls, sitting between the offices and shops of the new town and the tourist centre of the medieval city. It is targeted at the stylish end of the market: the furnishings are understated, cosy and chic, and the walls are decorated with portraits of trendy models and celebrities. Upstairs it doubles as a restaurant and chilled-out bar while downstairs you'll find the real dancing. In summer a large outdoor terrace is open.

Terrarium, Sadama 6.
Tel: 661 47 21 www.terrarium.ee
Open: 10pm–4am (5am Friday–Saturday). Closed Sunday–Tuesday.

Located next to the port area 10 minutes north of the Old Town, Terrarium combines a relaxed party atmosphere with a good-looking crowd, despite a less elitist approach than other leading city clubs. Open since 2001 in this redeveloped industrial area, now home to some of Tallinn's trendiest nightspots, this is a medium-sized club that offers decent party music in a fun layout, with a podium and an upstairs balcony that encircles it. The club's best party-trick is the smoky, see-through mirror in the loos, allowing men and women to view each other's shadows on the other side. Thursday nights are best for classic club dance music, while Fridays and Saturdays usually come in 1980s or

1990s flavours. It's famous also for its student party nights, so call ahead to check what's on.

● **Venus, Vana-Viru 14.**
Tel: 641 81 84 www.venusclub.ee
Open: 10pm–4am (5am Friday–Saturday). Closed Sunday–Tuesday.

Don't be put off by the neon-lit exterior – Venus is smaller and more intimate than you might expect, and cosier than most of the other larger clubs. In Tallinn's ethnically differentiated nightlife, Venus weighs in on the Russian camp – although, like most places in Estonia, there is more mingling than before, especially on Thursdays. Meanwhile, the club's ethnic leaning gives it a special party spirit: its voluptuous classical theme – nude statuettes of the goddess holding lamps (and oil paintings of more

nudes) – resonates with more flamboyant, less Scandinavian tastes. Most of the action – including live acts and go-go dancers – takes place in one large ballroom, with plush velvet curtains, a grand stairway and a balcony for viewing. Behind the bar, which runs the length of one wall, you can find the vast VIP area – crack it if you can. For some reason the waitresses here wear bosomy medieval outfits. Expect more mainstream, chart music than some clubs, and experiment with Ukrainian or Russian champagne if you're feeling lucky.

Von Krahli Baar, Rataskaevu 10–12.
Tel: 626 90 96 www.vonkrahl.ee.
Open: noon–1am (3am Saurday) daily

Estonian students and arty types flock to Von Krahli for the reasonable prices and the excellent vibe in this friendly, unpretentious venue bang in the middle of the Old Town. If you are looking for an edgy, Berlin feel with a touch of grunge then this is the place to come – warm wooden furniture, cheap beer and large rooms on several floors make for a great atmosphere and an excellent place to meet with talkative locals. Krahli is a nightclub, a theatre and a music venue (the stage is upstairs), hosting a variety of live acts with a strong focus on alternative music. With its arty credentials the club attracts good-quality DJs for dance nights – but call ahead to check the schedule before you turn up.

MUSIC CLUBS

Café Amigo, Sokos Hotel Viru, Viru väljak 4.
Tel: 631 53 33 www.viru.ee
Open: 9pm–4am (5am Friday–Saturday) daily

This large venue has weathered changing fashions and the fading
popularity of hotel nightclubs by reinventing itself as one of
Tallinn's regular live music venues. Situated in the basement of
the landmark Viru hotel, Amigo can guarantee a regular stream of
business from the thousands of guests who pass through the
hotel each year. And with a strong line-up of Estonian bands, it
also draws a reasonable local crowd. Rock and blues acts are the
focus – with such greats as Hot Rod, Ultima Thule and Bisquit
Rollers on their list of artists. Depending on the band, the clientele can vary but tend to verge on the older, drunker and pre-
dominantly Finnish. You'll spot plenty of middle-aged groups
occupying the large seating areas surrounding the dance-floor.

Guitar Safari, Müürivahe 22.
Tel: 641 16 07 safari@hot.ee
Open: noon–3am Monday–Friday; 2pm–3am Saturday;
1pm–3am Sunday

One of the only venues in Tallinn dedicated to live music, Guitar
Safari defies its vaguely reggae-sounding name with a heavy rock
atmosphere and an interior full of blues souvenirs. The bar is

found downstairs in an old-fashioned basement tucked away in one of the Old Town's narrowest alleys. Check the schedule next to the front door for the music line-up: there is a different band playing almost every night, with acts that range from unplugged rock to pop and blues. They have even been known to host line-dancing courses!

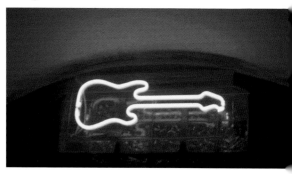

Kristostomus Kolumbus, Viru 24.
Tel: 627 74 64 kristostomus.kolumbus@mail.ee
Open: noon–midnight (1am Friday–Saturday) daily

This enormous, charismatic upstairs pub by the gates of the Old Town doubles as a fun-filled, live music venue, featuring local bands as well as karaoke nights on Tuesdays. A favourite with the locals, and not yet discovered by the tourists, Kristostomus Kolumbus takes up the entire upper floor of a corner right next

to the Viru gates. You emerge into a massive room decorated with cheerful animal designs on the walls and long wooden tables, to be welcomed by medieval-costumed waitresses heaving steins of beer. There is a pleasant party atmosphere, and a predominance of local youngsters who come here to socialize and drink in large groups or in the niches tucked around the back. If you're tired of the crowds find the side room that serves hot meals. Call ahead for the music schedule.

Von Krahli Baar, Rataskaevu 10–12.
Tel: 626 90 96 www.vonkrahl.ee
Open: noon–1am (3am Saturday) daily

Von Krahli is the nightspot of choice for the arty, grungy set – incorporating a theatre and much-loved music venue as well as a nightclub. The club runs a full schedule of live gigs in its theatre space, with acts that range from cutting-edge Berlin electronica to Estonian rock music, and from dance to folk. Warm wooden furniture, cheap beer and large rooms on several floors make for a great atmosphere and an excellent place to meet talkative and alternative locals. Call ahead to check the schedule before you turn up – the website can be hard to decode for English speakers.

CASINOS

Bally's Casino, Köleri 2.
Tel: 606 19 50 www.ballys.ee
Open: 24 hours daily

Set within easy reach of the centre of Tallinn, Bally's aims for a
private members' bar feel, with an opulent, gentleman's club
atmosphere and discreet location in the beautiful Kadriorg district. It's less tacky than some of the other large casinos –
although, despite the piped music and business news on wall-
mounted TVs, the sound of fruit machines is never far away.
Bally's is a medium-sized casino, with eight tables for poker,
roulette and blackjack – and 45 one-armed bandits. Downstairs
the casino has leased the restaurant to an excellent Italian venture – offering high-quality meals to gamblers and public alike.
And if you're looking for a late-night drink find the laid-back
24-hour bar in the middle of the gaming floor, open to all. Bally's
has the feel of a grand old residence taken over by a London
members' club. Glitzy, but fun – and more intimate than many of
its competitors.

Casino London, Mere pst, 8b.
Tel: 667 46 98
Open: 7pm–6am daily

Located in the unpromising modern block that is the Metropol
hotel just outside the Old Town, the London surprises with its
tasteful, comfortable interior and its atmosphere of a gentleman's
casino (complete with Churchill's portrait behind the cashier's
desk). With only five gaming tables and ten slot machines, this is
one of the smallest casinos in Tallinn, but also the most intimate
– with a crew of regulars who return frequently. With one
English and one Estonian shareholder the casino is popular with
both ex-pats and locals. Slot machines are open in the morning,
for the benefit of hotel guests (and Finnish day-trippers), but the
casino proper opens in the evenings. Blackjack tournaments are
held from time to time.

Casino Metropol Monte Carlo, Vabaduse väljak 10.
Tel: 640 46 88 www.mckasiinod.ee
Open: 24 hours daily

Housed inside a listed Jewish cinema built in 1926, this down-stairs casino has an appealing baroque charm despite the corporate chain carpet and unavoidable piped music. With six gaming and four poker tables, Monte Carlo is smaller than it used to be, answering competition from other casinos by focusing on a more intimate customer base – almost all are local, despite its central location on Vabaduse Square right next to the Old Town. The Metropol is the only casino that offers six-card poker – a Russian and Latvian game not well known outside the region, although its bi-annual international tournaments draw a crowd from all over Europe. Dress code is formal and the atmosphere discreet, perhaps reflecting the casino's origins – it's owned by former physics and chemistry professors from Tartu.

Olympic Casino, Reval Park Hotel, Kreutzwaldi 23.
Tel: 630 55 37 www.olympic-casino.net
Open: 24 hours daily

Located underneath the Reval Park Hotel, the Olympic is part of the largest casino chain in the Baltic, with 14 outlets throughout Estonia. While most of their outlets are coin machine parlours, this flagship branch includes a full set of gaming tables for poker, roulette and blackjack players. Like many Tallinn casinos, the Olympic marks its territory with a podium-mounted prize-car which sits outside the hotel enticing punters to come and try their luck. Once inside you are hit by a volley of glitzy lights and aspirational Vegas touches – from the waxwork of Robert de Niro to the dolly-bird croupiers and slick-haired staff. Frequented mainly by Scandinavian tourists and battle-hardened locals, the Olympic offers dance shows every Friday and Saturday from 10pm.

ADULT ENTERTAINMENT

Atlantida, Inseneri 1/Aia 10.
Tel: 627 36 00 www.mr-robinson.ee
Open: 9pm–6am daily

You will find Atlantida underneath one of Tallinn's most insanely Russian nightspots, Mr Robinson – a late night disco-bar full of teenage girls drinking Soviet champagne and dancing with each other (because there appear to be no men). You pay for your ticket to the strip-club at the door of Mr Robinson, meaning that you can relax with some amusing 1980s pop and Russian hits before (or after) chancing it with the pole dancers downstairs – and you can come and go without any pressure, a rarity in adult clubs. Atlantida has an intimate, laid-back atmosphere and is often full of couples (apparently on dates) as well as friends of the staff and strippers, in a small, low-lit room decorated with weirdly atmospheric alien seaweed murals in fluorescent paint. The quality of the dancing varies, but at best it's as good as anywhere. Be careful not to offend – you are in foreign territory.

Börsi Bar, Lai 7.
Tel: 641 19 59
Open: 11am–6pm daily

Börsi's striking red sign hangs outside a row of ancient buildings in one of Tallinn's prettiest medieval streets. Despite the setting, you will forget about your Hanseatic environment as soon as

you step inside the club: an intimate cellar space with a small bar and warm staff. After an inexpensive entrance fee (only 50kr), the house approach is to hit customers with double service: a personal hostess will join your group to chat and squeeze out drinks for herself as well as you, while you watch the dancing and leave tips. However, the extortion is done with politeness and good humour, rather than hard sell. Most of the dancers and staff are Russian.

Cabaret Le Galaxy, Müürivahe 23a.
Tel: 631 43 36
Open: 2pm–4am daily

Advertised by a whirligig of lights beamed onto the wall of the building opposite, Galaxy does its best to jump out of the confines of its cellar space in this busy Old Town alley. Housed underneath a popular crêperie, it is known for its thumping music and beautiful dancers with their balletic dance routines. The menus standing on the tables openly advertise the range of services available, from 20-minute private dances to an hour or longer 'sessions'. The main room is small, so you are never far from the dance-floor – or requests for tips. Friendly and attentive staff keep you supplied with drinks.

X Club, Harju 6.
Tel: 631 05 75 www.xclub.ee
Open: 6pm–6am daily

This large and well-known strip club beside the old city wall targets a more up-market, business-entertainment clientele than the traditional run of cellar strip-joints. X-Club is a sprawling complex of rooms that includes a main show hall, sauna and private rooms as well as an 'Oriental Hall' – a colonial-style gallery divided into tented booths where clients can enjoy belly-dancing in both the Middle Eastern and Indian style. Guests can keep it mild but the club also caters to the traditional strip-show customer, with continuous topless shows in the main bar and even a 'Marquis de Sade' room for 'bizarre' shows.

culture...

Two thousand years of foreign rule by Teutonics, Scandinavians and Russians have left Tallinn with a rich and varied cultural history – as well as a tradition of being extremely open to outside influence. Today Estonia is an independent country, but its past is still written into the walls of its ancient capital – from the alleys and fortifications of the Old Town, built by the Germanic merchants who lived here for a thousand years, to the gorgeous arts and crafts of the Baltic and Scandinavian cultures to be found all around the country.

Sightseeing in Tallinn can take many forms: you can learn about the city's rich heritage from a range of fascinating and topical museums; or admire the fabulous churches, palaces and castles that are living edifices and tangible proof of the town's noble past; or simply wander the streets and soak up the vibrant mix of architectural styles that juxtaposes medieval walls and modern skyscrapers.

Take time, if you can, to visit the Occupation Museum and learn something of what the Estonians lived through under Soviet rule; walk up Toompea Hill and admire the castle, the parliament and the splendour of the Nevsky Cathedral; and wander the narrow streets of the Old Town. These streets and the central

square bear all the hallmarks of the city's medieval past, which has been beautifully restored and preserved.

Tallinn's most interesting streets are walkable in a few hours – and its museums tend to be small and well designed, providing visitors with a great opportunity to cram in all the necessary cultural background before they duck into a few of its beautiful churches and old buildings. Most of the city's best stuff can be done in the course of one day. And in the evening there is plenty of excellent entertainment, whether it's cosmopolitan opera, folksy choral music or a children's puppet show you're after.

Note, however, that most Estonian museums and art galleries are closed on Mondays and/or Tuesdays, as well as national holidays. 18 May is International Museum Day and entry to museums is free. Should you decide to go for a culture blitz, you can buy Tallinn Cards from visitor centres and some hotels. These are no-nonsense passports that allow you free entry to all museums for periods of a day or longer.

SIGHTSEEING

Estonian Maritime Museum, Pikk 70.
Tel: 641 14 08 www.aktivist.ee/meremuuseum
Open: 10am–6pm Wednesday–Sunday

Tucked into a corner just inside the northernmost gate of the
Old Town, the Maritime Museum is well positioned – with the
Baltic just a few hundred yards away, you can see the gulls and
hear the ferry horns, reminding us that Tallinn still depends as
much as ever on sea trade for its prosperity (although today it
comes more in the form of people than goods). The first thing
you should notice when you arrive is the plaque on the front
wall commemorating the British naval forces who gave their lives
assisting Estonia in its fight against the Bolsheviks in 1918–20,
winning its first period of independence. This excellent museum,
housed inside a 16th-century fortified tower and former prison,
is worth seeing for its setting alone, and the view it offers of
Estonia's history through the filter of maritime events, from the
Viking raids right up to the tragic loss of the ferry *Estonia* in
1994. Medieval stairways take you past a spectacular collection
of sea-going and military hardware, maps and diagrams across
five floors. Emerge from vast, 6-metre walls to the open-air roof
of the tower for unbeatable views of the Old Town and the sea.

Kadriorg Palace – Museum of Foreign Art, Weizenbergi 37.
Tel: 606 64 00 www.ekm.ee
Open: 10am–5pm. Closed Monday.

About 5 minutes' drive from the centre of Tallinn, Kadriorg is the
leafy equivalent of London's Kensington – with a rustic, English-
style park and historic palace. Around the park, elegant wooden
houses built during the late Russian period remain the home of
Tallinn's smart set, while the Estonian Art Museum is the only
place you're going to find European art of any real quality in the
country. Housed in a grand, Italianate chateau complete with formal gardens and topiary, the museum was once Kadriorg Palace
– built by Peter the Great in the early 18th century for his wife
Catherine I and today a rare counterpoint to Tallinn's weighty
medieval charm. The collection includes European art from the
Renaissance onwards – and although you wouldn't come here
for world-famous masterpieces there are enough pieces to keep
the art lover happy for an hour or two in beautiful surroundings.

Kiek in de Kök, Harjumägi, off Vabaduse Square.
Open: 10am–5pm. Closed Tuesday.

This chunky military tower encapsulates everything you need to
know about the city walls and their romantic-looking fortifications – actually fairly serious weapons of war until they became

obsolete in the 19th century. Built in the 15th century and extended in the 17th, Kiek in de Kök has six storeys of gun positions and arrow-slit windows looking out over the town (hence the name, which means 'peek in the kitchen'). Today it is a museum, located conveniently underneath Toompea Hill – which it was originally designed to defend. Inside you will find a fascinating scatter-gun history of warfare and general life in old Estonia.

Laboratorium, Kooli and Gümnaasiumi streets.

You won't find these alleys listed in any guide to Tallinn museums but it is well worth making a quick visit to this back yard of the Old Town to take in the truly medieval atmosphere of the city wall. Unlike the busier Müürivahe – which skirts the ancient city wall near the Viru gateway, full of shops and bars – these contiguous lanes lie quiet and unnoticed beneath the massive walls and

ramparts of the Old Town on the north-western side. Here can be found the densest collection of fortified towers in Tallinn – a quick walk down the three streets reveals eight or nine medieval bastions, lining the wall like illustrations from a French battle painting. Look also for the tiny, Rapunzel-like Church of the Blessed Virgin, a Ukrainian chapel with the smallest windows outside toyland. On the side of the wall, in the street, there is a little public prayer box. Above is written: 'She is the protector of the innocent who have been wrongfully convicted, deceived and sinned against. The priest will pray for settlement of your question.'

Niguliste Church Museum/Concert Hall, Niguliste 13.
Tel: 644 99 11
Open: 10am–6pm Wednesday–Friday; 11.30am–6pm
Saturday–Sunday.

This sturdy 13th-century church was built to withstand military attack – making it the only fortified holy spot in town, still full of hiding places and secret exits. Standing proudly below the approach to Toompea Hill, Niguliste has the second highest spire in the Old Town, and is today an interesting museum as well as a popular concert venue. Have a look at the splendid silver pendants and coats of arms in the treasury – for once not the preserve of archbishops and lords but commissioned in times gone by for the tailors, potters, hatters and the other tradesmen who made Tallinn great. In the crypt-side chapel lurks a striking and malicious Dance of Death painting by Bernt Notke – including a large song addressed to the bad king, the bad emperor, and the

bad pope – all of them viewed here getting their just deserts.

● **Occupation Museum, Toompea 8.**
Tel: 650 52 80 www.okupatsioon.ee
Open: 10am–5.30pm. Closed Monday.

The period between 1940 and 1991 brought two major military
occupations and much suffering to the people of Estonia. The
impressive Occupation Museum, opened in 2003, is run by a
foundation whose aim is to keep the history of this time alive,
documenting the 'catastrophes and cataclysms... and to find
detailed proof about the past based on facts and analysis'. It's a
startling reminder of recent history – which few Estonians have
forgotten but will often not talk about. The museum uses artefacts, audio-visual displays and sound recordings to build a picture of those troubled times, and it also shows how ordinary
people got through their normal lives in tough conditions.
Housed in a striking glass and steel structure on the edge of the
Old Town, the museum has aroused controversy as well as admi-
ration, and well deserves a visit.

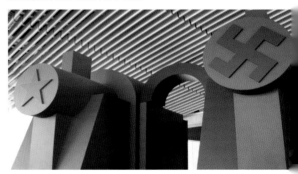

● **St Olav's Church (Oleviste Kirik), Pikk 48.**
Tel: 641 22 41 www.oleviste.ee
Open: 10am–2pm daily

Once the tallest structure in the known world, the spire of St
Olav's ('Oleviste' in Estonian) is still an awesome sight, although

it's 20 metres smaller than the original steeple, which was struck by lightning in 1820. One of Tallinn's most recognizable landmarks, St Olav's may well be the first thing you see as you arrive by boat or by air, and it is visible along the coast for miles out of town. Built in 1267, when the city was first emerging as a thriving merchant capital of the Baltic, St Olav's sums up the confidence and wealth of the people's town – a counterpoint to feudal Toompea Hill dominated by Estonia's Teutonic overlords. The church is named after the then king of Norway, although it contains German inscriptions written in honour of Russian tsars – a perfect reflection of Tallinn's multi-cultural past. Today it remains active as a Baptist church and also hosts concerts and musical events, especially around Christmas time.

Tallinn City Museum, Vene 17.
Tel: 644 65 53 www.linnamuuseum.ee
Open: 11am–5pm. Closed Tuesday.

If you're looking for a quick download of Tallinn's history before exploring the sights, go immediately to the the City Museum (Linnamuuseum), the town's best laid-out and annotated guide to its rich past. Small enough to cover in half an hour if you are rushing, the museum is built inside a 14th-century merchant's house across several floors – providing a perfect background for artefacts, costumes and pictures that date from Estonia's earliest history up until the present day. Attractions include examples of the extraordinary crafts and treasures that made the Tallinn

guilds great – while clear and informative labels in English give potted histories and explanations about Hanseatic life through the ages. Upstairs there is a comfy café, and rooms dedicated to the 20th century – its wars and troubles – as well as videos that evocatively conjure up the Soviet period in Estonia.

Toompea Hill.

On 20 August 1991, during the failed Soviet coup against Yeltsin, Estonia finally declared its independence. On that day Toompea Hill – once the seat of Tallinn's feudal overlords – regained its position at the heart of Estonian politics and has remained there since. Cresting the Old Town on a fortified outcrop, the Hill is a tiny city in its own right – full of compact government buildings and lords' houses dating from the 14th century onwards. Today

the modern parliament stands here (a 1920s building easily recognizable by its pink walls), as well as the onion-domed
Alexander Nevsky Russian Orthodox cathedral – a controversial
and striking symbol of Russian power for the last hundred years,
built only 17 years before the fall of the Tsar. It was here, on the
same patch as the parliament and the cathedral, that Tallinn's earliest fort was built, in 1227 – and the heavy, military walls that
circle the Hill still date from that time. Other attractions on
Toompea include the Dome Church (Toomkirik), built in 1240
and added to over the years, which was the religious centre for
the grand German families that ruled Tallinn – and the Baltic –
for centuries. The Estonian Art Museum stands opposite, with
exhibits limited mainly to relatively unknown local artists.
Around the corner from the museum don't miss the celebrated
vantage-point over Tallinn – a favourite spot with tourists, locals
and dog-walkers throughout the year.

Town Hall and Town Hall Square, Raekoja plats 1.
Tel: 645 79 00 www.tallinn.ee/raekoda

Back in the 16th century when Tallinn was still tiny (only 5,000
people) it was ethnic Germans who ruled the city – not just up
on the hill where the feudal lords held sway but also in the Old
Town where Germanic merchant guilds directed government and
every aspect of the city's life from the Town Hall. Today this
Gothic wonder still looms over the main square exactly as it
must have done 600 years earlier; only the iconic weathervane

'Old Thomas' – Tallinn's soldier mascot complete with large cod-piece – needing replacement after war damage. Inside the Hall, look for the opulent woodcarvings and coats of arms, speaking of centuries of Venetian-style merchant rule – from the heavy money chests to the comic carvings of Socrates being beaten by his wife. The square itself has been the centre of Tallinn's social and political life for centuries – festivals, weddings and executions have all taken place here, and possibly the earliest recorded public Christmas tree was erected in 1441. Across the square from the Town Hall, now surrounded by cafés and restaurants, find Europe's oldest pharmacy, which opened in 1422.

OPERA AND BALLET

For tickets to cultural events take yourself to the box office of the Estonian Theatre (better known as the National Opera – see below), which sells tickets for a range of classical performance venues; or the Kaubamaja Ticket Centre, located in the large department store of the same name (Gonsiori 2, tel: 667 3337, www.piletipunkt.ee).

Estonia Concert Hall, Estonia Avenue 4.
Tel: 626 02 60/14 www.concert.ee

Sitting aloof from the Old Town, this grand building, with its sweeping Italianate plasterwork, is home to the Estonian National Opera, which produces a full calendar of opera classics as well as ballet and more family-oriented musical events (such as children's opera). Performances are held from Tuesday or Wednesday to Sunday nights, with matinees at weekends.

CLASSICAL MUSIC, CHORAL AND JAZZ

Estonian choirs are famous for their verve and spirit: look for performances of traditional as well as classical songs for the full Estonian experience. Among classical music composers Estonia is proud to count the world-famous composer Arvo Pärt as its own, fêted by music lovers for his dark, medieval-influenced Modernism. Catch a piece of the action in one of the venues below. During music festivals and holidays a whole range of Tallinn churches get pressed into service as concert halls.

Estonia Concert Hall, Estonia pst.4.
Tel: 614 77 60 www.concert.ee

Tallinn's imposing national concert hall is the residence of the National Opera and also plays host to many of the best music concerts, including performances by the National and the Tallinn symphony orchestras, the Philharmonic Chamber Choir and the Estonian National Male Choir. The ticket office also acts as box office for other venues throughout Tallinn.

House of the Brotherhood of the Blackheads, Pikk 26.
Tel: 631 31 99 www.mustpeademaja.ee

This evocative venue, nestling in the middle of Old Tallinn, was formerly the home of one of Tallinn's leading medieval guilds. Today it operates as a small classical music and dance venue. It's worth a visit, if only for its highly unusual atmosphere and the colourful carved-wooden door: look out for the 'black head'.

Kadriorg Palace, Weizenbergi 37.
Tel: 606 64 00

A grand old baroque palace sitting in the grounds of Tallinn's gracious parkland next to the Baltic Sea, the Kadriorg Palace was built by Peter the Great and today holds Estonia's principal collection of European art. It also stages some classical music events.

Linnahall, Mere pst. 20.
Tel: 641 22 50 www.linnahall.ee

An imposing Soviet concert hall built to wow the visitors during Estonia's 1980s Winter Olympics, the Linnahall now plays host to major conferences and concerts, with all the audio-visual facilities – and charm – of the United Nations General Assembly.

Niguliste Church Museum/Concert Hall, Niguliste 3.
Tel: 644 99 11 www.ekm.ee

This thick, fortified church, standing proudly in a corner of the
Old Town next to ruins of buildings bombed during the war, has
today been turned into a museum and a successful concert
venue: a top circuit spot for classical and jazz music.

Song Festival Grounds, Narva mnt. 95.
Tel: 611 21 00 www.lauluvaljak.ee

Huge pop concerts and festivals are held here in this vast open-
air venue every summer. Bands have included rock greats such as
the Rolling Stones.

THEATRE

In general, theatre productions in Tallinn are performed in
Estonian. However, there can be exceptions. Call or visit the
websites for more details.

Estonian Puppet Theatre, Lai 1.
Tel: 667 95 55 www.nukuteater.ee

Located on the corner of Tallinn's medieval theatreland, bang in
the middle of the Old Town, this theatre with its arresting audio-
visual street display stages classic and less well-known puppet
acts produced mainly for children.

Town Theatre (Linnateater), Lai 23.
Tel: 665 08 50/00 www.linnateater.ee

This striking medieval theatre includes seven different performance spaces and an amazing open-air auditorium, perfect for the
summer. The venue and its much-loved resident company was
founded in 1965 by Estonian director Voldemar Panso.

CINEMAS

Coca-Cola Plaza, Hobujaama 5.
Tel: 1182 www.superkinod.ee

If you're put off by the name you probably shouldn't be here anyway – this is Tallinn's largest multiplex, which would look at home anywhere in the Western World. With 11 screens, the Plaza is usually showing at least one Hollywood film of interest – as well as some more intriguing local stuff from time to time, if you feel up to it. Well run and convenient, with bars, diners and shops, it is less than 5 minutes' walk from the Old Town, opposite the giant Viru hotel. If there are enough of you, why not hire the private screening room for your own personal cinema extravaganza?

Kinomaja, Uus 3.
Tel: 646 45 10 www.sabadik.pri.ee

A tiny art cinema just inside the Old City walls near Viru gate. Why not pass by this pretty old movie theatre to find out what's on? Kinomaja holds sporadic screenings of repertory, local and cult foreign films, and is a great place to spot Tallinn's film crowd hanging out. There's a cosy café tucked in the back near the medieval wall.

shop...

Tallinn is a city built on the toil and prosperity of craftsmen and merchant traders: its powerful artisan guilds dominated the political life of the town for centuries. Today the guilds are gone – or have a largely honorary role – but their influence can still be seen everywhere, making Tallinn today a thriving centre of craft and arts. Estonia may not be the place to come for top designers and famous brands, but Old Tallinn is still a gratifying place to browse for gifts and household items, from glassware, woodwork and ceramics to antiques, jewellery and woollen goods.

More street-wise, sporty or fashion-conscious customers will need to look outside the Old Town walls where Tallinn's main department stores sit alongside a smattering of luxury brand hotels and shopping centres opened in the last five years.

Shops generally open between 10am and pm, with most closed on Sundays (except the big malls) and many of the smaller shops closing early on Saturday. Prices are relatively low compared with Western Europe, although the amazing bargains of the 1990s have gone. On the other hand Tallinn is still cheap enough to attract millions of bargain hunters and booze cruisers every year from

Finland. If you're interested in buying alcohol, you may as well pick up some Vana Tallinn, a recent invention dressed up as tradition with a taste not far off Jägermeister – a handy gift.

Note that you may need a licence to take antiques out of the country, so check with the shop before purchasing anything that looks pre-war.

OLD TOWN

The Old Town is where you will find the densest collection of craft, antiques and souvenir shops – as well as a few small, designer boutiques. Virtually every street offers something of interest for the knick-knack hunter, but the main Old Town shopping streets are Viru, Müürivahe, Suur-Karja, Pikk and around Town Hall Square. Hidden passages such as Katariina käik (see below) will make a rewarding discovery for the craft-lover, containing entire small communities of artisan's workshops and small boutiques.

Town Hall Square (and Christmas market), Raekoja plats.

Lurking in the alleys off Town Hall Square are enough souvenir shops to fill 15 Christmas stockings with gifts. The quality of these can be really quite high, with hand-made, authentic craftwork far outweighing machine-made tat and cheesy postcards. From late November the entire square is transformed into a festive, German-style Christmas market – packed with wooden stalls selling everything from clothes and crafts to mulled wine and Estonian food. Fun.

Antiik religious icons, some dating back to the 17th century
Aurum jewellery
Gold Market jewellery
Horveit Estonian hand-made linen, clothes, sweaters and amber
Jardin crafty, good-quality woollens and gifts
Sangla Juveelisalong jewellery
Villa Nella gifts and souvenirs

Pikk, Vene and Lai streets.

Three long streets snake up from the middle of the Old Town towards the northern walls. Running parallel with each other, these narrow lanes also boast Tallinn's best craft and artisan shops.

Antique Military Collection characterful military memorabilia shop
Bally classic and smart gentleman's shoes
Bogapott up the ramp that leads to Toompea Hill: a pottery studio, café and shop all rolled into one
Draakoni galerii local and foreign contemporary art (for sale)
Keraamika Ateljee weird and wonderful ceramics, with kiln in full view
Kiika Kööki craftwork
Master's Courtyard jewellery
Mihkli Guild's ceramics studio ceramics
Puupood wooden crafts and wickerwork, from knives to furniture
Reval Antiik antiques
Rewill Handicraft a range of Estonian handicrafts made of wool, wood, fur and stone

Katariina käik (Katarina passage), off Vene.

Katariina Gild a small collection of shops and ateliers where craftsmen (and women) make and sell their goods from the same door. Peer through the windows of this medieval passage at quilt-makers and hatters busy at their work. Linens, glassware and other quality souvenirs are also made on the spot.

Viru and the City Centre.

The main gateway to the Old Town from the big bad world outside, with sportswear, mainstream and high-street fashion shops, as well as boutiques and a couple of shopping malls all crammed into one short street.

Adidas trendy sportswear, shell-suits and plastic dummies
Aureus antique crystal ware
Bastion women's clothing by a local designer
De La Gardie department store selling mainstream clothes and concessions
Demini Centre bijou shopping centre with small clothing boutiques
Molen off-beat jewellery, leather and ceramics
Monton leading Estonian clothes brand
Vana-Viru Kingaäri nightclub gear, cool music, sullen staff,

Puma trainers, T-shirts, jeans and bags

WW Passaa shopping centre – includes Kairi Vilderson, local women's clothes designer

Müürivahe.

Literally 'between the walls', Müürivahe skirts the inside of the Old City wall next to the busy Viru gate – the main entrance to old Tallinn. Today it is home to many little shops, thriving off the dense tourist traffic that swells the streets.

Woollen market A famous and apparently permanent knitwear market offers hats, gloves, jumpers and virtually anything you can make out of wool from a series of open stalls

propped against the old city wall – shopping as it might have looked 500 years ago.

Kodukäsitöö gifts and souvenirs

Loitsukeller gifts and souvenirs

Myy Art a trio of artists sell their own ceramics and textiles as well as some graphic art

Lühike jalg.

On the steps up to sinister Toompea Hill a range of art gallery/craft stores have settled this corner of the Old Town, offering glassware and ceramics and other pretty things.

Galerii 36 art and ceramics

Galerii Kaks jewellery, textiles, ceramics

Lühikese Jala Galerii glass, textiles, ceramics, silk paintings

Other shopping opportunities

A-Gallery, Hobusepea 8 original hand-made jewellery of a high quality

Armiin, Suur-Karja 3 Estonian furs for women

MaxMara, Harju 6 shoes, handbags, jeans, clothing for women and men

Nina Ricci, Väike Karja 10 stylish women's fashion and accessories

Nu Nordik, Vabaduse väljak 8 ultra-trendy new Scandinvian designer store: household goods, clothes and club music

OUTSIDE THE OLD TOWN

There are plenty of shops outside the Old Town, although most of it goes on inside the two mighty flagship department stores that stand within the same square kilometre south-east of the city walls. Around them a few good shops have sprung up – on Pärnu mnt. and Estonia pst. – although these will be of more interest to those in need of practical items of clothing than to browsers seeking local treasure.

City Centre

Tallinna Kaubamaja, Gonsiori 2.
www.kaubamaja.ee

The Selfridges of Tallinn… although not quite…

Stockmann, Liivalaia 53.
www.stockmann.ee

Another Tallinn institution, slightly more upmarket.

Melon/Lemon, Estonia pst. 1-3.

A collection of local clothes chains (Absolu, Monton, NS King), a salon (Tiia Ilusalong), an excellent 24-hour shop and café (Deli 24) and lovely cosmetics and candles from Occitane.

Parnu mnt.

Calvin Klein men's fashion and famous underwear
Hippo children's clothes and footwear
JOOP! clothes and perfumes by German designer Wolfgang Joop
Villeroy & Boch up-market kitchen and dinnerware, furniture

Viru Centre.

Tallinn's newest shopping mall sits right outside the old city walls, forming a bridge of commerce between the old and new town. Opened in 2004 to much fanfare, the centre forms part of the Viru Hotel and merges into the Kaubamaja department store. With more than 70 shops and services across two floors, professional consumers can make use of more than 10 cafes and restaurants.

Diesel modern fashion for successful living

Mango attractive street fashion for ladies

Naomi frocks and shirts for girls in candy colours

Silk House gifts, jewellery and household items

Terranova Italian casualwear for men and women

Trendexpress fashionable shoes with a wild boar's head trophy

The City Outskirts

Kristiine Centre, Endla 46.

Tallinn's biggest shopping centre, a good place to buy trainers and CDs.

Rocca Al Mare, Paldiski mnt. 102.
www.roccalmare.ee

Mini-shopping centre along the coast to the West: good sports-wear, bikewear, surf and skate kit. There's also a bowling alley and a (private) sports club, frequented by Tallinn's rich and discreet.

play...

Estonia provides a wealth of outdoor activities – a fact that may come as a relief to those who've had their fill of medieval architecture. Its position on the Baltic and its relatively unspoilt countryside mean that there are plenty of opportunities to get out and enjoy yourself, both in the sea and on land. You can participate in traditional sports, simply watch the professionals, or maybe turn your hand to something a little different.

Estonia's favourite spectator sports are football and basketball, both domestic and foreign leagues. You can sit down in a pub, enjoy a drink and watch the latest game, or, alternatively, take a trip to a stadium and watch Flora Tallinn in action on the pitch or spend time admiring the slam dunks of Kalev's leading players.

Tallinn's proximity to the countryside makes it an ideal base if you fancy spending an afternoon hacking around the forests on horses, or riding the trails on a mountain bike. Hiking is a popular pastime and there are several beautiful national parks within easy reach of the town. While you are here, why not try something a little different? Estonia has a fantastic range of flora and fauna, some of which can be legally hunted. The winter season provides opportunities to pit one's skills against wild boar, moose and elk – but watch out for the wolves!

Tallinn has been catering to a Finnish tourist trade for a while – which has meant providing playgrounds for the boys. It isn't uncommon to see groups of them pitting themselves against each other on the go-kart track, playing paint-ball or even bowling. There are some more adventurous challenges for those so inclined: days out with former Estonian and Russian special forces can be arranged where it's possible to practise with all the newest and biggest guns, play 'hide and seek' and even fly an old fighter plane.

While the boys are off killing things or each other Tallinn has a range of decent spas in which the girls can relax and get ready for the evening ahead. While many offer purely therapeutic treatments, others mix in some of those wonder-fully relaxing massages and facials. A day spent in Pirita, having lunch on the beach, followed by a manicure and pedicure, might just be the way to unwind. Of course a trip to Estonia is always incomplete without a visit to a traditional sauna, where you will be expected to self-flagellate with birch branches.

We have included here only a selection of the huge variety of outdoor and indoor pursuits available in Estonia, some of them close to and inside Tallinn itself, others quite a distance from the city. If you are in doubt, or looking for something a little closer to home, the Tourist Information Centre can always help you with further details of sports and leisure activities. It is located at:

Tallinn Tourist Information Centre, Kullassepa 4 / Niguliste 2. Tel: 645 77 77
www.tourism.tallinn.ee

BASKETBALL

Basketball leads the field as Estonia's favourite spectator sport. The leading local team is called Kalev, after the mythical ancient giant of Tallinn, and plays in regular local and national leagues and tournaments. See www.basket.ee for a detailed calendar of events.

BOWLING

Ku:Sa:l, Mere pst. 6e.
Tel: 661 66 82 www.kuulsaal.ee

This club is 5 minutes' walk from town, in the post-industrial area between the Old Town and the port, and surrounded by interesting clubs and restaurants.

Rocca Al Mare Bowling, Merivälja tee 5.
Tel: 630 01 21 www.bowlingclub.ee

Come for spectacular views of the wild waves at Rocca Al Mare, a large bowling alley in a little shopping centre overlooking the Baltic Sea. It shares the building with a sports shop and a private gym.

CANOEING AND KAYAKING

One of Estonia's most popular outdoor pursuits: dash down a fast river or take a few days for a lazy float. Package trips normally last one to three days, including light meals and equipment rental, and guides are usually available. Make sure you book some time in advance.

Hotel Pesa, Uus 5, Põlva.
Tel: 799 85 30 www.kagureis.ee

Adventurous canoe trips offered on the Ahja and Võhandu rivers, accompanied by experienced guides. Accommodation is offered.

Seikleja Sea Kayaking.
Tel: 502 72 00 www.seikleja.com

Seikleja organizes fun sea-kayak tours around the coastline of
Estonia, with English-speaking guides for day trips or longer
expeditions around coastal islands such as Hiiumaa, Väinameri
and Pakri. Prices start at 320kr per day for single kayaks.

CYCLING

Estonia's untouched, rather flat countryside makes it the perfect
location for cycling tours – especially in summer when the going
is good all through the night (if you feel like it). The cobbles of
Old Tallinn don't single it out as a great cycling city, but in the
countryside there is a large network of safe, unmarked cycle
routes – free from the hassle of passing traffic. For bicycle rental,
try the following suppliers:

Jalgrattakeskus, Tartu mnt. 73. Tel: 637 67 79
Velo Pood, Tartu mnt. 30. Tel: 601 01 66

FISHING

Estonia has a long coastline and more waterways than any other
European country except Finland – so is an excellent place to
enjoy this ancient Baltic activity. Permits are not required for
simple hand lines unless your line is more than one and a half
times the length of your rod. The companies below should advise
you on how to get hold of a standard permit.

FOOTBALL

Estonia's national team includes players from the Danish league
and Derby County – but thus far the big time has proved elusive. Flora Tallinn FC is probably the country's most celebrated
local team. They play at A Le Coq arena, Asula 4c (check out
their website www.fcflora.ee for games). The Estonian Football
Association can be found at Võidu 16, or tel: 654 27 15.

GOLF

Tallinna Golfiklubi, Niitvälja, Keila vald, Harjumaa.
Tel: 678 04 54 www.egk-golf.ee

Escape from the tourist rush with 18 leisurely holes at Tallinn's finest golf club. Completed in 1994, the course is set among the woods and water of the Estonian countryside. Green fees start at 690kr, and with clubs, caddies and carts available there is no reason not to play the course in style. A professional is on hand to offer advice or provide lessons if needed.

HIKING

One of Estonia's strongest cards: take advantage of the vast tracts of wild forest and waterlands (never very far away). There are four national parks and several local nature reserves in Estonia, full of rare plants, birds and animals – including ancient oaks and marsh rosemary.

Estonian Fund for Nature (ELF), Riia 185a, Tartu.
Tel: 742 84 43 (ask for Jüri) www.elfond.ee/reisid

ELF organizes nature tours to locations throughout Estonia, although its head office is based in Tartu, 100 miles south of Tallinn. Contact them for more information or see the website for the list of seasonal events.

RMK.
Tel: 628 15 00 www.rmk.ee/eng

The state-run forestry centre administers camping, hiking and hunting throughout Estonia's primeval forest and countryside.

Tackendorf Holiday House, Tahkuranna, Pärnu province (150km from Tallinn).
Tel: 521 97 22 www.hot.ee/tranna

Shooting, hiking, archery and sea boats way out of town and near the seashore close to the Via Baltica. Accommodation available.

HORSE-RACING

Tallinna Hipodroom, Paldiski mnt. 50.
Tel: 677 16 77 www.hipodroom.ee

Come and have a bet. Built in 1923, Tallinna Hipodroom is the only racecourse in the Baltic States, and plenty of Scandinavians bring their horses. The racecourse is situated close to town. In the restaurant there is a *totalisaator* for remote gamblers.

HORSE-RIDING

There are plenty of trekking opportunities in Estonia's empty outback. Escape for one or more nights to get the most out of the countryside. The best riding is some way out of Tallinn and worth organizing in advance.

Kohala Manor, Kohala Sõmeru vald.
Tel: 325 77 96 www.kohalamois.ee

For some deep country action, drive to picturesque Kohala Manor on the banks of the Kunda River, 120km from Tallinn, towards St Petersburg. Accommodation is available at the hotel, and riding tours on Icelandic horses can be organized all year around.

Niitvälja Riding Club.
Tel: 501 63 36.

About 25 minutes outside Tallinn.

Pallase Tallid, Arbavere 67 (outside Tallinn).
Tel: 503 65 62 pallas@estpak.ee

Single or multi-day tours and sleigh rides in winter.

HUNTING

Although it has been relatively easy in the past to hunt in Estonia
without the proper paperwork, the law has tightened in recent
years and today hunting requires a valid licence and a gun
licence. Most associations (such as the State Forestry administra-
tion RMK, tel: 628 15 00 www.rmk.ee/eng) can help by providing
weapon import licences, hunting licences and a certificate to
allow the transport of trophies out of Estonia.

Estonian game seasons

Beaver	August to mid-April
Wild boar	all year round
Moose	mid-September to mid-December
Elk	September to end January
Pheasant	October to end February

RMK.
Tel: 628 15 00 www.rmk.ee/eng

The state-run forestry assocation administers camping, hiking
and hunting throughout the Estonia's primeval forest and
countryside – and can help you secure the right licences and
paperwork.

Special Place, a custom tour operator, can organize big-game
hunting provided you bring your own licence. Contact
toby@specialplaces.co.uk or dial the London number 020 7313
6655 for details and made-to-measure deals.

Taagepera Castle, Taagepera, Valga province.
Tel: 766 63 90 www.taageperaloss.ee

A grandiose conference centre and all-round leisure palace

200km from Tallinn near the Latvian border. As well as canoeing, cycling, paintball and horse-riding, the Castle also offers hunting: beaver, boar, moose, elk and pheasant. You must supply your own licence and gun.

Tammemäe Boarding Farm, Tõrve küla, Jõgeva province.
Tel: 776 35 00 www.tammemae.ee

Roe deer, European moose and wild boar found just a couple of hours' drive (160m from Tallinn). See their website for prices.

ICE-SKATING

Linnahall, Mere pst. 20.
Tel: 641 22 66.
Open: 9–10.30pm Friday; noon–8pm Saturday–Sunday

An indoor ice rink, open from mid-July. You can hire skates at the centre.

Jeti Jäähall, Suur-Sõjamäe 14b.
Tel: 610 10 35 www.jeti.ee
Open: 10am–10pm daily

An indoor ice rink where you can hire skates by the hour – it's also possible to rent the whole rink for about 2,300kr an hour. An on-site sauna can help to soothe away those traumatic post-skating aches and pains.

KARTING

FK Keskus, Paldiski mnt 229a.
Tel: 654 81 01

About 730 metres of hobby-kart track. Maximum speed is 70km/h and the track is equipped with a digital timing system, giving every competitor his or her own personal race report. It also offers laser gun sessions and paintball.

PAINTBALL

FK Keskus, Paldiski mnt 229a.
Tel: 654 81 01 www.fkkeskus.ee

Paintball and laser-gun venue that also offers a go-kart track.

SAILING AND DIVING

Estonia has both coastal and inland waters, and plenty of them. Take a boat out and make like a Baltic merchant. A blue flag on the beach indicates that it has been cleared for environmental cleanliness and may be used for swimming. Visit the seikleja.com website for more details.

SHOOTING AND MILITARY EXCURSIONS

Deserted countryside military zones and the proximity of cheap ex-Soviet equipment make a perfect setting for a bit of shoot-'em-up.

Special Places, a highly experienced specialist tour operator, can provide all the hijinks you're looking for, not only with defunct guns but also with state-of-the-art special forces weapons and trainers. Visit toby@specialplaces.co.uk or tel: (London) 020 7313 6655 for details and made-to-measure deals. Special Places can also organize weekend house trips, hunting and even a flight in a Czech fighter plane – no experience necessary!

Laulasmaa Side Holiday Centre, Laulasmaa Keila vald, Harju.
Tel: 672 19 89 www.puhkekeskus.ee

Trips in open Russian jeeps in a limestone coastal region, including 'geo-hide and seek' using GPS equipment, 35km from Tallinn. Paintball is also available.

SPAS

Club 26, Reval Hotel Olümpia, Liivalaia 33.
Tel: 631 55 85 www.revalhotels.com
Open: 6.30am–11pm daily

The view from this 26th floor fitness centre alone makes it well
worth the visit – it's possibly the only swimming pool in the world
which offers a direct view of the Baltic while you breaststroke. You
can also enjoy the sauna, jacuzzi or gym from the dizzy heights of
Reval's enormous Olümpia Hotel. Little Club 26 is in fact open to
everyone, although it has a reputation for attracting famous
clients and it's cheaper for hotel guests and First Client (loyalty
card) holders. Full-body sport massage and group training sessions are on offer, including coaching by Estonia's champion body
builder (ranked sixth in the world). Basic use of the fitness centre
costs 130kr during the week and 150kr at weekends. The sauna
room can accommodate groups of up to 10 people.

Finnisage, Merivälja tee 1, Regata Maja (in Pirita).
Tel: 606 22 14 finissage@finissage.ee
Open: 10am–8pm Monday–Friday; 11am–5pm Saturday.
Closed Sunday.

Finnisage is a smart, boutique-like salon catering to image-
conscious Tallinites looking for something more exclusive than
the typical manicure/beauty salon treatment. Opened in late
2002, this stylish little outlet is already popular with ladies-who-
lunch, who are attracted by the chic design, the trendy atmosphere and the discreet private rooms. Come here for the standard facials and massage or try something more interesting –
Finnisage is the only place in Estonia that offers 'Plasmalite' therapy, a Swedish technology that regenerates old cells and can permanently remove unwanted hair or tattoos. The salon is not
geared towards tourists – most customers are locals or Russians
– but it is very welcoming to all visitors. It's located in Pirita, a
short drive outside central Tallinn on the coastal road, and you'd
be well advised to book time in advance.

Hedone, Sauna I.
Tel: 631 34 04 www.hedone.ee
Open: 4pm–2am daily

This luxurious new massage parlour in the centre of the Old Town approaches relaxation the oriental way. Clients don dressing-gowns and have a drink and a chat before choosing a therapy, which can range from sport and aromatic to erotic or sensual massage (although it emphasizes therapy rather than sex, with professionally trained staff who take their craft seriously despite flirtatious belly-dancer costumes). Sessions take place in small, well-equipped rooms, while the lounge area is decorated like an up-market harem – full of red satin, soft banquettes, hookah pipes and a jacuzzi.

Kalma Sauna, Vana-Kalamaja 9a.
Tel: 627 18 11
Open: 10am–11pm daily

If you are looking for the real Baltic sauna experience, then jump in a cab and head to Kalma Sauna, a traditional public sauna that has been open since 1928, servicing the needs of Estonians, Finns and Soviets for decades. Housed inside a period building a short walk from Tallinn train station (only 10 minutes north of the Old Town), this old institution keeps alive the tradition of municipal heat treatment – with no-nonsense attendants, locker rooms and a large area for cooling off, equipped with bar and TV. Once inside you will hire a towel and a plastic mat to sit on (you'll need it), as well as a birch for self-flagellation – which is done by most sauna regulars to improve the circulation. The sauna itself is vast, capable of accommodating dozens of bodies, although it is not usually too crowded. Men and women are put in entirely separate rooms, so if you arrive as a couple you won't see each other until you're finished.

Pirita TOP Spa, Regati pst. I.
Tel: 639 88 22 www.topspa.ee

Tallinn's largest residential health and beauty centre, the TOP Spa is 15 minutes' drive from central Tallinn on the main coastal road to Pirita – the summer hang-out for city dwellers who don't have the energy to leave town completely when it gets hot. The SPA is housed inside a concrete structure that calls to mind a gulag-sized World War II bunker – but once inside this drab exterior the foyer is reassuringly clean and warm, with the look and feel of a giant sports centre complete with gym and swimming pool. Come here for an amazing range of health treatments, therapies and massage as well as the great facilities, including saunas and steam rooms, which are available for day use or as part of longer treatment packages.

SPA Hotell Viimsi Tervis, Randvere tee 11.
Tel: 606 10 00 www.viimsitervis.ee

Opened in 2002, the still-sparkling Tervis spa in Viimsi is a 20-minute drive out of the city, past some of Tallinn's most interesting coastline, flanked to the south by forest and the houses of the super-rich. The Tervis has fewer residential rooms than the equally mega-sized TOP Spa in Pirita but has more health and beauty facilities – attracting visitors from across the Baltic for the excellently priced therapies, massage and even plastic surgery. Guests usually book into the spa for week or half-week treatment holidays – but it is equally open to day visitors not wanting accommodation. Tervis boasts a 25-metre swimming pool and gym, as well as sauna and steam rooms. Day packages start from as little as 480kr, and can include consultations with a doctor. The spa is busiest during the bleak spring and autumn months.

Hg2 Tallinn

info...

DANGERS

There is little to worry about in the centre of Tallinn, although locals will comment darkly on rising crime rates and you may hear stories of muggings in the Old Town late at night. Tallinn is so much safer than any major European city that unless you are very unlucky you could pass an entire lifetime here without incident. The locals tend to be modest and respectful (unless they are very drunk), making it a safe city both at night and during the day. Alcohol can be a problem for the Finns and other foreign visitors, however, who often visit Tallinn with the express aim of getting wasted – and few evenings go by without the sight of a drunk Scandinavian tottering down the road, alone or in a pack. Women will want to give them a wide berth, although they are usually too drunk to make trouble.

MONEY

The Estonian kroon is the national currency, in circulation since 1992. At the time of writing, exchange rates are roughly £1 = 23kr; $1 = 13kr; €1 = 16k. You should have no trouble getting cash from ATMs, which are to be found all over Tallinn and accept all normal credit and debit cards.

PUBLIC TRANSPORT

Trams are everywhere, and if you take the trouble to learn the routes they can prove an excellent and rather atmospheric way of getting around. Tickets cost 10kr a ride from newsagent's kiosks or 15kr from the driver. There are also regular buses. Online schedules can be found at www.tallinn.ee.

QUEUING

Estonians are almost as fond of queuing as the English, and sometimes more so. Take care not to fall foul of this orderly culture when ordering drinks at the bar: Estonians will form a clear line in one direction and wait as if they are at a bus stop. If you walk right up to the barman no one will stop you, but no one will take your order either.

RUSSIANS AND ESTONIANS

Estonia's two main ethnic groups share a fraught history and a certain resentment and bitterness still hangs between them. Russians make up 40% of the population of the country (50% of Tallinn's) – but still live in different areas, frequent different bars and (if you believe the Estonians) have completely different taste in food, music, fashion and everything else. On the other hand, there is little open expression of dislike and absolutely no violence. And things are getting better – younger Tallinites remember little of the Soviet era. However, it is something to be aware of as you get to know the locals, all of them charming in their own way.

TAXIS

Taxis (*takso*) are generally trustworthy and easy to find. Drivers tend to be honest and friendly, and not too talkative! A taxi journey around the city centre should not usually cost more than 50 or 60kr. Twenty-four hour ranks can be found in Suur-Karja – and just outside the Viru gates, between old and new town. Airport taxis should cost about 80kr into Tallinn, but there is no fixed rate – so this will depend on where exactly you are going. Always make sure the meter is on, to avoid arguments. Some useful numbers for taxi companies are: Krooni Takso 638 11 11; Kiisu Takso 655 07 77; Peretakso 646 00 06.

TELEPHONES AND MOBILES

Local calls are not expensive. To use a pay phone you will need to buy a card from one of the newspaper kiosks around town. If you're phoning Tallinn from the UK, you'll need to dial the prefix 00 372 2 – all places listed here have had the country and city code removed.

TIPPING

There is little tradition and no real etiquette with regard to tipping; most places leave it to your discretion. One should aim to leave between 10 and 15% in restaurants, rounding up for taxis, bars and cafés.

index

index